Mathematics
GCSE
and Standard Grade

Book 1

David Rayner

Head of Mathematics
Richard Hale School, Hertford

Oxford University Press

Oxford University Press, Walton Street, Oxford OX2 6DP

Oxford New York Toronto
Delhi Bombay Calcutta Madras Karachi
Petaling Jaya Singapore Hong Kong Tokyo
Nairobi Dar es Salaam Cape Town
Melbourne Auckland

and associated companies in
Berlin Ibadan

Oxford is a trade mark of Oxford University Press

ISBN 0 19 914245 9

First published 1987
Reprinted 1987, 1988

Cartoons by David Simonds

Printed by Butler and Tanner Ltd, Frome
Typeset by Katerprint Typesetting Services

PREFACE

This two-book course hs been written for the majority of secondary school pupils attempting the GCSE or Standard Grade in mathematics and can be used in the two to three years leading to the examination. It provides practice in all the topics of Lists 1 and 2 of the National Criteria and of the syllabuses of the examining groups at this level.

The many practice questions are arranged in exercises which are graded to match the abilities of pupils in a given class. Because the books cover a wide range of abilities, it is not expected that all the questions in every exercise will be attempted. It is the author's experience that pupils who find mathematics difficult will derive much pleasure and satisfaction from the subject in doing questions that help to build up their confidence. If the work can be covered systematically, an appreciation of the purpose and the power of the subject can be developed, leading to a realisation of the use of mathematics in everyday practical situations and in future employment.

An important part of each book is to be found in the 'Think about it' sections. In these, the projects form a lively platform for investigational work and discussion which can be extended at the discretion of the teacher and used as a basis for assessment. They are intended to develop the pupil's ability to reason logically, to appreciate patterns and relationships and to stimulate powers of creative imagination. The exercises inserted between these projects aim to widen the perceptive abilities of the pupil.

Each book also includes a section of mental arithmetic tests in which questions are read out to the class with books closed. A competitive element can be enjoyed here with the text later used for pupils to check their errors. The numerical answers to both books are provided in one separate answer book.

The author wishes to record his thanks to Micheline Dubois, Philip Cutts and all his colleagues at school for all their help. Thanks are also due to the following examination boards for kindly allowing the use of questions in Book 2 from their past mathematics papers.

London and East Anglian Group for GCSE [L]
Midland Examining Group [M]
Northern Examining Association [N]
Southern Examining Group [S]
Welsh Joint Education Committee [W]

CONTENTS

Part 1

1.1   WHOLE NUMBERS

Exercise 1

Work out
1. 27 + 31
2. 45 + 22
3. 234 + 17
4. 316 + 204
5. 50 + 911
6. 291 + 46
7. 299 + 197
8. 306 + 205
9. 45 + 275
10. 903 + 89

11. 415 + 207 + 25
12. 41 + 607 + 423
13. 206 + 114 + 8
14. 9 + 19 + 912
15. 157 + 16 + 24
16. 16 + 2341 + 27
17. 3047 + 265
18. 274 + 5061
19. 2941 + 4067
20. 8046 + 147

21. 401 + 609 + 21
22. 506 + 2615
23. 2947 + 4 + 590
24. 209 + 607 + 11
25. 6672 + 11 + 207
26. 994 + 27
27. 604 + 12 407
28. 9150 + 12 694
29. 53246 + 62141
30. 19 274 + 27 + 584

Exercise 2

Work out
1. 97 − 63
2. 69 − 41
3. 83 − 60
4. 87 − 5
5. 192 − 81
6. 214 − 10
7. 86 − 29
8. 52 − 37
9. 74 − 18
10. 91 − 68

11. 265 − 128
12. 642 − 181
13. 562 − 181
14. 816 − 274
15. 509 − 208
16. 604 − 491
17. 808 − 275
18. 250 − 127
19. 640 − 118
20. 265 − 184

21. 484 − 219
22. 6064 − 418
23. 5126 − 307
24. 6417 − 29
25. 8050 − 218
26. 406 − 22
27. 649 − 250
28. 6009 − 205
29. 1717 − 356
30. 843 − 295

31. 641 − 286
32. 2719 − 394
33. 7416 − 286
34. 5417 − 346

35. 2098 − 364   **36.** 2006 − 507
37. 4017 − 2138   **38.** 2094 − 1846
39. 4075 − 999   **40.** 732 − 159

41. Two hundred and six take away forty-eight.

42. Five hundred and seventeen take away one hundred and twenty.

43. Two thousand, four hundred and eight take away six hundred and eleven.

44. Ten thousand and twenty take away eight thousand six hundred and four.

45. Six hundred and nineteen take away two hundred and thirty-seven.

46. Nineteen thousand and twelve take away ten thousand.

47. Six hundred and seven take away five hundred and sixty.

48. Ten thousand take away six hundred and forty.

49. Six hundred and fifty take away two hundred and ninety-one.

50. Seventeen thousand and seventeen take away six hundred and eighty-four.

Exercise 3

In a 'magic square' you get the same number when you add across each row (↔), add down each column (↕) and add diagonally (↗, ↘). Copy and complete the following magic squares.

1.

3		
2		
7	0	

2.

9	7	5
		10

3.

8	1	6
4		

4.

7		
	6	4
		5

5.

12		14
	11	
8		

6.

17		
12		16
13		

7.

		7	14
	13	2	
	3	16	5
15			4

8.

		6	4
10		16	
		2	
1	12	7	14

9.

	10		
14	15		8
	4	18	
16	13		6

10.

18		12	7
	6		
11	16	5	14
4			

11.

11		7	20	3
	12	25		16
	5	13		9
	18		14	
		19	2	15

12.

16		10	17	4
3	15		9	21
20		14		8
		19		
24			5	12

13. This one is slightly different because there are not enough numbers given. Try different numbers for ∗ until you find one which makes the square magic.

10		
5		
6		∗

Tables test

Exercise 4

Copy and complete the multiplication squares.

1.

×	4	7	3	5	9	11	8	6	2	12
4										
7										
3					27					
5										
9										
11									22	
8		24								
6										
2										
12										

2.

×	7	5	9	6	8	11	4	2	12	3
7										
5										
9										
6										
8										
11										
4										
2										
12										
3										

Multiplication

Exercise 5

Work out

1. 21×3 **2.** 32×3
3. 42×6 **4.** 35×4
5. 213×3 **6.** 46×5
7. 205×6 **8.** 28×6
9. 211×7 **10.** 302×7

11. 213×5 **12.** 641×3
13. 21×8 **14.** 314×6
15. 131×9 **16.** 214×8
17. 820×6 **18.** 921×4
19. 2141×6 **20.** 3025×5

21. 324×8 **22.** 643×7
23. 295×9 **24.** 641×10
25. 846×10 **26.** 275×8
27. 631×7 **28.** 885×9
29. 497×8 **30.** 2153×6

Exercise 6

Work out

1. 23×15 **2.** 27×17
3. 41×23 **4.** 36×23
5. 61×25 **6.** 25×47
7. 73×61 **8.** 80×43
9. 29×16 **10.** 211×23

11. 406×24 **12.** 291×31
13. 382×42 **14.** 611×52
15. 952×73 **16.** 211×312
17. 314×215 **18.** 234×614
19. 812×316 **20.** 911×806

Division

Exercise 7

Work out

1. $69 \div 3$ **2.** $286 \div 2$
3. $844 \div 4$ **4.** $345 \div 3$
5. $712 \div 4$ **6.** $1160 \div 5$
7. $1581 \div 3$ **8.** $2112 \div 4$
9. $415 \div 5$ **10.** $994 \div 2$

11. $1092 \div 4$ **12.** $18\ 072 \div 3$
13. $3020 \div 5$ **14.** $1626 \div 6$
15. $1660 \div 4$ **16.** $1915 \div 5$
17. $4944 \div 6$ **18.** $5616 \div 6$
19. $2247 \div 7$ **20.** $10\ 710 \div 5$

21. $18\ 972 \div 2$ **22.** $9256 \div 4$
23. $1928 \div 8$ **24.** $14\ 010 \div 2$
25. $5859 \div 7$ **26.** $55\ 305 \div 9$
27. $21\ 104 \div 8$ **28.** $3735 \div 9$
29. $12\ 360 \div 6$ **30.** $24\ 832 \div 8$

Exercise 8

Work out

1. $1300 \div 4$ **2.** $1863 \div 9$
3. $2508 \div 6$ **4.** $1664 \div 4$

5. 31 805 ÷ 5
6. 3175 ÷ 5
7. 24 267 ÷ 3
8. 19 976 ÷ 8
9. 39 389 ÷ 7
10. 69 984 ÷ 4

There are 'remainders' in the next 10 questions.
11. 2143 ÷ 4
12. 6418 ÷ 5
13. 6027 ÷ 4
14. 24 081 × 7
15. 4135 ÷ 6
16. 1173 ÷ 9
17. 6798 ÷ 7
18. 7048 ÷ 3
19. 2035 ÷ 8
20. 26 525 ÷ 6

Sequences

Write down the next two numbers in each sequence.

(a) 2, 6, 10, 14,
(b) 60, 59, 57, 54,
(c) 240, 120, 60, 30,

(a) 2, 6, 10, 14, **18, 22**.
(b) 60, 59, 57, 54, **50, 45**.
(c) 240, 120, 60, 30, **15, 7½**

Exercise 9

Write down each sequence and find the next two numbers.

1. 2, 5, 8, 11,
2. 1, 6, 11, 16,
3. 20, 18, 16, 14,
4. 2, 9, 16, 23,
5. 74, 62, 50, 38,
6. 1, 2, 4, 7, 11,

7. 5, 7, 10, 14,
8. 50, 49, 47, 44,
9. 50, 43, 36, 29,
10. 44, 53, 62, 71,
11. 90, 82, 75, 69,
12. −4, −2, 0, 2,
13. −5, −2, 1, 4,
14. 6, 2, −2, −6,
15. 5, 8, 12, 17,
16. 10, 8, 5, 1,
17. −20, −14, −8, −2,
18. 93, 81, 70, 60,
19. 31, 40, 51, 64, 79,
20. 55, 49, 42, 34,

Exercise 10

Write down each sequence and find the next two numbers or letters.

1. 1, 2, 4, 8,
2. 1, 3, 9, 27,
3. 400, 200, 100, 50
4. 22, 31, 40, 49,
5. 3, 30, 300, 3000,
6. 128, 64, 32, 16,
7. 85, 92, 99, 106,
8. 40, 38, 35, 31,
9. A, C, E, G,
10. B, E, H, K,
11. A, B, D, G, K,
12. W, U, S, Q,
13. 2480, 1240, 620, 310,
14. 1, 4, 9, 16,
15. 1, 1, 2, 6, 24,
16. −5, −4, −2, 1,
17. A, D, G, J,
18. 7, 4, 0, −5,
19. 8, 11, 15, 20,
20. 3, 10, 19, 30,

The next ten are more difficult.
21. −21, −18, −13, −6,
22. 162, 54, 18, 6,
23. 63, 51, 65, 49,
24. 27, 9, 3, 1,
25. 1, 1, 2, 3, 5, 8,
26. C, C, D, F, I,
27. 1, 4, 20, 120,
28. 100, 79, 59, 40,
29. 2, 5, 11, 20,
30. 2, 3, 5, 7, 11, 13,

1.2 DECIMALS

Place value

Exercise 11

In questions **1** to **12** write down the line which is correct.
1. (a) 0.06 is equal to 0.6
(b) 0.06 is greater than 0.6
(c) 0.06 is less than 0.6

2. (a) 0.14 is equal to 0.41
(b) 0.14 is greater than 0.41
(c) 0.14 is less than 0.41

3. (a) 0.61 is equal to 0.6
(b) 0.61 is greater than 0.6
(c) 0.61 is less than 0.6

4. (a) 0.04 is equal to 0.040
(b) 0.04 is greater than 0.040
(c) 0.04 is less than 0.040

5. (a) 0.12 is equal to 0.1
(b) 0.12 is greater than 0.1
(c) 0.12 is less than 0.1

[In the following questions:
> means 'is greater than' (e.g. 9 > 5)
< means 'is less than' (e.g. 7 < 10)]

6. (a) 0.03 = 0.3
(b) 0.03 > 0.3
(c) 0.03 < 0.3

7. (a) 0.214 = 0.241
(b) 0.214 > 0.241
(c) 0.214 < 0.241

8. (a) $0.06 = 0.60$
  (b) $0.06 > 0.60$
  (c) $0.06 < 0.60$

9. (a) $2.01 = 2.010$
  (b) $2.01 > 2.010$
  (c) $2.01 < 2.010$

10. (a) $0.15 = 0.153$
  (b) $0.15 > 0.153$
  (c) $0.15 < 0.153$

11. (a) $0.313 = 0.331$
  (b) $0.313 > 0.331$
  (c) $0.313 < 0.331$

12. (a) $0.071 = 0.08$
  (b) $0.071 > 0.08$
  (c) $0.071 < 0.08$

In the remaining questions answer 'true' or 'false'

13. $0.8 = 0.08$
14. $0.7 < 0.71$
15. $0.61 > 0.16$
16. $0.08 > 0.008$
17. $0.5 = 0.500$
18. $0.4 < 0.35$
19. $0.613 < 0.631$
20. $0.06 > 0.055$
21. $8 = 8.00$
22. $7 = 0.7$
23. $0.63 > 0.36$
24. $8.2 < 8.022$
25. $6.04 < 6.40$
26. $0.75 = 0.075$
27. $5 = 0.5$
28. $0.001 > 0.0001$
29. $0.078 < 0.08$
30. $9 = 9.0$
31. $0.9 > 0.085$
32. $6.2 < 6.02$
33. $0.05 < 0.005$
34. $0.718 < 0.871$
35. $0.09 > 0.1$
36. $11 = 0.11$
37. $0.88 > 0.088$
38. $0.65 > 0.605$
39. $2.42 = 2.420$
40. $0.31 = 0.3100$

Exercise 12

Arrange the numbers in order of size, smallest first.

1. 0.21, 0.31, 0.12
2. 0.04, 0.4, 0.35
3. 0.67, 0.672, 0.7
4. 0.05, 0.045, 0.07
5. 0.1, 0.09, 0.089
6. 0.75, 0.57, 0.705
7. 0.41, 0.041, 0.14
8. 0.809, 0.81, 0.8
9. 0.006, 0.6, 0.059
10. 0.15, 0.143, 0.2

11. 0.04, 0.14, 0.2, 0.53
12. 1.2, 0.12, 0.21, 1.12
13. 2.3, 2.03, 0.75, 0.08
14. 0.62, 0.26, 0.602, 0.3
15. 0.5, 1.3, 1.03, 1.003
16. 0.79, 0.792, 0.709, 0.97
17. 1.23, 0.321, 0.312, 1.04
18. 0.008, 0.09, 0.091, 0.0075
19. 2.05, 2.5, 2, 2.046
20. 1.95, 9.51, 5.19, 5.1

21. 0.76, 0.674, 0.706, 0.71
22. 1, 0.99, 0.989, 0.09
23. 0.42, 0.24, 1, 0.204
24. 0.3, 0.33, 0.303, 0.222
25. 1.2, 1.02, 1.21, 0.95
26. 3.62, 0.632, 0.362, 0.662
27. 0.08, 0.096, 1, 0.4
28. 0.72, 0.732, 0.722, 0.7
29. 4.03, 3.99, 4, 4.025
30. 0.66, 0.658, 0.685, 0.08

Addition and subtraction

Exercise 13

Work out the following, without a calculator.

1. $2.84 + 7.3$
2. $18.6 + 2.34$
3. $25.96 + 0.75$
4. $212.7 + 4.256$
5. $3.6 + 6$
6. $7 + 16.1$
7. $8 + 3.4 + 0.85$
8. $12 + 5.32 + 0.08$
9. $0.004 + 0.0583$
10. $7.77 + 77.7$

11. $4.81 - 3.7$
12. $6.92 - 2.56$
13. $8.27 - 5.86$
14. $19.7 - 8.9$
15. $3.6 - 2.24$
16. $8.4 - 2.17$
17. $8.24 - 5.78$
18. $19.6 - 7.36$
19. $15.4 - 7$
20. $23.96 - 8$

21. $8 - 5.2$
22. $9 - 6.8$
23. $13 - 2.7$
24. $25 - 3.2$
25. $0.325 - 0.188$
26. $0.484 - 0.4352$
27. $7 - 0.35$
28. $6 - 1.28$
29. $2.38 - 1.814$
30. $11 - 7.4$

Multiplication

Work out (a) 5.2×0.6,   (b) 12.4×1.3

(a) $\begin{array}{r} 52 \\ \times\ 6 \\ \hline 312 \\ \hline \end{array}$ (b) $\begin{array}{r} 124 \\ \times\ 13 \\ \hline 1240 \\ 372 \\ \hline 1612 \\ \hline \end{array}$

So $5.2 \times 0.6 = 3.12$ So $12.4 \times 1.3 = 16.12$

Exercise 14

Work out the following, without a calculator

1. 2.3×0.4
2. 3.6×0.3
3. 4.7×0.5
4. 21.3×0.4
5. 62.5×0.8
6. 4.26×0.7

7. 4.2×0.03
8. 6.04×0.05
9. 17.3×0.004
10. 25.2×0.002

11. 0.51×0.9
12. 0.063×0.04
13. 212×0.6
14. 543×0.02
15. 7104×0.04
16. 0.085×0.5
17. 1.33×0.04
18. 4.004×0.9
19. 1.09×0.0002
20. 584×0.001

21. 2.3×1.3
22. 3.4×1.4
23. 5.21×1.5
24. 6.22×0.21
25. 7.34×0.32
26. 0.831×1.5
27. 8.42×0.022
28. 81.4×0.26
29. 76.4×0.043
30. 0.708×0.034

Division

> Work out $7.63 \div 0.4$
>
> $7.63 \div 0.4 = 76.3 \div 4$
>
> $\begin{array}{r} 19.075 \\ \hline 4)\overline{76.300} \end{array}$

Exercise 15

Work out the following, without a calculator.
1. $8.76 \div 4$
2. $19.74 \div 2$
3. $7.02 \div 3$
4. $9.24 \div 4$
5. $8.34 \div 5$
6. $20.7 \div 6$
7. $0.318 \div 2$
8. $2.51 \div 8$
9. $40.88 \div 7$
10. $13.26 \div 5$

11. $17.2 \div 8$
12. $3.15 \div 9$
13. $25.96 \div 11$
14. $60.13 \div 7$
15. $525 \div 6$
16. $0.92 \div 5$
17. $0.638 \div 0.2$
18. $0.852 \div 0.4$
19. $5.73 \div 0.5$
20. $2.912 \div 0.8$

21. $0.3504 \div 0.06$
22. $2.527 \div 0.07$
23. $5.616 \div 0.9$
24. $0.004\ 384 \div 0.008$
25. $0.446\ 74 \div 0.07$
26. $0.028\ 49 \div 0.11$
27. $0.039\ 282 \div 0.006$
28. $5.2 \div 0.05$
29. $14.3 \div 0.004$
30. $2.63 \div 0.0008$

31. $51.093 \div 9$
32. $68.618 \div 11$
33. $0.347\ 41 \div 0.7$
34. $7 \div 0.005$
35. $0.7612 \div 0.011$
36. $8 \div 0.002$
37. $0.643\ 06 \div 1.1$
38. $0.015\ 54 \div 6$
39. $5 \div 0.08$
40. $27.34 \div 0.000\ 01$

Multiplication and division by 10's, 100's, 1000's

Exercise 16

Write down the answer to each of the following.
1. 0.634×10
2. 0.838×10
3. 0.815×100
4. 0.074×100
5. 7.245×1000
6. 0.6105×100
7. 0.064×100
8. 0.0075×1000
9. 27×10
10. 351×100

11. $6.24 \div 10$
12. $8.97 \div 10$
13. $17.5 \div 100$
14. $23.6 \div 1000$
15. $4.8 \div 100$
16. $0.73 \div 10$
17. $127 \div 1000$
18. $16.3 \div 100$
19. $580 \div 10$
20. $6300 \div 1000$

21. 0.751×100
22. $0.084 \div 10$
23. $0.111 \div 10$
24. 0.0084×1000
25. 16×1000
26. $7 \div 100$
27. $0.8 \div 100$
28. 317×10
29. $254 \div 1000$
30. 99×1000

There is another exercise on this topic in section 2.1 (page 15) on the metric system.

The next two exercises are more difficult because they contain a mixture of questions on addition, subtraction, multiplication and division.

Exercise 17

1. $3.7 + 0.62$
2. $8.45 - 2.7$
3. $11.3 - 2.14$
4. 2.52×0.4
5. $3.74 \div 5$
6. $17 + 3.24$
7. $12 - 1.8$
8. $23.6 \div 8$
9. 82.1×0.06
10. 0.034×1000

11. $62.1 \div 100$
12. $11.4 - 3.16$
13. 0.153×0.8
14. $2.16 + 9.99$
15. $18.606 \div 7$
16. 6.042×11
17. 34.1×1000
18. $0.41 \div 100$
19. 52.6×0.04
20. $0.365 - 0.08$

21. $2.329\ 56 \div 9$
22. 654×0.005
23. $0.7 + 0.77 + 0.777$
24. $54 \div 100$
25. 27×0.001
26. 6.007×1.1
27. $8.2 - 1.64$
28. $47.04 \div 6$
29. $58.4 \div 10\ 000$
30. 0.742×1 million

Exercise 18

1. 2.06×0.05
2. $43.75 \div 7$
3. $19.1 - 7$
4. $7 - 3.6$
5. 0.62×1000
6. $82.6 \div 10$
7. $43.6 - 2.18$
8. $0.5 + 0.55 + 0.555$
9. $0.072 \div 8$
10. 850×0.0004
11. 0.026×1 million
12. $962.4 \div 100\ 000$
13. $54 - 6.2$
14. 28.3×0.011
15. $586.26 \div 9$
16. $2.84 \div 0.5$
17. 48.6×0.07
18. $0.392 \div 0.04$
19. $7 + 0.7 + 0.77$
20. $180 - 2.5$
21. $0.0714 \div 0.08$
22. 0.004×10 million
23. 333×0.007
24. $17 + 8.8$
25. $82 \div 10\ 000$
26. $0.458\ 36 \div 0.07$
27. $206 - 74.2$
28. $18 + 1.8 + 0.18$
29. $0.190\ 47 \div 0.003$
30. $2.6 \div 0.005$

1.3   PERCENTAGES

> Change 15 out of 25 into a percentage.
>
> As a fraction 15 out of 25 $= \dfrac{15}{25}$
>
> $$\dfrac{15}{25} = \dfrac{15}{25} \times \dfrac{100}{1}\%$$
>
> $$= 60\%$$

Exercise 19

Change to percentages

1. $\frac{3}{4}$
2. $\frac{2}{5}$
3. $\frac{1}{2}$
4. $\frac{4}{5}$
5. $\frac{1}{4}$
6. $\frac{5}{8}$
7. $\frac{9}{10}$
8. $\frac{17}{20}$
9. $\frac{5}{20}$
10. $\frac{7}{8}$
11. $\frac{17}{25}$
12. $\frac{7}{20}$
13. $\frac{7}{100}$
14. $\frac{1}{3}$
15. $\frac{2}{3}$
16. $\frac{1}{8}$
17. $\frac{49}{50}$
18. $\frac{15}{60}$
19. $\frac{61}{100}$
20. $\frac{250}{1000}$
21. $\frac{16}{50}$
22. $\frac{27}{40}$
23. $\frac{4}{12}$
24. $\frac{235}{1000}$

25. 17 marks out of 25
26. 18 marks out of 20
27. 52 marks out of 80
28. 12 marks out of 30
29. £45 out of £200
30. £17 out of £50
31. £98 out of £100
32. £65 out of £260
33. 19 kg out of 40 kg
34. 300 kg out of 900 kg
35. $67 out of $1000

Exercise 20

1. (a) In a test Ann obtained 11 marks out of 25. What is her percentage mark?

   (b) In a second test she obtained 13 marks out of 20. What is her percentage mark?

2. A motorist has to drive a distance of 400 km. After an hour he has driven 84 km. What percentage of his journey has he completed?

3. In a survey 1600 people were asked which television channel they preferred.
   800 chose ITV
   640 chose BBC
   160 had no television set.
   (a) What percentage chose ITV?
   (b) What percentage chose BBC?
   (c) What percentage had no television?

4. Of the people in a room 11 are men and 14 are women.
   (a) How many people are in the room?
   (b) What percentage of the people are men?
   (c) What percentage of the people are women?

5. Three girls in different classes all had maths tests on the same day.
   Jane scored 27 out of 50.
   Susan scored 28 out of 40.
   Jackie scored 39 out of 75.
   Work out their marks as percentages and put them in order with the highest first.

6. In a car park 23 cars are British made and 27 cars are imported. What percentage of the cars in the car park are imported?

7. The children in a class were asked to state which was their least favourite subject.

       7 chose Maths
      12 chose Music
      6 chose R.E.

(a) What percentage of the class chose Music?

(b) What percentage of the class chose Maths or Music?

8. In an opinion poll 37% of the people preferred the Conservatives, 35% preferred Labour, 24% preferred Liberal/S.D.P. and the rest were 'Don't knows'. What percentage were 'Don't knows'?

9. John throws a die several times and obtains the following results

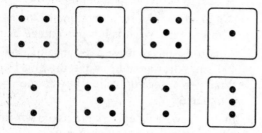

(a) What percentage of his throws gave a 'two'?

(b) What percentage of his throws gave a 'four'?

(c) What percentage of his throws gave a 'six'?

(d) What percentage of his throws gave more than three?

10. In a group of people 17 came from France, 22 came from Spain, 32 came from Germany and 9 came from Italy. What percentage of the group came from Germany?

Percentage of a number

Work out 22% of £40.

$$\frac{22}{100} \times \frac{40}{1} = \frac{880}{100}$$

Answer: £8.80

Exercise 21

Work out
1. 20% of £60
2. 10% of £80
3. 5% of £200
4. 6% of £50
5. 4% of £60
6. 30% of £80
7. 9% of £500
8. 18% of £400
9. 61% of £400
10. 12% of £80

11. 6% of $700
12. 11% of $800
13. 5% of 160 kg
14. 20% of 60 kg
15. 68% of 400 g
16. 15% of 300 m
17. 2% of 2000 km
18. 71% of $1000
19. 26% of 19 kg
20. 1% of 6000 g

21. 67% of £2000
22. 35% of 700 kg
23. 22% of £440
24. 17% of £560
25. 26% of £85
26. 73% of £96
27. 110% of £60
28. 125% of £90
29. 140% of £80
30. 117% of £145

Work out 6.5% of £17.50 correct to the nearest penny.

$$\frac{6.5}{100} \times \frac{17.5}{1} = \frac{113.75}{100}$$

$$= £1.1375$$

Answer: £1.14 to the nearest penny.

Exercise 22

Give the answers to the nearest penny where necessary.
1. 4.5% of £6.22
2. 17% of £6.84
3. 15% of £8.11
4. 17% of £17.07
5. 37% of £9.64
6. 3.5% of £12.90
7. 8% of £11.64
8. 68% of £54.45
9. 73% of £23.24
10. 2.5% of £15.20

11. 6.3% of £12.50
12. 8.2% of £19.50
13. 87% of £15.40
14. 80% of £62.50
15. 12% of £24.50
16. $12\frac{1}{2}$% of £88.50
17. $7\frac{1}{2}$% of £16.40
18. $5\frac{1}{2}$% of £80
19. $12\frac{1}{2}$% of £90
20. 19% of £119.50

21. 1% of £11.79
22. 1% of £2.73
23. $6\frac{1}{2}$% of £17
24. 110% of £85
25. 117% of £82
26. 153% of £279
27. 1% of £3.51
28. 2% of £6.38
29. 19.1% of £35.60
30. 8.7% of £10.10

A coat originally cost £24. Calculate the new price after a 5% reduction.

Price reduction $= 5\%$ of £24

$$= \frac{5}{100} \times \frac{24}{1} = £1.20$$

New price of coat $= £24 - £1.20$

$$= £22.80$$

Exercise 23

1. Increase a price of £12 by 10%
2. Increase a price of £40 by 5%
3. Increase a price of £60 by 15%
4. Increase a price of £84 by 4%
5. Increase a price of £70 by 20%
6. Reduce a price of £50 by 8%
7. Reduce a price of £75 by 40%
8. Reduce a price of £64 by 5%
9. Reduce a price of £8.40 by 10%
10. Reduce a price of £9.90 by 10%

11. Increase a price of £60 by 5%
12. Reduce a price of £800 by 8%
13. Reduce a price of £82.50 by 6%
14. Increase a price of £65 by 60%
15. Reduce a price of £2000 by 2%
16. Increase a price of £440 by 80%
17. Increase a price of £66 by 100%
18. Reduce a price of £91.50 by 50%
19. Increase a price of £88.24 by 25%
20. Reduce a price of £63 by $33\frac{1}{3}\%$

In the remaining questions give the answers to the nearest penny.
21. Increase a price of £8.24 by 46%
22. Increase a price of £7.65 by 24%
23. Increase a price of £5.61 by 31%
24. Reduce a price of £8.99 by 22%
25. Increase a price of £11.12 by 11%
26. Reduce a price of £17.62 by 4%
27. Increase a price of £28.20 by 13%
28. Increase a price of £8.55 by $5\frac{1}{2}\%$
29. Reduce a price of £9.60 by $7\frac{1}{2}\%$
30. Increase a price of £12.80 by $10\frac{1}{2}\%$

Exercise 24

1. In a closing-down sale a shop reduces all its prices by 20%. Find the sale price of a coat which previously cost £44.
2. The price of a car was £5400 but it is increased by 6%. What is the new price?
3. The price of a sideboard was £245 but, because the sideboard is scratched, the price is reduced by 30%. What is the new price?
4. A hi-fi shop offers a 7% discount for cash. How much does a cash-paying customer pay for an amplifier advertised at £95?
5. A rabbit weighs 2.8 kg. After being shot its weight is increased by 1%. How much does it weigh now?

6. The insurance premium for a car is normally £90. With a 'no-claim bonus' the premium is reduced by 35%. What is the reduced premium?
7. Myxomatosis kills 92% of a colony of 300 rabbits. How many rabbits survive?
8. The population of a town increased by 32% between 1945 and 1985. If there were 45 000 people in 1945, what was the 1985 population?
9. A restaurant adds a 12% 'service charge' onto the basic price of meals. How much do I pay for a meal with a basic price of £8.50?
10. A new-born baby weighs 3.1 kg. Her weight increases by 8% over the next fortnight. What does she weigh then?
11. A large snake normally weighs 12.2 kg. After swallowing a rat, the weight of the snake is increased by 7%. How much does it weigh after dinner?
12. At the beginning of the year a car is valued at £3250. During the year its value falls by 15%. How much is it worth at the end of the year?

13. Copy and complete the table.

Basic price	VAT at 15%	Final price
(a) £24	£3.60	£27.60
(b) £38		
(c) £42		
(d) £212		
(e) £8.20		

14. During a sale a shopkeeper reduces prices by various amounts. Copy and complete the table.

Normal price	% reduction	Sale price
(a) £28	10%	
(b) £35	5%	
(c) £55	15%	
(d) £240	35%	
(e) £8.40	5%	

Exercise 25

(This exercise contains some harder questions.)
In questions **1** to **4** find the total bill.

1. 2 hammers at £5.30 each
50 screws at 25p for 10
5 bulbs at 38p each
1 tape measure at £1.15
VAT at 15% is added to the total cost.

2. 5 litres of oil at 85p per litre
3 spanners at £1.25 each
2 manuals at £4.30 each
200 bolts at 90p for 10
VAT at 15% is added to the total cost.

3. 12 rolls of wallpaper at £3.70 per roll
3 packets of paste at £0.55 per packet
2 brushes at £2.40 each
1 stepladder at £15.50
VAT at 15% is added to the total cost.

4. 5 golf clubs at £12.45 each
48 golf balls at £15 per dozen
100 tees at 1p each
1 bag at £21.50
1 umbrella at £12.99
VAT at 15% is added to the total cost.

5. In a sale a dress priced at £35 is reduced by 20%. At the end of the week the *sale price* is reduced by a further 25%. Calculate
(a) the price in the original sale
(b) the final price.

6. In a sale a coat priced at £85 is reduced by 40%. At the end of the week the *sale price* is reduced by a further 20%. Calculate
(a) the price in the original sale
(b) the final price.

7. A dishonest shopkeeper increases all his prices by 10% and keeps the new prices for a week. At the end of the week he has a sale of 'all goods at 10% off!' What is the sale price of an article which cost £400 before the increase?

8. (a) In 1985 a club has 40 members who each pay £12 annual subscription. What is the total income from subscriptions?
(b) In 1986 the subscription is increased by 35% and the membership increases to 65.
 (i) What is the 1986 subscription?
 (ii) What is the total income from subscriptions in 1986?

Exercise 26

1. A jacket costs £32 to make and the shopkeeper adds 25% to give the 'marked price'. During a sale all goods, are labelled 'Sale Price – 10% off Marked Price'.
(a) What was the 'marked price' for the jacket?
(b) What was the 'Sale Price' for the jacket?
(c) How much profit did the shopkeeper make, if he sold 20 of these jackets in the sale?

2. The table shows the normal price of some television sets and how much they are reduced in a sale.

Make	Normal price	% reduction	Actual reduction
Sony	£280	10%	
ITT	£315	5%	
Phillips	£440		£44
Ferguson	£310	12%	
Sanyo	£250		£50

Copy and complete the table.

3. A car bought for £5950 loses £950 of its value during the first year, and then an annual depreciation of 20% of its value at the beginning of each following year.
   (a) What is the value of the car after one year?
   (b) By how much does the value decrease over the second year?
   (c) Work out the value of the car after
       (i) 2 years   (ii) 3 years   (iii) 4 years

4. A cooker is purchased by taking out a bank loan for £450, to which the bank adds interest equivalent to 10% of the loan.

   (a) How much interest is charged?
   (b) What is the total cost?
   (c) The bank loan plus interest has to be repaid by 12 equal monthly payments. How much is repaid each month?

5. In a survey 10 000 people were asked which television channel they liked best.
       4000 chose ITV
       3500 chose BBC1
       1000 chose BBC2
        500 chose Channel 4
       1000 did not have TV.

   What percentage chose
   (a) ITV   (b) BBC1   (c) BBC2
   (d) Channel 4?

6. A shopkeeper bought 50 articles for £20 and sold them all at 50p each.
   Find the missing numbers below.
   (a) The cost price of each article was * p
   (b) The total selling price of all the articles was £*
   (c) The total profit was £*.

7. At blast-off a rocket consists of a structure of mass 800 kg together with 4000 kg of fuel. Calculate the total mass of the rocket when 15% of the fuel has been burned away.

8. A man bought a house in 1982, for £30 000. He sold it, in 1985, for £35 000.
   (a) What was his profit, in £'s?
   (b) Express this profit as a percentage of the 1982 cost price.

1.4   RATIO

> Share £60 in the ratio 2:3
>
> Total number of shares = 2 + 3 = 5
> ∴ One share = £60 ÷ 5 = £12
> ∴ The two amounts are £24 and £36

Exercise 27

1. Share £30 in the ratio 1:2.
2. Share £60 in the ratio 3:1.
3. Share £20 in the ratio 3:2.
4. Share £42 in the ratio 1:5.
5. Divide 880 g of food between the cat and the dog in the ratio 3:5.

6. Divide $1080 between Sam and Chris in the ratio 4:5.
7. Share 126 gallons of petrol between Steve and Dave in the ratio 2:5.
8. Share £60 in the ratio 1:2:3.
9. Share £400 in the ratio 2:3:3.
10. Share £96 in the ratio 1:3:4.
11. Divide $5400 in the ratio 2:3:4.
12. Share out 260 marbles between three children in the ratio 2:3:5.
13. Divide 880 g of wedding cake between three guests in the ratio 2:4:5.
14. Alan, Brian and Dawn divided £560 between them in the ratio 2:1:5. How much did Brian receive?

15. A sum of £120 is divided in the ratio 3:4:5. What is the largest share?

16. Find the largest share when £192.50 is divided in the ratio 2:5.

17. Find the smallest share when 260 g is divided in the ratio 4:2:7.

18. At an election 7800 people voted Labour, Conservative or Alliance in the ratio 4:3:5. How many people voted Alliance?

19. Find the largest share when £1 is divided in the ratio 5:6:9.

20. £109.80 is divided between James and his twin sisters in the ratio 5:2:2. How much does each twin receive?

Exercise 28

(This exercise is more difficult.)

1. Divide $45 in the ratio 2:4:3:1.

2. Divide £330 in the ratio 3:2:5:5.

3. Share 4200 kg in the ratio 2:5:1:6.

4. Find the largest share when 480 g is divided in the ratio 1:3:4:7.

5. Find the smallest share when £91 is divided in the ratio 5:2:6:7.

6. £80 is divided between Sally and Jane in the ratio 2:3. How much more does Jane get than Sally?

7. $388.50 is divided between Charles and Jack in the ratio 2:5. How much more does Jack get than Charles?

8. Share £96 so that A has twice as much as B.

9. Share £120 so that A has one third as much as B.

10. Share £84 so that A has twice as much as B, who has twice as much as C.

11. Share £600 so that A has twice as much as B, who has three times as much as C.

12. Share £252 so that A has half as much as B, who has four times as much as C.

13. Share £350 so that A has half as much as C, who has half as much as B. (Make it clear how much each person receives).

14. Share £168 so that A has twice as much as C, who has twice as much as B.

15. Share £54 so that B has three times as much as C, who has twice as much as A.

In a class, the ratio of boys to girls is 3:4. If there are 9 boys, how many girls are there?

> Boys:Girls = 3:4
> Multiply both parts by 3.
> Boys:Girls = 9:12
> So there are 9 boys and 12 girls.

Exercise 29

1. In a room, the ratio of boys to girls is 3:2. If there are 12 boys, how many girls are there?

2. In a room, the ratio of men to women is 4:1. If there are 20 men, how many women are there?

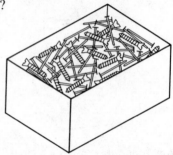

3. In a box, the ratio of nails to screws is 5:3. If there are 15 nails, how many screws are there?

4. A sum of money is divided in the ratio 4:5. If the smaller amount is £80, find the larger amount.

5. A sum of money is divided in the ratio 7:3. If the smaller amount is £18, find the larger amount.

6. An alloy consists of copper, zinc and tin in the ratios 1:3:4. If there is 10 g of copper in the alloy, find the weights of zinc and tin.

7. In a shop the ratio of oranges to apples is 2:5. If there are 60 apples, how many oranges are there?

8. In a train the ratio of adults to children is 7:2. If there are 126 adults, how many children are there?

9. In a bag, the ratio of red beads to white beads to green beads is 7:2:1. If there are 56 red beads, how many white beads are there and how many green beads?

10. On a farm, the ratio of cows to horses to sheep is 8:1:3. If there are 48 sheep, how many horses are there and how many cows?

1.5 PROPORTION

Direct proportion

> If 12 calculators cost £54, find the cost of 17 calculators.
>
> 12 calculators cost £54
> ∴ 1 calculator costs £54 ÷ 12 = £4.50
> ∴ 17 calculators cost £4.50 × 17
> = £76.50

Exercise 30

1. If 5 books cost £15, find the cost of 8.
2. If 7 apples cost 63p, find the cost of 12.
3. If 4 batteries cost 180p, find the cost of 7.
4. If 5 bottles of beer cost £2.45, find the cost of 12.
5. Toy cars cost £3.36 for 8. Find the cost of
   (a) 3 toy cars
   (b) 10 toy cars.
6. Crisps cost £1.32 for 12 packets. Find the cost of
   (a) 20 packets
   (b) 200 packets.
7. Stair carpet costs £78 for 12 m. Find the cost of 15 m.
8. The total weight of 7 ceramic tiles is 1750 g. How much do 11 tiles weigh?
9. A machine fills 2000 bottles in 10 minutes. How many bottles will it fill in 7 minutes?
10. The total contents of 8 cartons of fruit drink is 12 litres. How much fruit drink is there in 3 cartons?
11. Find the cost of 15 cakes if 9 cakes cost £2.07.
12. Find the cost of 7 screws if 20 screws cost £4.60.
13. How much would 7 cauliflowers cost, if 10 cauliflowers cost £5.70?
14. A machine takes 20 seconds to make 8 coins. How long does it take to make 50 coins?
15. A plane flies 50 km in 15 minutes. How long will it take to fly 300 km?

Exercise 31

1. If 8 pencils cost 56p, how many can be bought for 70p?
2. If 6 pineapples can be bought for £3.12, how many can be bought for £5.20?
3. If 20 m² of carpet costs £150, what area of carpet can be bought for £90?
4. Oranges cost £1.68 for 12. How many can be bought for (a) £2.80 (b) £4.90?

£1.68 — 12 oranges

5. Twenty men produce 500 articles in 6 days. How many articles would 4 men produce in 6 days?
6. Forty women take 8 days to produce 400 articles. How many articles would 16 women produce in 8 days?
7. 12 men produce 600 components in 12 hours. How many components would 9 men produce in 12 hours?
8. 7 cycles cost £623.
   (a) What is the cost of 3 cycles?
   (b) How many cycles can be bought for £979?
9. 11 cassettes cost £9.35.
   (a) What is the cost of 15 cassettes?
   (b) How many cassettes can be bought for £17?
10. 2½ m of metal tube cost £1.40. Find the cost of (a) 4 m (b) 7½ m.
11. 3¼ kg of sweets costs £2.60. Find the cost of (a) 2 kg (b) 4½ kg.
12. A car travels 210 km on 30 litres of petrol. How much petrol is needed for a journey of 245 km?
13. A light aircraft flies 375 km on 150 litres of fuel. How much fuel is needed for a journey of 500 km?
14. A tank travels 140 miles on 40 gallons of fuel. How much fuel is needed for a journey of 245 miles?

Inverse proportion

> If 12 men can build a wall in 8 hours, how long will it take 4 men?
>
> The less men there are, the more time it takes.
>
> 12 men take 8 hours
> 1 man takes 96 hours
> 4 men take 24 hours

Exercise 32

1. If 15 men can build a wall in 6 hours, how long will it take 5 men?

2. If 6 men can dig a trench in 12 hours, how long will it take 24 men?

3. A ship has enough food to supply 600 passengers for 3 days. How long would the food last for 300 passengers?

4. Four men can build a shed in 9 hours. How long would it take six men?

5. A farmer has enough hay to feed 8 horses for 2 days. How long would the hay last for
   (a) 2 horses   (b) 32 horses?

6. Eight dockers can unload a ship in 15 hours. How long will it take 3 men?

7. A farmer employs 12 men to do a job in 10 days. How long would it have taken 5 men?

8. A bridge was painted by 8 men in 6 days. How long would it have taken 12 men?

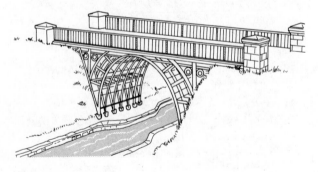

9. Four men can do a job in 12 hours. How many men would it take to do the job in 2 hours?

10. Six women can do a job in 8 hours. How many women would it take to do the job in 6 hours?

11. 8 sacks of corn will feed 30 hens for 6 days. Copy and complete the following:
    (a) 16 sacks of corn will feed 30 hens for * days.
    (b) 4 sacks of corn will feed 30 hens for * days.
    (c) 8 sacks of corn will feed 45 hens for * days.
    (d) 4 sacks of corn will feed 60 hens for * days (use part (b)).

12. 200 kg of food will feed 40 prisoners for 6 days. Copy and complete the following:
    (a) 200 kg of food will feed * prisoners for 3 days.
    (b) 200 kg of food will feed 10 prisoners for * days.
    (c) * kg of food will feed 40 prisoners for 30 days.
    (d) 50 kg of food will feed 40 prisoners for * days.

13. 6 swallows eat 300 flies in 5 hours. Copy and complete the following:
    (a) 30 swallows eat * flies in 5 hours.
    (b) 30 swallows eat * flies in 10 hours.
    (c) 6 swallows eat 60 flies in * hours.
    (d) * swallows eat 6000 flies in 5 hours.

14. Usually it takes 5 hours for 12 men to do a job. How many men are needed to do the job in 2 hours?

15. A car travelling at 80 km/h completes a certain journey in 60 minutes. How long would it take for a car travelling at
    (a) 40 km/h   (b) 120 km/h?

16. A car travelling at 60 km/h completes a journey in 90 minutes. How long would it take for a car travelling at
    (a) 180 km/h   (b) 15 km/h?

Part 2

2.1 THE METRIC SYSTEM

> (a) 0.314×100
> $= 31.4$
>
> (b) $17.4 \div 1000$
> $= 0.0174$
>
> (c) 1.2×1000
> $= 1200$
>
> (d) $8 \div 100$
> $= 0.08$

Exercise 1

This exercise provides revision of multiplying and dividing by 10's, 100's and 1000's. Do not use a calculator.

Work out

1. 0.724×10
2. 0.41×10
3. 1.625×100
4. 0.231×100
5. 8×100
6. 17×10
7. 6×1000
8. 0.6×100
9. 0.2×1000
10. 1.3×1000
11. 1.1×100
12. 0.04×100
13. 3.2×1000
14. 15.6×100
15. 7×1000
16. 0.7×1000
17. 0.007×100
18. 0.002×100
19. 0.74×100
20. 6.23×1000

21. $82.4 \div 10$
22. $79.6 \div 10$
23. $97.3 \div 100$
24. $111.2 \div 100$
25. $27 \div 10$
26. $373 \div 100$
27. $24.2 \div 100$
28. $8.2 \div 100$
29. $6 \div 100$
30. $11 \div 100$
31. $4 \div 1000$
32. $2 \div 1000$
33. $2.3 \div 1000$
34. $1 \div 100$
35. $182 \div 1000$
36. $79 \div 1000$
37. $0.2 \div 10$
38. $0.71 \div 100$
39. $1.3 \div 100$
40. $84 \div 1000$

41. 2.3×100
42. $8.2 \div 10$
43. 0.41×1000
44. 17×100
45. $17 \div 10$
46. $0.6 \div 10$
47. 89.7×100
48. 1.1×1000
49. $8 \div 100$
50. $600 \div 100$
51. 20×100
52. 18×1000

Length	Weight	Volume
10 mm = 1 cm	1000 g = 1 kg	1000 ml = 1 l
100 cm = 1 m	1000 kg = 1 t	1000 l = 1 m³
1000 m = 1 km	(t for tonne)	(l for litre)

Exercise 2

Copy and complete.

1. 1.27 m =   cm
2. 0.65 m =   cm
3. 3 m =   cm
4. 0.07 m =   cm
5. 11 m =   cm
6. 8.1 m =   cm
7. 2.34 m =   cm
8. 0.002 m =   cm
9. 17 cm =   m
10. 24 cm =   m
11. 240 cm =   m
12. 11 cm =   m
13. 2 cm =   m
14. 18.2 cm =   m
15. 3.1 cm =   m
16. 5000 cm =   m
17. 6.3 m =   cm
18. 0.24 m =   cm
19. 67 cm =   m
20. 9 cm =   m

21. 17 mm =   cm
22. 25 mm =   cm
23. 250 mm =   cm
24. 12 mm =   cm
25. 2 cm =   mm
26. 15 cm =   mm
27. 2.8 cm =   mm
28. 9.6 cm =   mm
29. 2 km =   m
30. 1.5 km =   m
31. 1.24 km =   m
32. 0.324 km =   m
33. 0.076 km =   m
34. 18 km =   m
35. 7.1 km =   m
36. 0.07 km =   m
37. 400 m =   km
38. 875 m =   km
39. 25 mm =   cm
40. 65 m =   km

41. 450 g =   kg
42. 200 g =   kg
43. 1400 g =   kg
44. 2650 g =   kg

45. 40 g =   kg
46. 55 g =   kg
47. 7 g =   kg
48. 7000 g =   kg
49. 2.2 kg =   g
50. 0.65 kg =   g
51. 2 t =   kg
52. 3.2 t =   kg
53. 500 ml =   l
54. 4000 l =   m³
55. 6000 l =   m³
56. 8000 ml =   l
57. 455 ml =   l
58. 2.45 l =   ml
59. 2.8 t =   kg
60. 67 g =   kg

Exercise 3

Copy and complete.

1. 32 cm =   m
2. 15 mm =   cm
3. 234 g =   kg
4. 72 m =   km
5. 7.5 m =   cm
6. 0.041 kg =   g
7. 260 ml =   l
8. 0.71 cm =   mm
9. 9 cm =   m
10. 100 km =   m
11. 27 g =   kg
12. 7 mm =   cm
13. 18 kg =   g
14. 800 ml =   l
15. 0.2 km =   m
16. 11.1 m =   cm
17. 400 kg =   t
18. 1000 kg =   g
19. 85 m =   km
20. 0.3 mm =   cm

21. 8 cm =   m
22. 6 g =   kg
23. 100 mm =   cm
24. 950 ml =   l
25. 7.8 t =   kg
26. 0.07 kg =   g
27. 20 cm =   m
28. 60 m =   cm
29. 18 g =   kg
30. 880 m =   km
31. 7000 cm =   km
32. 600 mm =   m
33. 0.03 m =   mm
34. 0.71 km =   m
35. 20 000 g =   t
36. 50 000 ml =   m³
37. 600 cm =   km
38. 17 g =   kg
39. 250 m =   cm
40. 0.1 mm =   m

2.2 PROBLEMS

Exercise 4

1. John makes a tower using nine identical bricks, each of thickness 2.7 cm. How high is the tower?

2. Mrs Johnson bought 8 kg of potatoes at 31p a kilogram. She paid for her purchase with a £5 note. How much change did she receive?

3. A car dealer bought twelve cars. He bought a number of tyres so that each car had five new tyres and he had 13 left over. How many tyres did he buy?

4. A theatre has 460 seats arranged in 20 rows of equal length. How many seats are in each row?

5. The population of a town near a nuclear power station decreased from 8854 to 6278. How many people left the town?

6. A man bought five articles at £2.40 each and six articles at 95p each. How much did he spend altogether?

7. A chef cooks a Christmas pudding which weighs 24 kg. The pudding is shared equally between 40 people. How much does each person receive?

8. Find the next two numbers in each sequence
   (a) 61, 52, 43, . . .
   (b) 120, 60, 30, . . .
   (c) 2, 3, 5, 8, . . .
   (d) 80, 68, 56, . . .

9. John and Steven each have the same amount of money. How much must John give to Steve if Steve is then to have £10 more than John?

10. In a simple code A = 1, B = 2, C = 3, . . . Z = 26.
    Decode the following messages.
    (a) 23, 8, 1, 20
        20, 9, 13, 5
        4, 15
        23, 5
        6, 9, 14, 9, 19, 8.
    (b) 19, 4^2, (3×7), 18, $(90 - 71)$
        1^3, (9×2), $(2^2 + 1^2)$
        18, $(\frac{1}{5}$ of 105$)$, 2, $(1 \div \frac{1}{2})$, 3^2, 19, 2^3.
    (c) 23, $(100 \div 20)$
        1, $(2 \times 3 \times 3)$, $(2^2 + 1^2)$
        21, $(100 - 86)$, $(100 \div 25)$, 5, $(2^4 + 2)$
        1, (5×4), $(10 \div \frac{1}{2})$, 1, $(27 \div 9)$, $(99 \div 9)$.

Exercise 5

1. There are 1128 pupils in a school and there are 36 more girls than boys. How many girls attend the school?

2. A generous, but not very bright, teacher decides to award 1p to the person coming 10th in a test, 2p to the person coming 9th, 4p to the person coming 8th and so on, doubling the amount each time. How much does the teacher award to the person who came top?

3. A tree was planted when James Wilkinson was born. He died in 1920, aged 75. How old was the tree in 1975?

4. Washing-up liquid is sold in 200 ml containers. Each container costs 57p. How much will it cost to buy 10 litres of the liquid?

5. A train is supposed to leave London at 11 24 and arrive in Brighton at 12 40. The train was delayed and arrived $2\frac{1}{4}$ hours late. At what time did the train arrive?

6. Big Ben stopped for repairs at 17 15 on Tuesday and restarted at 08 20 on Wednesday. For how long had it been stopped?

7 How much would I pay for nine litres of paint if two litres cost £2.30?

8. A television set was advertised at £282.50 for cash, or by 12 equal instalments of £25.30. How much would be saved by paying cash?

9. Eggs are packed twelve to a box. A farmer has enough eggs to fill 316 boxes with unbroken eggs and he has 62 cracked eggs left over. How many eggs had he to start with?

10. A car travels 30 miles on a gallon of petrol and petrol costs £2.20 per gallon. Over a period of one year the car travels a distance of 9600 miles. How much does the petrol cost for the whole year?

Exercise 6

1. In a rugby match the total number of points scored was 58. The home team won by 16 points. How many points did the away team score?

2. Every day at school a teacher uses 10 g of chalk. He teaches 200 days a year. How much chalk will he use if he teaches for 25 years? Give the answer in kg.

3. Mrs James saw flour on sale at 200 g for 28p. How much does she pay if she buys 650 g of flour?

4. A half is a third of it. What is it?

5. A third is a half of it. What is it?

6. A hotel manager was able to buy loaves of bread at £4.44 per dozen, whereas the shop price was 43p per loaf. How much did he save on each loaf?

7. David bought seven apples and received 88p change from £2.00. What was the average price of the apples?

8. In a cycle time-trial, John took 6 min 11 s for the course and Bill took only 5 min 47 s. By how many seconds was Bill quicker than John?

9. One day a third of the class is absent and 16 children are present. How many children are in the class when no one is away?

10. A train leaves Manchester at 09 00 and travels towards London at 100 mph. Another train leaves London for Manchester, also at 09 00, and travels at 80 mph. Which train is nearer to London when they meet?

Exercise 7

1. A special new cheese is on offer at £3.48 per kilogram. Mrs Mann buys half a kilogram. How much change does she receive if she pays with a £5 note?

2. A cup and a saucer together cost £2.80. The cup costs 60p more than the saucer. How much does the cup cost?

3. What number must be subtracted from both 25 and 42 so that one number is twice the other?

4. A generous school teacher gave each of her 30 pupils five sweets. There were 65 sweets left in the box. How many sweets were in the box to start with?

5. Six lamp posts lie at equal distances from each other along a straight road. If the distance between each pair of lamp posts is 20 m, how far is it from the first lamp post to the sixth?

6. A man worked 7 hours per day from Monday to Friday and 4 hours overtime on Saturday. The rate of pay from Monday to Friday is £4.50 per hour and the overtime rate is time and a half. How much did he earn during the week?

7. A man smokes 40 cigarettes a day and each packet of 20 cigarettes costs £1.15. How much does he spend on cigarettes in a whole year of 365 days?

8. A dealer bought a shirt for £4, sold it for £5, bought it back for £6 and finally sold it for £7. How much profit did he make?

9. Five 2's can make 25: $25 = 22 + 2 + \frac{2}{2}$
 (a) Use four 9's to make 100
 (b) Use three 6's to make 7
 (c) Use three 5's to make 60
 (d) Use five 5's to make 61
 (e) Use four 7's to make 1
 (f) Use three 8's to make 11

10. Find the missing digits.

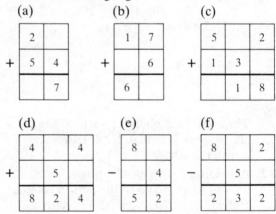

Exercise 8

1. If gas costs 31p for every therm used, what will be the cost in £'s of 200 therms?

2. The rent for a flat is £19 per week. How much rent is paid over a period of 30 weeks?

3. A man works from 07 30 until 16 45. How many hours and minutes has he worked?

4. A rectangular room measures 3.8 m by 2.7 m. A carpet measuring 4 m by 3 m is cut to fit the room.
 (a) Calculate the area of the room.
 (b) Calculate the area of carpet wasted.

5. Calculate the number of seconds in a day.

6. Write down the next two numbers in each of the following sequences
   (a) 2, 5, 8, 11, . . .
   (b) 7, 7, 8, 10, 13, . . .
   (c) 12, 11, 9, 6, . . .
   (d) 1, 3, 7, 15, 31, . . .

7. A roll of wallpaper is cut into five strips. A wall requires 35 strips of paper. How much will it cost if one roll of wallpaper costs £5.40?

8. A television set which costs £300 in England was on sale in France at 3630 francs. Assuming that the television set has the same value as in England, calculate the rate of exchange (i.e. how many francs to the pound?).

9. (a) Last season in the Football League 3 points were awarded for a win, 1 point for a draw and 0 points for a defeat. Copy and complete the table below.

Team	P	W	D	L	Points
Liverpool	18	12	3	3	
Notts. Forest	19	11	5	3	
Man. Utd	18	12	2	4	
West Ham	19	10	6	3	
Spurs	18	11	2	5	
QPR	19	9	4	5	
Everton	17	10	0	7	
Ipswich	17	8	4	5	

   (b) Calculate also how many points each team would have using the old system of
   2 points for a win
   1 point for a draw
   0 points for a defeat.

10. A shopkeeper buys coffee at £3.65 per kg and sells it at 95p per 100 g. How much profit does he make per kg?

Exercise 9

1. Mrs Jackson buys nine 15p stamps and twenty 18p stamps. How much change will she receive from a £5 note?

2. Place the following numbers in order of size, smallest first: 0.12, 0.012, 0.21, 0.021, 0.03.

3. The outline of a 50p coin is shown below.

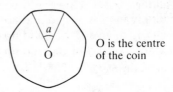

O is the centre of the coin

Calculate the size of the angle a, to the nearest $\frac{1}{10}$ of a degree.

4. Which would cost less and by how much: 35 tins at 25p each or 23 jars at 37p each?

5. A car travels 12 km on 1 litre of petrol. How much petrol will it need on a journey of 54 km?

6. A wooden rod of length 4 m is cut into two pieces so that one piece is 10 cm longer than the other. How long is each piece?

7. (a) Increase £60 by 10%.
   (b) Decrease £900 by 20%.
   (c) Increase £2000 by 2%.

8. A 12-day holiday in Spain costs £285. Find the average cost per day, correct to the nearest pound.

9. Write as a single number:
   (a) 3^2 (b) 2^3 (c) 5^2
   (d) 10^3 (e) 2×4^2 (f) 3×2^4

10. In order to make the service more popular, bus fares are reduced by 40%. Find the new price of a ticket which used to cost (a) 10p, (b) 50p, (c) 35p.

Exercise 10

1. Twelve calculators cost £102. How many calculators could be bought for £76.50?

2. A car travels 35 m in 0.7 seconds. How far does it travel in
   (a) 0.1 s? (b) 1 s? (c) 2 minutes?

3. Class 4P has 22 pupils and class 4N has 20 pupils. Pupils in 4P give an average of 5p each to charity and pupils in 4N give an average of 7p each. How much was given to charity altogether?

4. Find two numbers which:
   (a) multiply to give 12 and add up to 7.
   (b) multiply to give 42 and add up to 13.
   (c) multiply to give 32 and add up to 12.
   (d) multiply to give 48 and add up to 26.

5. Copy and complete

	Fraction	Decimal
(a)	$\frac{4}{5}$	0.8
(b)	$\frac{1}{4}$	
(c)		0.3
(d)	$\frac{1}{8}$	
(e)		0.05

6. An engineering firm offers all of its workers
   a choice of two pay rises. Workers can
   choose either an 8% increase on their
   salaries or they can accept a rise of £800.
   (a) A fitter earns £5200 a year. Which pay
       rise should he choose?
   (b) The personnel manager earns £11 500 a
       year. Which pay rise should he choose?

7. A ship's voyage started at 20 30 on Tuesday
   and finished at 07 00 on the next day. How
   long was the journey in hours and minutes?

8. Work out, without using a calculator.
   (a) 0.6 − 0.06   (b) 0.04 × 1000
   (c) 0.4 ÷ 100   (d) 7.2 − 5
   (e) 10% of £90   (f) 25% of £160.

9. In 1984 the population of the United States
   was 232 million. The population was
   expected to grow by 12% by the end of the
   century. Find the expected population at the
   end of the century, correct to the nearest
   million.

10. Amongst other ingredients, 350 g of flour
    and 2 tablespoons of milk are needed to
    make 4 cakes.
    (a) What weight of flour is need to make 12
        cakes?
    (b) How many tablespoons of milk are
        needed to make 6 cakes?

Exercise 11

1. How many oranges costing 9p each can be
   bought with £2?

2. A film lasting 1 hour 40 minutes finishes at
   21 15. At what time does the film start?

3. Find the angle between the hands of a clock
   showing 4.00 p.m.

4. A roll of wallpaper costs £5.60 and each roll
   is sufficient for 6 strips. How much will it
   cost to paper a room which requires 24 strips
   of wallpaper?

5. Arrange the following numbers in order,
   smallest first:
   3210, 3120, 2333, 3211, 3301, 3102.

6. Work out, without a calculator:
   (a) 2.7 × 100,
   (b) 0.41 × 10 000,
   (c) 0.84 ÷ 100,
   (d) 0.005 23 × 1000.

7. How many seconds are there in 5 hours?

8. In a rugby match the total number of points
   scored was 50. The home team won by 14
   points. How many points did the away team
   score?

9. A milkman delivers 2 bottles of milk to
   every house on his round.
   (a) If there are 648 houses on his round,
       how many bottles does he deliver?
   (b) After he has delivered to 487 houses,
       how many more bottles has he still to
       deliver?

10. Which of the shapes below can be drawn
    without going over any line twice and
    without taking the pencil from the paper?
    Write 'yes' or 'no' for each shape.

(a)   (b)

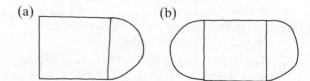

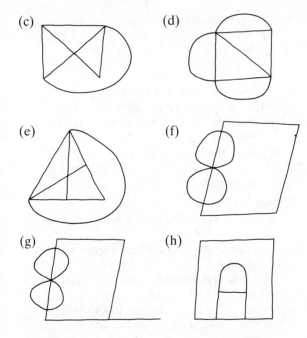

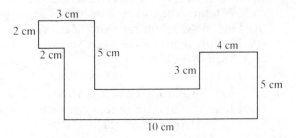

4. Calculate the perimeter of the shape below.

Exercise 12

1. A worker is paid £3.40 per hour for a 40 hour week. In addition to his basic pay he works 6 hours overtime at time and a half. Calculate
   (a) his basic pay for 40 hours
   (b) his overtime pay
   (c) his take-home pay, if he pays £8.75 National Insurance and £15.80 income tax.

2. Calculate the area of a square which has a perimeter of 20 cm.

3. The table below gives the cost of sending parcels by post. (Parts of a kilogram are charged as a whole kilogram).

Parcel not over	Cost
1 kg	£1.80
2 kg	£2.15
3 kg	£2.45
4 kg	£2.72
5 kg	£2.93

State the cost of posting a parcel of weight:
(a) 2 kg
(b) 2.8 kg
(c) 4.2 kg.

5. A hi-fi system is priced as follows:

Stereo amplifier	£119.50
Cassette deck	£92.50
Record deck	£46.00
Tuner	£75.50
Speakers	£124.00
Cabinet	£65.50

   (a) Find the total cash price of this system.
   (b) This system can also be bought using hire purchase with a deposit of £120 and 18 monthly payments of £28. Find the total hire purchase price.
   (c) In a sale the prices of all items are reduced by 30%. Find the cash price of the whole system in the sale.

6. The houses in a street are numbered from 1 to 60. How many times does the number '2' appear?

7. Draw a large copy of the square below.

1	2	3	4

Your task is to fill up all 16 squares using four 1's, four 2's, four 3's and four 4's. Each number may appear only once in any row (↔) or column (↕). The first row has been drawn already.

8. Between the times 11 57 and 12 27 the mileometer of a car changes from 23793 miles to 23825 miles. At what average speed is the car travelling?

9. In a simple code A = 1, B = 2, C = 3 and so on. When the word 'BAT' is written in code its total score is (2 + 1 + 20) = 23.
   (a) Find the score for the word 'ZOOM'
   (b) Find the score for the word 'ALPHABET'
   (c) Find a word with a score of 40.

10. Alan has 28p and John has 20p. How much must John give to Alan so that Alan has twice as much money as John?

Exercise 13

1. A woman hires a car from a car hire firm which charges £12 per day plus 8p per km travelled.
   (a) How much does it cost to hire a car for four days and drive 200 km?
   (b) How much does it cost to hire a car for six days and drive 650 km?
   (c) A woman hired a car for two days and had to pay £32. How far did she drive?

2. The table shows how much £100 amounts to when invested at the given rates for periods of 1, 3 or 5 years.

Period in years	Amount		
	6% per annum	8% per annum	10% per annum
1	£106	£108	£110
3	£119	£126	£133
5	£134	£147	£161

   (a) What does £100 amount to when invested
      (i) at 6% for 1 year
      (ii) at 10% for 5 years
      (iii) at 8% for 3 years
      (iv) at 6% for 3 years?
   (b) How much interest is earned when £100 is invested at 8% per annum for 5 years?
   (c) What does £500 amount to when invested at 10% for 3 years?
   (d) What is the interest on £2000 at 6% per annum for 3 years?

3. Find the missing numbers
   (a)   3 * 4
       + * 2 *
       ‾‾‾‾‾‾‾
         5 8 9

   (b)   * 4 7
         + 8 * *
         ‾‾‾‾‾‾‾‾
          * 1 5 9

4. A restaurant adds a service charge of 10% to the basic price of meals.
   (a) Find the total cost of a meal with a basic price of £15.
   (b) Find the basic price of a meal which costs £22 after the service charge has been added.

5. Due to overproduction, the E.E.C. destroyed 41 cauliflowers for each minute of the year in 1984.
   (a) How many cauliflowers were destroyed per day?
   (b) How many cauliflowers were destroyed in the whole year?
   (c) If each cauliflower had been sold for 20p, how much money would have been raised by actually selling the cauliflowers?

2.3 IMPERIAL UNITS

(a) 12 inches = 1 foot
3 feet = 1 yard
1760 yards = 1 mile

(b) 16 ounces = 1 pound
14 pounds = 1 stone
2240 pounds = 1 ton

(c) 8 pints = 1 gallon

29. $\frac{1}{2}$ mile =   yards
30. $\frac{1}{2}$ gallon =   pints
31. 4 feet 6 inches =   inches
32. 3 pounds 6 ounces =   ounces
33. 5 stones 2 pounds =   pounds
34. 7 stones 4 pounds =   pounds
35. 10 stones 12 pounds =   pounds
36. 5 feet 3 inches =   inches
37. 6 feet 1 inch =   inches
38. 4 feet 10 inches =   inches

Exercise 14

1. How many inches are there in two feet?
2. How many feet are there in three yards?
3. How many ounces are there in two pounds?
4. How many pints are there in two gallons?
5. How many pounds are there in three stones?
6. How many inches are there in five feet?
7. How many yards are there in ten miles?
8. How many ounces are there in five pounds?
9. How many pounds are there in two tons?
10. How many inches are there in a yard?
11. How many pounds are there in ten stones?
12. How many ounces are there in a stone?
13. How many inches are there in half a yard?
14. How many ounces are there in half a pound?
15. How many yards are there in a quarter of a mile?
16. How many inches are there in ten yards?

In questions **17** to **38** copy each statement and fill in the missing numbers.

17. 12 feet =   yards.
18. 32 ounces =   pounds
19. 4 stones =   pounds
20. 2 gallons =   pints
21. 6 feet =   inches
22. 2 miles =   yards
23. 40 pints =   gallons
24. 4480 pounds =   tons
25. 28 pounds =   stones
26. 6 gallons =   pints
27. 3 yards =   inches
28. $1\frac{1}{2}$ feet =   inches

Changing units

Exercise 15

You may use the following approximate conversions.

1 inch = 2.54 cm   1 gallon = 4.55 litres
1 mile = 1.61 km   1 km = 0.621 mile
1 pound = 0.454 kg   1 litre = 0.22 gallon
1 pint = 0.568 litre   1 kg = 2.2 pounds

Copy each statement and fill in the missing numbers.

1. 10 inches =   cm
2. 10 gallons =   litres
3. 100 pounds =   kg
4. 100 pints =   litres
5. 2 miles =   km
6. 2 pounds =   kg
7. 10 miles =   km
8. 4 inches =   cm
9. 5 pounds =   kg
10. $\frac{1}{2}$ pint =   litre
11. 10 km =   miles
12. 100 litres =   gallons
13. 3 kg =   pounds
14. 100 km =   miles
15. 400 litres =   gallons
16. 2 kg =   pounds
17. 2 km =   miles
18. 5 litres =   gallons
19. 20 kg =   pounds
20. 20 km =   miles
21. 1 foot =   cm
22. 5 pints =   litres
23. 3 litres =   gallons
24. 3 inches =   cm
25. 4 pounds =   kg

2.4   FOREIGN CURRENCY

In this section we will use the following rates of exchange:

Country	Unit of money	Rate of exchange
France	franc	F12 = £1
Germany	mark	DM4 = £1
Greece	drachma	DR150 = £1
Spain	peseta	Ptas200 = £1
U.S.A.	dollar	$1.40 = £1

Exercise 16

Change the British money into the foreign currency stated.

1. £10 = F
2. £20 = DM
3. £3 = DR
4. £100 = Ptas
5. £1000 = $
6. £8 = DR
7. £7 = F
8. £100 = $
9. £16 = DM
10. £500 = DM
11. £0.50 = F
12. £0.50 = Ptas
13. £0.50 = $
14. £1000 = DR
15. £1000 = Ptas
16. £0.25 = DM
17. £0.25 = F
18. £50 = $
19. £200 = DR
20. £0.10 = Ptas
21. £500 = $
22. £600 = F
23. £65 = DM
24. £30 = DR
25. £1.50 = F
26. £1 = $
27. £1.50 = DR
28. £2.50 = Ptas
29. £11 = Ptas
30. £12.50 = $

Convert $50 into British money to the nearest penny.

$1.40 = £1   (from above)

$\therefore $1 = £\frac{1}{1.40}$

$\therefore $50 = £\frac{1}{1.40} \times 50 = £35.7142$

$= £35.71$ (to the nearest penny)

Exercise 17

Change the foreign currency into British money, correct to the nearest penny where necessary.

1. F36
2. DM40
3. $2.80
4. Ptas1000
5. DR600
6. F120
7. $140
8. DM80
9. Ptas5000
10. DR1500
11. F96
12. $70
13. DM6
14. Ptas900
15. DR80
16. F65
17. $60
18. DM82
19. F105
20. Ptas6500
21. DM62
22. $900
23. DR70
24. F240
25. Ptas10 000
26. DR95
27. $22.50
28. Ptas965
29. DM88.40
30. F72.65
31. Ptas8500
32. $71
33. DR640
34. DR191
35. $760
36. DM317
37. DM19 000
38. Ptas600 000
39. F22 500
40. $255

Exercise 18

Give answers correct to the nearest penny where necessary. In questions **1** to **10** fill in the spaces.

1. £20 = F
2. £15 = DM
3. $14 = £
4. DR450 = £
5. £5 = Ptas
6. F108 = £
7. DM60 = £
8. £600 = $
9. F27 = £
10. DM84 = £

11. A record costs $5.50 in the United States. What is the price in British money?

12. A car costs F40 000 in France. What is the price in British money?

13. A television costs £320 in Britain. What is the price in Greek money?

14. A bottle of wine costs Ptas185 in Spain. What is the price in British money?

15. A video recorder costs £500 in Britain and DM1900 in Germany. In which country is it cheaper and by how much (in £)?

16. A car costs F37 920 in France and Ptas680 000 in Spain. In which country is it cheaper and by how much (to the nearest £)?

17. A book costs DM26 in Germany and $8.40 in the United States. In which country is it cheaper and by how much (in £)?

18. Copy and complete
    (a) $140 = £   (b) £100 = F
    (c) $140 = F

2.5 MAP SCALES

The map below is drawn to a scale of 1:50 000. In other words 1 cm on the map represents 50 000 cm on the land.

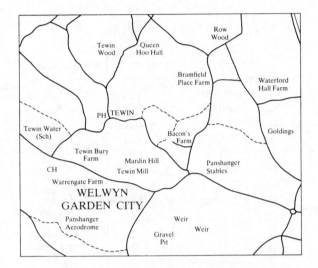

On a map of scale 1:25 000 two towns appear 10 cm apart. What is the actual distance between the towns in km?

1 cm on map = 25 000 cm on land
10 cm on map = 250 000 cm on land
250 000 cm = 2500 m
= 2.5 km

The towns are 2.5 km apart.

Exercise 19

1. The scale of a map is 1:1000. Find the actual length in metres represented on the map by 20 cm.

2. The scale of a map is 1:10 000. Find the actual length in metres represented on the map by 5 cm.

3. The scale of a map is 1:20 000. Find the actual length in kilometres represented on the map by
   (a) 10 cm   (b) 15 cm   (c) 4 cm

4. The scale of a map is 1:50 000. Find the actual length in kilometres represented on the map by
   (a) 10 cm   (b) 6 cm   (c) 12 cm

5. Copy and complete the table

Map scale	Length on map	Actual length on land
(a) 1:10 000	10 cm	1 km
(b) 1:2000	10 cm	m
(c) 1:25 000	4 cm	km
(d) 1:10 000	6 cm	km
(e) 1:50 000	3 cm	km
(f) 1:25 000	10 cm	km
(g) 1:100 000	2.2 cm	km
(h) 1:25 000	8 cm	km
(i) 1:50 000	3.1 cm	km
(j) 1:10 000	2.7 cm	m

6. How far apart are two places if they are 5.4 cm apart on a map whose scale is 1:20 000?

7. Find the actual distance in metres between two points which are 6.3 cm apart on a map whose scale is 1:1000.

8. On a map of scale 1:300 000 the distance between York and Harrogate is 8 cm. What is the actual distance in km?

9. On a map of scale 1:320 000 the distance between Adwick le Street and Knottingley is 6.1 cm. What is the actual distance in km?

10. On a map of scale 1:64 000 the distance between Pudsey Town Hall and Beeston cemetery is 9.2 cm. What is the actual distance in km?

11. A builder's plan is drawn to a scale of 1 cm to 10 m. How long is a road which is 12 cm on the plan.

12. A plan is drawn to a scale of 1 cm to 1 m. How long is a wall which is 5.6 cm on the plan?

13. The plan of a house is drawn to a scale of 1 cm to 5 m. How wide is the kitchen if its width is 1 cm on the plan?

14. The scale of a drawing is 1 cm to 10 m. How long is a road which is 9 cm on the drawing?

15. The scale of a drawing is 1 cm to 5 m. How long is a path which is 2.1 cm on the drawing?

The distance between two towns is 18 km. How far apart will they be on a map of scale 1:50 000?

18 km = 1 800 000 cm

1 800 000 cm on land = $\frac{1}{50\,000} \times 1\,800\,000$ cm on map

Distance between towns on map = 36 cm

Exercise 20

1. The distance between two towns is 15 km. How far apart will they be on a map of scale 1:10 000?

2. The distance between two points is 25 km. How far apart will they be on a map of scale 1:20 000?

3. The length of a road is 2.8 km. How long will the road be on a map of scale 1:10 000?

4. The length of a reservoir is 5.9 km. How long will it be on a map of scale 1:100 000?

5. Copy and complete the table.

	Map scale	Actual length on land	Length on map
(a)	1:20 000	12 km	cm
(b)	1:10 000	8.4 km	cm
(c)	1:50 000	28 km	cm
(d)	1:40 000	56 km	cm
(e)	1:5000	5 km	cm
(f)	1:1000	60 m	cm
(g)	1:60 000	30 km	cm
(h)	1:250 000	550 km	cm
(i)	1:2000	12 m	cm

6. The plan of a house is drawn to a scale of 1 cm to 1 m. The length of the house is 13 m. What length will the house be on the plan?

7. The scale of a drawing is 1 cm to 10 m. The length of a wall is 25 m. What length will the wall be on the drawing?

8. A builder's plan is drawn to a scale of 1 cm to 10 m. The length of a garden is 15 m. What length will the garden be on the plan?

Exercise 21

1. On a map of scale 1:55 000 the distance between two places is 8 cm. What is the actual distance in km?

2. The length of a canal is 50 km. How long will it be on a map of scale 1:20 000?

3. Copy and complete the table.

	Map scale	Length on map	Actual length on land
(a)	1:10 000	5 cm	* km
(b)	1:10 000	* cm	12 km
(c)	1:20 000	8.4 cm	* km
(d)	1:50 000	* cm	8 km
(e)	1:200 000	3.2 cm	* km
(f)	1:1000	* cm	2 m
(g)	1:250	1.2 cm	* m
(h)	1:20 000	7.7 cm	* km
(i)	*	20 cm	2 km
(j)	*	8 cm	1.6 km
(k)	*	3 cm	3 km
(l)	*	9 cm	1.8 km
(m)	*	2.7 cm	1.35 km

4. A farmer's field is 5 cm long on a map. If the field is actually 500 m long, find the scale of the map.

5. A road is 12 cm on a map. If the road is actually 2.4 km long, find the scale of the map.

6. Two towns are 14 km apart, but the distance between them on a map is 28 cm. Find the scale of the map.

7. The plan of the room below is drawn to a scale of 1 cm to 1.2 m.

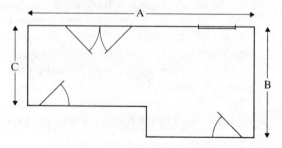

Use a ruler to find the actual dimensions marked A, B and C.

Part 3

3.1 APPROXIMATIONS

Significant figures

Write the following numbers correct to three significant figures (3 s.f.).

(a) $2.6582 = 2.66$ (to 3 s.f.)
          ↑

(b) $0.5142 = 0.514$ (to 3 s.f.)
          ↑

(c) $84\ 660 = 84\ 700$ (to 3 s.f.)
        ↑

(d) $0.04031 = 0.0403$ (to 3 s.f.)
            ↑

In each case we look at the number marked with an arrow to see if it is 'five or more'.

Exercise 1

In questions **1** to **20** write the numbers correct to three significant figures.

1. 3.1782	**2.** 14.762
3. 8.0491	**4.** 2.6324
5. 51.252	**6.** 0.5567
7. 0.832 41	**8.** 7.3668
9. 0.076 14	**10.** 18.294
11. 426.72	**12.** 315.23
13. 6.0074	**14.** 11.355
15. 2.0943	**16.** 0.007 422
17. 318.24	**18.** 2418
19. 3561	**20.** 38 684

In questions **21** to **40** write the numbers correct to two significant figures.

21. 5.674	**22.** 18.34
23. 0.7666	**24.** 0.5151

25. 8.333
27. 11.624
29. 18.555
31. 0.071 38
33. 30.542
35. 18 740
37. 889
39. 40 027

26. 7.2461
28. 25.09
30. 0.008 26
32. 17.802
34. 60.91
36. 34 265
38. 71 623
40. 163.4

In questions **41** to **60** write the numbers correct to four significant figures.
41. 28.666
43. 2.994 81
45. 8.0455
47. 0.031 111
49. 65 525
51. 5.6777
53. 568.83
55. 0.038 1111
57. 80.0455
59. 77 777

42. 3.0407
44. 316.252
46. 0.007 1652
48. 84 207
50. 124 860
52. 193.24
54. 2001.76
56. 76.0583
58. 6.0666
60. 400 289

Decimal places

Write the following numbers correct to two decimal places (2 D.P.)

(a) 8.358 = 8.36 (to 2 D.P.)
     ↑

(b) 0.0328 = 0.03 (to 2 D.P.)
     ↑

(c) 74.355 = 74.36 (to 2 D.P.)
     ↑

In each case we look at the number marked with an arrow to see if it is 'five or more'.

Exercise 2

In questions **1** to **20** write the numbers correct to two decimal places.
1. 8.486
3. 1.042
5. 11.618
7. 0.555
9. 2.0492
11. 13.6241
13. 0.0743
15. 7.823
17. 4.114
19. 206.125

2. 6.041
4. 12.135
6. 6.049
8. 18.076
10. 8.946
12. 216.841
14. 0.0714
16. 3.126
18. 24.521
20. 8.0895

In questions **21** to **40** write the numbers correct to one decimal place.
21. 8.621
23. 9.047
25. 8.614
27. 0.714
29. 8.826
31. 207.15
33. 0.0923
35. 4.261
37. 217.14
39. 0.85

22. 12.55
24. 2.608
26. 5.672
28. 0.0961
30. 0.666
32. 10.72
34. 8.041
36. 88.74
38. 3.961
40. 4.972

In questions **41** to **60** write the numbers to the degree of accuracy indicated.
41. 8.052 (2 D.P.)
43. 6.777 (1 D.P.)
45. 0.0714 (3 D.P.)
47. 19.62 (1 D.P.)
49. 8.092 (2 D.P.)
51. 3.3355 (3 D.P.)
53. 8.0496 (2 D.P.)
55. 0.07145 (4 D.P.)
57. 8.0715 (3 D.P.)
59. 9.942 (1 D.P.)

42. 17.62 (1 D.P.)
44. 9.094 (2 D.P.)
46. 0.03328 (4 D.P.)
48. 8.0755 (3 D.P.)
50. 4.076 (2 D.P.)
52. 8.921 (1 D.P.)
54 .0.078 (2 D.P.)
56. 2.342 (1 D.P.)
58. 1.3498 (3 D.P.)
60. 15.981 (1 D.P.)

61. Use a ruler to measure the dimensions of the rectangles below.
(a) Write down the length and width in cm correct to one decimal place.
(b) Work out the area of each rectangle and give the answer in cm^2 correct to one decimal place.

(i)
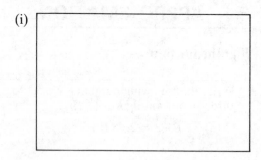

(ii)
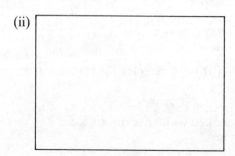

3.2 ESTIMATING

Estimate the answers to the following
questions:

(a) $9.7 \times 3.1 \approx 10 \times 3$. About 30.
(b) $81.4 \times 98.2 \approx 80 \times 100$. About 8000.
(c) $19.2 \times 49.1 \approx 20 \times 50$. About 1000.
(d) $102.7 \div 19.6 \approx 100 \div 20$. About 5.

Exercise 3

In the table below there are 30 questions, each followed by three possible
answers. In each case only one answer is correct.
Write down each question and decide (by estimating) which answer is
correct. No calculating is required.

Question	Answer A	Answer B	Answer C
1. 5.1×9.9	4.69	94.69	50.49
2. 9×7.2	64.8	23.4	201.8
3. 1.01×80.6	19.302	81.406	304.206
4. 58.4×102	600.4	5956.8	2450.4
5. 6.8×11.4	19.32	280.14	77.52
6. 97×1.08	104.76	55.66	1062.3
7. 972×20.2	2112.4	19 634.4	8862.4
8. 7.1×103	74.3	731.3	7210.3
9. 18.9×21	396.9	58.7	201.9
10. 2.1×96	19.6	507.6	201.6
11. 3.85×1010	394.6	3002.5	3888.5
12. 11.6×40.3	467.48	811.48	48.48
13. 1.95×21	212.65	40.95	19.85
14. 6.9×103	710.7	2350.7	70.9
15. 207×3.9	317.3	8140.3	807.3
16. 21.1×19.2	708.12	405.12	41.12
17. 97.1×98	963.8	4810.8	9515.8
18. 4.01×960	3849.6	417.4	894.2
19. 33×2.7	35.1	89.1	342.1
20. 43×0.95	4.95	40.85	407.65
21. 7.8×9	20.4	711.2	70.2
22. 11.1×8.9	98.79	58.69	504.6
23. 88×4.9	195.4	431.2	904.2
24. 201×1.87	38.63	916.87	375.87
25. 0.9×115	103.5	62.5	309.5
26. 1200×0.89	121.4	1068	364.4
27. 10.9×61	61.8	2444.9	664.9
28. 0.1×98.2	29.42	9.82	98.2
29. 0.104×980	9.82	984.2	101.92
30. 0.21×1050	22.5	220.5	485.5

Exercise 4

In the table below there are 30 questions, each followed by three possible answers. In each case only one answer is correct.

Write down each question and decide (by estimating) which answer is correct. Do not do the calculations exactly.

Question	Answer A	Answer B	Answer C
1. $7.79 \div 1.9$	8.2	4.1	1.9
2. $27.03 \div 5.1$	5.3	0.5	8.7
3. $59.78 \div 9.8$	12.2	2.8	6.1
4. $13.32 \div 1.8$	7.4	4.7	12.1
5. $18.05 \div 0.95$	1.9	19	7.6
6. $29.82 \div 7.1$	1.8	8.6	4.2
7. $34.68 \div 10.2$	3.4	7.1	11.4
8. $93.84 \div 9.2$	7.6	10.2	19.4
9. $711 \div 7.9$	90	51	175
10. $1.078 \div 0.98$	6.4	10.4	1.1
11. $1250.5 \div 6.1$	21.4	205	66.2
12. $20.48 \div 3.2$	6.4	12.2	2.8
13. $25.25 \div 10.1$	5.6	25	2.5
14. $881.1 \div 99$	8.9	4.9	19.9
15. $1155 \div 105$	3.5	11	23
16. 32×98	3136	1754	24 806
17. 2.1×5.01	7.641	10.521	17.21
18. 103×0.96	9.78	65.78	98.88
19. 7.2×6.9	112.68	49.68	73.48
20. $19.11 \div 9.1$	5.2	2.1	0.23
21. $25.11 \div 3.1$	8.1	15.1	19.3
22. $216 \div 0.9$	56.3	24.3	240
23. $19.2 + 0.41$	23.3	8.41	19.61
24. $207 + 18.34$	25.34	225.34	1248
25. $68.2 - 1.38$	97.82	48.82	66.82
26. $7 - 0.64$	6.36	1.48	0.48
27. 974×0.11	9.14	107.14	563.14
28. $551.1 \div 11$	6.92	50.1	5623
29. $207.1 + 11.65$	310.75	23.75	218.75
30. 664×0.51	256.2	338.64	828.62

3.3   ORDER OF OPERATIONS

Work out $\times$ and $\div$ before $+$ and $-$

(a) $5 + 6 \times 2 = 5 + 12 = 17$
(b) $12 \div 3 - 2 = 4 - 2 = 2$
(c) $8 - 15 \div 3 = 8 - 5 = 3$
(d) $2 \times 4 + 3 \times 6 = 8 + 18 = 26$

Exercise 5

Work out

1. $6 \times 3 + 2$ 2. $5 + 2 \times 4$
3. $6 + 5 \times 2$ 4. $8 + 7 \times 2$
5. $8 - 1 \times 4$ 6. $7 + 18 \div 3$
7. $9 + 6 \div 2$ 8. $26 - 2 \times 8$

9. $20 - 3 \times 5$
10. $11 + 8 \div 2$
11. $5 \times 5 - 5$
12. $16 - 30 \div 3$
13. $10 - 20 \div 4$
14. $7 \times 7 - 2$
15. $9 + 7 \times 3$
16. $20 \div 10 + 20$
17. $50 - 8 \times 4$
18. $55 - 8 \times 5$
19. $22 - 3 \times 7$
20. $19 + 24 \div 6$
21. $11 + 8 \div 1$
22. $60 - 7 \times 8$
23. $15 - 2 \times 6$
24. $15 \div 5 - 3$
25. $30 + 15 \div 3$
26. $9 \times 5 + 15$
27. $40 - 3 \times 8$
28. $12 - 36 \div 6$
29. $3 + 20 \div 2$
30. $13 + 8 \div 8$

31. $2 \times 4 + 3 \times 5$
32. $6 \times 6 + 7 \times 5$
33. $1 \times 6 + 7 \times 2$
34. $2 \times 8 + 2 \times 10$
35. $3 \times 5 - 12 \div 2$
36. $3 \times 5 - 28 \div 4$
37. $7 \times 4 + 2 \times 2$
38. $30 \div 3 + 5 \times 4$
39. $20 \div 2 - 3 \times 2$
40. $8 \div 8 - 1 \times 1$
41. $7 \times 3 + 32 \div 2$
42. $7 \times 5 + 33 \div 3$
43. $40 \div 8 - 60 \div 12$
44. $40 \div 8 + 6 \times 5$
45. $4 \times 12 + 13 \times 2$
46. $7 \times 3 - 100 \div 5$
47. $5 + 3 \times 2 - 6$
48. $28 - 7 \times 4 + 7$
49. $10 - 4 \times 2 + 4$
50. $15 + 60 \div 3 - 15$
51. $10 + 12 \div 3 - 7$
52. $2 + 9 \times 10 + 3$
53. $15 - 36 \div 12 + 2$
54. $40 - 216 \div 6 + 3$
55. $6 + 3 \times 8 - 10$
56. $9 + 9 \times 9 - 1$
57. $7 \times 7 + 10 \div 10$
58. $3 \times 8 - 2 \times 8$
59. $50 \div 2 - 5 \times 4$
60. $20 \times 20 - 306 \div 9$

When a calculation involves brackets, do things in the following order:

  (i) brackets
  (ii) $\times$ and $\div$
  (iii) $+$ and $-$

(a) $15 - (7 - 2) = 15 - 5 = 10$
(b) $3 \times (8 \div 2) = 3 \times 4 = 12$
(c) $(12 + 8) \div (6 \div 3) = 20 \div 2 = 10$
(d) $24 - (3 + 2 \times 4) = 24 - 11 = 13$

Exercise 6

Work out
1. $6 + (3 \times 2) + 1$
2. $4 \times (4 - 2) + 7$
3. $8 + (8 - 3) \times 3$
4. $6 \times 6 - (3 \times 3)$
5. $(10 - 1) \times 2 - 3$
6. $8 \times (10 \div 2) - 12$
7. $7 + 3 \times (6 \times 5)$
8. $(3 \times 3) + 2 \times 4$

9. $8 - (3 \times 2) \div 6$
10. $5 \times (8 - 3) - 20$
11. $20 + 16 \div (4 \times 2)$
12. $12 + 8 \div (8 \div 4)$
13. $(5 - 2) \times 3 + 11$
14. $3 \times (12 - 7) - 10$
15. $15 \div (9 - 6) + 8$
16. $5 \times (9 + 1) + 8$
17. $8 + 3 \times (3 + 4)$
18. $85 - (15 + 45) \div 12$
19. $8 + (7 + 2) \div 9$
20. $6 + 16 \div (5 - 1)$
21. $(1 + 4) \times 7 - 15$
22. $10 + 8 \times (8 - 5)$
23. $24 - (9 + 21) \div 5$
24. $42 \div (11 - 5) - 2$
25. $(7 \times 2) \times 2 + 16$
26. $(11 - 7) \times 3 + 16$
27. $60 - (3 \times 20) + 13$
28. $17 + 5 \times (3 \times 1)$
29. $16 - 22 \div (23 - 21)$
30. $13 + (19 + 5) \div 3$

31. $(18 + 6) \div 6 + 13$
32. $(8 + 5) \times 2 + 10$
33. $15 + 8 \times (21 - 18)$
34. $129 - 7 \times (15 - 8)$
35. $(13 - 6) \times 8 - 5$
36. $35 \div (24 - 19) - 6$
37. $7 - (8 + 2) \div 5$
38. $12 + (5 + 2) \times 6$
39. $9 + (36 + 9) \div 9$
40. $(19 - 8) \times 6 + 12$
41. $(33 - 22) \times 4 + 7$
42. $7 + (21 + 7) \div 4$
43. $9 \times (9 + 2) - 2$
44. $6 \div (12 \div 2) + 3$
45. $96 - 8 \times (60 - 51)$
46. $8 \times 4 + (17 - 8)$
47. $7 \times (12 - 10) + 9$
48. $9 \times 3 - (20 \div 2)$
49. $37 - (26 - 19) \times 2$
50. $24 \div (12 \div 2) + 7$

51. $\dfrac{15}{(8 - 5)}$
52. $\dfrac{9 \times 2}{(9 - 6)}$
53. $\dfrac{18 + 2}{(3 + 2)}$
54. $\dfrac{15 + 15 - 2}{(8 - 1)}$
55. $\dfrac{27 + 3 \times 3}{(3 \times 2)}$
56. $\dfrac{6 + 8 \times 3}{(8 \times 2 - 10)}$
57. $\dfrac{13 - 12 \div 4}{4 + 3 \times 2}$
58. $\dfrac{11 + 6 \times 6}{5 - 8 \div 2}$
59. $\dfrac{12 + 3 \times 6}{4 + 3 \div 3}$
60. $\dfrac{24 - 18 \div 3}{1.5 + 4.5}$

The last ten questions are more difficult.

61. $(42 - 5 \times 6) \times (8 - 4 \times 2) + (7 + 3 \times 3)$
62. $(10 - 24 \div 3) + (8 + 3 \times 4) \div (8 - 6 \times 1)$
63. $7 + 9 \times (8 - 6 \div 2)$
64. $[(7 - 2) \times 5] - (6 \times 3 - 2 \times 4)$
65. $[(60 - 7 \times 5) \div 5] + (12 + 7 \times 10)$
66. $(15 - 3 \times 4) \times 4 + [60 \div (24 \div 2)]$
67. $[(9 - 7) \times 12] - (7 \times 3 - 5 \times 4)$
68. $(50 - 8 \times 6) \times 2 + [40 \div (5 \times 2)]$
69. $[(12 - 8) \times 4] \div (11 - 3 \times 1)$
70. $(7 \times 2 - 6) + (7 + 16 \div 8) \times (10 - 4 \times 2)$

3.4 USING A CALCULATOR

Exercise 7

Work out, correct to four significant figures.

1. 85.3×21.7
2. $18.6 \div 2.7$
3. $10.074 \div 8.3$
4. 0.112×3.74
5. $8 - 0.11111$
6. $19 + 0.3456$
7. $0.841 \div 17$
8. 11.02×20.1
9. $18.3 \div 0.751$
10. 0.982×6.74

11. $\dfrac{8.3 + 2.94}{3.4}$
12. $\dfrac{6.1 - 4.35}{0.76}$

13. $\dfrac{19.7 + 21.4}{0.985}$
14. $7.3 + \left(\dfrac{8.2}{9.5}\right)$

15. $\left(\dfrac{6.04}{18.7}\right) - 0.214$
16. $\dfrac{2.4 \times 0.871}{4.18}$

17. $19.3 + \left(\dfrac{2.6}{1.95}\right)$
18. $6.41 + \dfrac{9.58}{2.6}$

19. $\dfrac{19.3 \times 0.221}{0.689}$
20. $8.3 + \dfrac{0.64}{0.325}$

21. $2.4 + (9.7 \times 0.642)$
22. $11.2 + (9.75 \times 1.11)$

23. $0.325 + \dfrac{8.6}{11.2}$
24. $8.35^2 - 25$

25. $6.71^2 + 0.64$
26. $3.45^3 + 11.8$

27. $2.93^3 - 2.641$
28. $\dfrac{7.2^2 - 4.5}{8.64}$

29. $\dfrac{13.9 + 2.97^2}{4.31}$
30. $(3.3 - 2.84)^2$

31. $\dfrac{(12.9 - 8.45)^2}{4.3}$
32. $\left(\dfrac{4.4 + 6.23}{9.9}\right)^2$

Using the memory

Work out $\dfrac{4.2 + 1.75}{3.63 - 2.14}$, correct to 4 s.f., using the memory buttons.

Find the bottom line first:

| 3.63 | − | 2.14 | = | M+ | C |

| 4.2 | + | 1.75 | = | ÷ | MR | = | .

The calculator reads 3.9932886

∴ Answer = 3.993 (to 4 s.f.)

Exercise 8

Work out the following, correct to four significant figures. Use the memory buttons where necessary.

1. $\dfrac{7.3 + 2.14}{3.6 - 2.95}$
2. $\dfrac{2.3 + 0.924}{1.3 + 0.635}$

3. $\dfrac{5.89}{7 - 3.83}$
4. $\dfrac{102}{58.1 + 65.32}$

5. $\dfrac{18.8}{3.72 \times 1.86}$
6. $\dfrac{904}{65.3 \times 2.86}$

7. $12.2 - \left(\dfrac{2.6}{1.95}\right)$
8. $8.047 - \left(\dfrac{6.34}{10.2}\right)$

9. $14.2 - \left(\dfrac{1.7}{2.4}\right)$
10. $\dfrac{9.75 - 8.792}{4.31 - 3.014}$

11. $\dfrac{19.6 \times 3.01}{2.01 - 1.958}$
12. $3.7^2 - \left(\dfrac{8.59}{24}\right)$

13. $8.27 - 1.56^2$
14. $111.79 - 5.04^2$

15. $18.3 - 2.841^2$
16. $(2.93 + 71.5)^2$

17. $(8.3 - 6.34)^4$
18. $54.2 - 2.6^4$

19. $(8.7 - 5.95)^4$
20. $\sqrt{68.4} + 11.63$

21. $9.45 - \sqrt{8.248}$
22. $3.24^2 - \sqrt{1.962}$

23. $\dfrac{3.54 + 2.4}{8.47^2}$
24. $2065 - \sqrt{44\,000}$

25. $\sqrt{(5.69 - 0.0852)}$
26. $\sqrt{(0.976 + 1.03)}$

27. $\sqrt{\left(\dfrac{17.4}{2.16 - 1.83}\right)}$
28. $\sqrt{\left(\dfrac{28.9}{\sqrt{8.47}}\right)}$

29. $257 - \dfrac{6.32}{0.059}$
30. $75\,000 - 5.6^4$

31. $\dfrac{11.29 \times 2.09}{2.7 + 0.082}$
32. $85.5 - \sqrt{105.8}$

33. $\dfrac{4.45^2}{8.2^2 - 51.09}$
34. $\left(\dfrac{8.53 + 7.07}{6.04 - 4.32}\right)^4$

35. $2.75 + \dfrac{5}{8.2} + \dfrac{11.2}{4.3}$
36. $8.2 + \dfrac{6.3}{0.91} + \dfrac{2.74}{8.4}$

37. $\dfrac{18.5}{1.6} + \dfrac{7.1}{0.53} + \dfrac{11.9}{25.6}$
38. $\dfrac{83.6}{105} + \dfrac{2.95}{2.7} + \dfrac{81}{97}$

39. $\left(\dfrac{98.76}{103} + \dfrac{4.07}{3.6}\right)^2$
40. $\dfrac{(5.843 - \sqrt{2.07})^2}{88.4}$

3.5 STANDARD FORM

Very large numbers and very small numbers are more conveniently written using *standard form*.

$$260\,000\,000 = 2.6 \times 10^8$$
$$4\,187\,000\,000 = 4.187 \times 10^9$$
$$0.000\,000\,072 = 7.2 \times 10^{-8}$$
$$0.000\,05 = 5 \times 10^{-5}$$

Most calculators represent large and small numbers using standard form.

e.g. $\boxed{1.541^{\ 24}}$ means 1.541×10^{24}

Exercise 9

Write the following numbers in standard form.

1. 560 000
2. 244 000 000
3. 72 000
4. 131 000
5. 85 000 000
6. 900 000 000
7. 73 400 000 000
8. 8 420 000 000
9. 66 000
10. 2 000 000 000 000
11. 100 million
12. 2000 million
13. 440
14. 60 000
15. 160 000
16. 4 850 000 000
17. 18 472
18. 635 811
19. 3 333 333
20. 8 211 111

21. 0.000 004
22. 0.000 0052
23. 0.000 007 411
24. 0.004 32
25. 0.0075
26. 0.008 239
27. 0.000 000 007
28. 0.000 000 015
29. 0.000 000 000 2
30. 0.0046
31. 0.0074
32. 0.006 31
33. 84 000
34. 12 000 000
35. 0.000 002
36. 0.000 000 045 3
37. 16 000 000 000
38. 0.724
39. 284 444
40. 0.000 002 22

41. 320×10^4
42. 600×10^7
43. 18.2×10^5
44. 0.4×10^{-6}
45. 0.07×10^{-5}
46. 700×10^{-10}
47. 666×10^8
48. 7100×10^8
49. 320×10^{-10}
50. 16.2×10^{-7}

Exercise 10

Write the following numbers in the usual form.

1. 3.6×10^5
2. 7.22×10^7
3. 8.2×10^4
4. 6×10^6
5. 1.1×10^9
6. 3.24×10^5
7. 1×10^{11}
8. 6.36×10^6
9. 8.02×10^9
10. 3.2×10^4

11. 6.7×10^2
12. 3.03×10^4
13. 8.99×10^7
14. 1.02×10^{10}
15. 6.2×10^6
16. 2.6×10^{-4}
17. 8.1×10^{-2}
18. 1×10^{-5}
19. 3×10^{-6}
20. 4.4×10^{-7}
21. 8×10^{-3}
22. 1.2×10^{-7}
23. 9.5×10^{-8}
24. 4.6×10^{-11}
25. 8.8×10^4
26. 2.75×10^3
27. 1.01×10^{-3}
28. 9.6×10^{-6}
29. 7×10^{-5}
30. 3.2×10^2

Exercise 11

Work out
1. $10^2 \times 10^5$
2. $10^2 \times 10^7$
3. $10^4 \times 10^6$
4. $10^7 \times 10^{-2}$
5. $10^9 \times 10^{-3}$
6. $10^{-2} \times 10^4$
7. $10^{-5} \times 10^{-2}$
8. $10^8 \times 10^{-10}$
9. $10^4 \times 10^{-12}$
10. $10^{-2} \times 10^{-3}$
11. $10^{-1} \times 10^{-7}$
12. $10^8 \times 10^{-6}$
13. $10^6 \div 10^2$
14. $10^8 \div 10^3$
15. $10^{10} \div 10^2$
16. $10^5 \div 10^9$
17. $10^3 \div 10^{16}$
18. $10^4 \div 10^{-2}$
19. $10^7 \div 10^{-1}$
20. $10^8 \div 10^{-3}$
21. $10^{-3} \div 10^5$
22. $10^9 \times 10^{-2}$
23. $10^7 \times 10^{-10}$
24. $10^5 \div 10^{-3}$

Exercise 12

Work out the following and give the answer in standard form.

1. $(2 \times 10^4) \times (3 \times 10^5)$
2. $(1.5 \times 10^5) \times (2 \times 10^8)$
3. $(2.2 \times 10^7) \times (3 \times 10^{10})$
4. $(1 \times 10^{11}) \times (8.8 \times 10^2)$
5. $(4 \times 10^6) \times (2 \times 10^{-2})$
6. $(8.5 \times 10^{12}) \times (1 \times 10^{-3})$
7. $(2.3 \times 10^{-8}) \times (3 \times 10^2)$
8. $(3.5 \times 10^{-5}) \times (2 \times 10^{10})$
9. $(6.28 \times 10^8) \times (1 \times 10^8)$
10. $(7.2 \times 10^7) \times (1 \times 10^{-11})$

11. $(8.8 \times 10^8) \div (2 \times 10^2)$
12. $(9 \times 10^6) \div (2 \times 10^3)$
13. $(6 \times 10^8) \div (4 \times 10^2)$
14. $(8 \times 10^{11}) \div (1 \times 10^8)$
15. $(9 \times 10^5) \div (3 \times 10^{10})$
16. $(5 \times 10^3) \div (2.5 \times 10^9)$
17. $(7.2 \times 10^2) \div (2 \times 10^8)$
18. $(3.4 \times 10^4) \div (2 \times 10^{-2})$
19. $(7.5 \times 10^6) \div (2.5 \times 10^{-3})$
20. $(9.3 \times 10^5) \div (3 \times 10^{-2})$

Think about it 1

Project 1   **THE CHESS BOARD PROBLEM**

Look at the miniature chess board below. It is only a 4 × 4 square instead of 8 × 8. Your problem is to place four objects on the board so that nowhere are there two objects on the same row (↔), column (↕) or diagonal (↗) (↘).

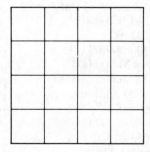

In the example below we have gone wrong because ① and ④ are on the same diagonal, and ② and ③ are on the other diagonal.

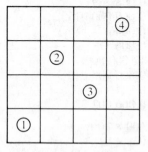

1. Find a correct solution for the 4 × 4 square.
2. Find a solution for a 5 × 5 square, using five objects.
3. Find a solution for a 6 × 6 square, using six objects.
4. Find a solution for a 7 × 7 square, using seven objects.
5. Finally, if you have been successful with the previous squares, try to find a solution for a full-size 8 × 8 square, using eight objects. It is called the chess board problem because one of the objects could be a 'Queen' which can move any number of squares in any direction.

Most people start off by trying to guess the solutions. After a little practice it is better to adopt a more systematic approach. Good luck!

Exercise A

$\frac{182}{8} = 22.75$

$22 \times 6 = 176, 6 \text{ left over}$

22 packets

42

$5090 \div 2 = 1545.$
$2545 + 260 = 2805$

$92 \text{ coins} \times 0.10$
$£9.00$

$210 \div 35 = 6$

$6 + 4$

172.8 km

740

82.5 mins

$\frac{360}{20} = 18$

18 sacks

1. Screws are sold in packets of eight and I need 182 screws for a job. How many packets must I buy and how many screws will be left over?

2. What number, when divided by 7 and then multiplied by 3, gives an answer of 18?

3. In an election 5090 votes were cast for the two candidates. Mr Wislon won by 260 votes. How many people voted for Wislon?

4. A 10p coin is 2 mm thick. Nicola has a pile of 10p coins which is 18.4 cm tall. What is the value of the money in Nicola's pile of coins?

5. The school morning lasts 3 hours 30 minutes. How many 35-minute lessons are there?

6. Find two numbers which multiply together to give 24 and which add up to 10.

7. A man runs around a rectangular field which is 160 m long and 90 m wide. How far does he run in km if he completes 12 laps of the field?

8. When a certain number is divided by 20 the answer is 37. What is the number?

9. An aircraft takes $2\frac{3}{4}$ hours to complete a journey. How long will the journey take if it travels at half the speed?

10. A garden 36 m long and 10 m wide is to be covered with peat, which is supplied in 60 kg sacks. 10 kg of peat covers an area of 20 m^2. How many sacks of peat are needed for the whole garden?

Project 2   PENTOMINOES

A pentomino is a set of five squares joined along their edges. You probably know of the game of dominoes. A domino is just two squares joined together; there is only one possible shape because the two shapes here count as the same.

counts the same as

1. See how many different pentominoes you can design on squared paper. Here are a few.

(a)   (b)   (c)

You may find that some of your designs are really the same, for example

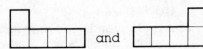

and

You can use a piece of tracing paper to check if some of your designs are really the same or different.

After about fifteen minutes, compare your designs with those of other people in your class. There are in fact twelve different pentomino shapes. Make a neat copy of these.

2. On squared paper, draw a square having eight units on each side. Somewhere inside the square draw a small square having two units on each side and shade it.

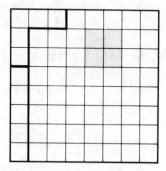

Now fill up the rest of the square with as many different pentominoes as you can. There should be no 'holes' left by the time you have finished.

A start has been made in the diagram above.

3. Take some more squared paper and draw a rectangle measuring 10 by 6. Fill up the rectangle with as many different pentominoes as you can.

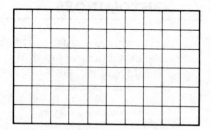

This problem is more difficult than the 8 by 8 square.

Exercise B

1. Find the result when two hundred and twelve thousand, five hundred and seven is added to sixty thousand, eight hundred and seventy.

2. Find the angle between the hands of a clock showing
(a) 8.00 pm
(b) 11.00 am

3. A badly typed three-digit number appears as 84*. It is known to be odd and divisible by 5. Find the number.

4. A car uses 9 litres of petrol for every 50 km travelled. Calculate the cost in £'s of travelling 750 km if petrol costs 43p per litre.

5. Add together the 19th odd number and the 12th even number. (The first odd number is 1 and the first even number is 2).

6. (a) Work out 8 × 125, without a calculator.
(b) Use the result above to work out 12 000 ÷ 125.

7. A play was attended by 240 adults, each paying 80p, and 164 children, each paying 50p. How much in £'s was paid altogether by the people attending the play?

8. The exchange rate in Spain is 220 pesetas to the £.
(a) How many pesetas will I receive for £20?
(b) A bottle of wine is priced at 550 pesetas. What is the equivalent cost in £'s?

9. An extract from Mrs Brown's bank statement is shown below.

Date	Customer details	Debit	Credit	Balance
April 1	Balance forward			334.13
April 4	495466	46.00		288.13
April 8	495468	85.00		x
April 15	Salary		574.08	y
April 20	495467	24.00		
April 21	495470	110.00		
April 25	495469	57.50		z

Calculate the values of the missing balances x, y and z.

10. A man smokes 60 cigarettes a day and a packet of 20 costs £1.25. How much does he spend on cigarettes in a seven day week?

Project 3   STAMPS

I have lots of 4p and 9p stamps but I have no stamps of other values.

I could post a package costing 30p by using 9p + 9p + 4p + 4p + 4p. It is, however, impossible to put on an amount of 14p exactly.

Copy and complete the list below and show how to make up the amounts given. If it is impossible, write 'impossible'.

1p Impossible	14p	27p	40p
2p Impossible	15p	28p	41p
3p Impossible	16p	29p	42p
4p = 4p	17p	30p	43p
5p Impossible	18p	31p	44p
6p Impossible	19p	32p	45p
7p Impossible	20p	33p	46p
8p 4p + 4p	21p	34p	47p
9p = 9p	22p	35p	48p
10p	23p	36p	49p
11p	24p	37p	50p
12p	25p	38p	
13p	26p	39p	

38

Exercise C   'SUPER LEAGUE' SOCCER

To avoid the football league programme becoming too crowded, an experimental 'super league' was formed with just six clubs: Liverpool, Manchester United, Nottingham Forest, West Ham, Arsenal and Everton.

Each team played each of the others at home and away and the results are shown below.

Home		Away		Attendance
Liverpool	2	Manchester United	1	46 250
Nottingham Forest	1	Liverpool	1	28 700
Liverpool	4	West Ham	1	33 610
Arsenal	0	Liverpool	2	47 420
Liverpool	1	Everton	1	49 840
Manchester United	2	Liverpool	0	56 815
Liverpool	2	Nottingham Forest	2	29 610
West Ham	1	Liverpool	2	28 250
Liverpool	2	Arsenal	1	36 460
Everton	1	Liverpool	1	48 890
Manchester United	3	Nottingham Forest	1	46 610
West Ham	0	Manchester United	1	31 295
Manchester United	2	Arsenal	0	51 605
Manchester United	1	Everton	1	46 240
Nottingham Forest	1	Manchester United	2	27 270
Manchester United	2	West Ham	0	38 615
Arsenal	1	Manchester United	0	43 720
Everton	2	Manchester United	1	45 610
Nottingham Forest	1	West Ham	2	19 265
Arsenal	1	Nottingham Forest	0	36 780
Nottingham Forest	1	Everton	1	24 815
West Ham	0	Nottingham Forest	1	23 370
Nottingham Forest	2	Arsenal	0	22 610
Everton	3	Nottingham Forest	1	35 470
West Ham	2	Arsenal	1	31 865
West Ham	1	Everton	1	25 700
Arsenal	1	West Ham	0	38 215
Everton	3	West Ham	1	28 320
Arsenal	2	Everton	2	32 610
Everton	2	Arsenal	1	35 815

1. Copy and complete the table of results for Liverpool.

Win	Draw	Lose
2-1		
	1-1	
4-1		
2-0		
	1-1	
		0-2

Games:
Won: 5
Drawn:
Lost:

Goals
For: 17
Against

2. Work out similar tables of results for Manchester United, Nottingham Forest, West Ham, Arsenal and Everton.

3. Use the information you have obtained to work out the final league table. A team obtains 3 points for a win, 1 point for a draw and 0 points for a loss. If two teams have the same number of points, the team with the better goal difference is placed higher.

Team	Games played	Won	Drawn	Lost	Goals For	Against	Points
Liverpool	10	5	4	1	17	11	19

Here is a list of prices charged by the six clubs.

Team	Average admission price	Price of programme
Liverpool	£2.50	50p
Man. Utd.	£2.00	40p
Notts Forest	£2.60	60p
West Ham	£2.60	50p
Arsenal	£2.40	60p
Everton	£2.70	65p

4. When Liverpool were at home to Manchester United the attendance was 46 250. Calculate the total sum of money paid for admission.

5. What was the total sum paid for admission to the Arsenal–Liverpool game? (i.e. Arsenal at home.)

6. Calculate the total sum paid for admission to Manchester United's five home games.

7. Exactly half of the people at the Arsenal–Notts Forest game bought a programme. Calculate the total money received from programme sales.

Project 4 — MATCHSTICK SHAPES

1. Triangles

Diagram 1

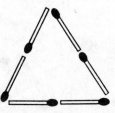
Diagram 2

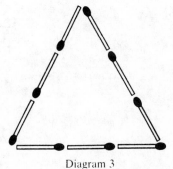
Diagram 3

Draw the next three triangles in the sequence.
Copy and complete this table.

Diagram number	1	2	3	4	5	6	10	30	45
Number of matches	3	6							150

2. Squares

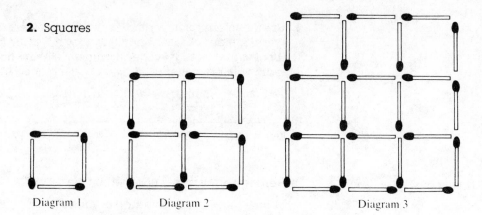

Diagram 1   Diagram 2   Diagram 3

Draw the next three diagrams in the sequence.
Copy and complete this table.

Diagram number	1	2	3	4	5	6	10	20	50
Number of matches									

3. Steps

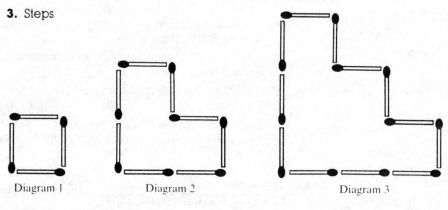

Diagram 1   Diagram 2   Diagram 3

Draw the next three diagrams in the sequence.
Copy and complete this table.

Diagram number	1	2	3	4	5	6	10	15	30
Number of matches								150	168

4. Triangle nets

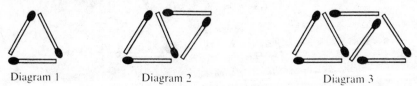

Diagram 1   Diagram 2   Diagram 3

Draw the next three diagrams in the sequence.
Copy and complete this table.

Diagram number	1	2	3	4	5	6	15	30	50
Number of matches								111	125

5. Finding a formula
  (a) For each of the four sequences of diagrams above, find a
      formula which connects the diagram number x with the number
      of matches n in the diagram, i.e. find an equation involving x
      and n.
  (b) Make two tables, one for the sequence of squares (part 2) and
      one for the sequence of triangle nets (part 4), to show the
      number of matches p on the perimeter of each shape.
      The table for the sequence of squares starts like this.

Diagram number x	1	2	3	4	5	6
Number of matches p on the perimeter	4	8	12			

If p is the number of matches on the perimeter, find a formula
(relationship) between p and x for each of the two sequences.

Exercise D

1. A suitcase is packed with 35 books, each weighing 420 g. The total
weight of the suitcase and books is 17 kg. Find the weight of the
suitcase.

2. Copy and complete the following:
  (a) 200 cm =   m,   (b) 2.3 m =   cm,
  (c) 7.2 km =   m,   (d) 0.8 m =   cm,
  (e) 28 m =   km,   (f) 25 mm =   cm.

3. A lady bought a car for £1200 and sold it six months later at a price
10% higher. At what price did she sell the car?

4. Copy and complete the pattern below.

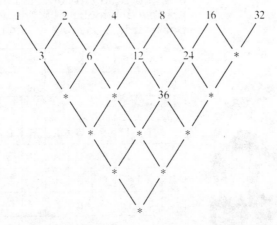

5. A box contains 200 assorted nails and screws and there are three
times as many nails as screws.
  (a) How many screws are there?
  (b) What is the probability that an item chosen at random from the
      box will be a nail?

6. A 9-day holiday in Italy costs £170. Find the average cost per day,
correct to the nearest pound.

7. In 1984 British Euro-MPs were paid a basic salary of £18 000 per year. The allowance for accommodation and subsistence was £75 a day. Travel allowances were 30p per mile travelled. Work out how much money was paid in one year to an MP who drew the accommodation allowance for 150 days and travelled a total of 80 000 miles during the year.

8. Mr Black's salary is £7800 per year. He pays no tax on the first £1600 of his salary but pays 30% on each remaining £. How much tax does he pay?

9. A man bought 20 plants at 85p each and a number of plants costing 45p each. In all he spent £22.40. How many of the less expensive plants did he buy?

10. ABCD is a square of side 10 cm. Side AB is increased by 30% to form rectangle AXYD.

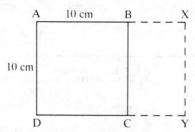

Calculate
(a) the area of ABCD   (b) the length BX   (c) the area BXYC

Project 5   **MATHEMATICAL WORDSEARCH**

Copy the square below. Find as many mathematical words as possible and make a list. The words appear written forwards or backwards in any row, column or diagonal.

A	M	P	T	R	I	A	N	G	L	E	O
R	N	C	Z	J	S	X	I	R	N	M	F
P	E	D	B	O	N	E	D	A	H	U	P
E	T	D	E	G	R	E	E	M	E	L	S
N	L	F	K	C	A	U	B	T	O	O	F
C	H	R	C	S	I	Q	L	D	G	V	T
I	C	A	J	E	R	M	O	E	S	D	U
L	N	C	D	V	Q	Z	A	N	R	D	L
E	I	T	H	E	E	U	R	L	T	A	V
Z	M	I	S	N	N	F	E	V	T	B	W
K	Y	O	W	T	X	O	A	O	R	U	N
C	E	N	T	I	M	E	T	R	E	C	O

Your rating:

10 Average
15 Good
18 Very good
20 Excellent

Exercise E

1. What is the weight of 15 biscuits if 9 biscuits weigh 288 g?

2. The area of an ordinary postage stamp is approximately (a) 5 mm^2 (b) 50 mm^2 (c) 5 cm^2 (d) 0.5 m^2. Select the correct answer.

3. An aircraft flies 210 m in 0.3 seconds.

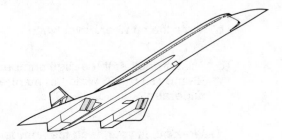

   (a) How far does it fly in 0.1 seconds?
   (b) How far does it fly in 1 second?
   (c) How far does it fly in 1 minute?

4. Nine mugs cost £7.65 and weigh 3.78 kg.
   Find (a) the cost and (b) the weight of 20 of these mugs.

5. The charges for parking a car at a car park are as follows:
   0–1 hour   10p
   1–3 hours   20p
   3–8 hours   50p
   Over 8 hours   80p
   Find the charge for a car parked from 08 40 to 12 20.

6. Which is more: (5% of £80) or (8% of £40)?

7. Write down the square root of the following (without a calculator)
   (a) 25   (b) 900   (c) 144
   (d) 10 000   (e) 81   (f) 0.01

8. Copy and complete

Percentage	Fraction
(a) 20%	
(b) 75%	
(c)	$\frac{1}{2}$
(d) 90%	
(e)	$\frac{1}{4}$
(f) 10%	

9. A box contains 45 assorted sweets and there are twice as many toffees as chocolates.
   (a) How many are toffees?
   (b) What is the probability that a sweet chosen at random from the box will be a chocolate?

10. A special offer for engine oil says: 'Buy 2 cans at £3.50 each and get a third can at half price'. Calculate the total cost of the 3 cans of oil.

Project 6 **MATHSMAGIC**

Here is a trick which you can perform to demonstrate your amazing powers of mental arithmetic. You will incidentally be learning some mathematics as you do it.

(a) Ask someone to give you a three-digit number. He may say '327'

(b) Write the number down twice

327 327

(c) Ask for another three-digit number. He may say '652'. Write this number underneath one of the 327's.

327 327
652

(d) Work out in your head the number which when added to 652 gives 999, in this case 347. Pretend you are just thinking of another number at random and write the 347 underneath the other 327.

327 327
652 347

(e) Pretend to concentrate very hard and 'in your head' you multiply 327 by 652 and add the result to 327 × 347

$$\begin{array}{r} 327 \\ \times\, 652 \\ \hline \end{array} \quad + \quad \begin{array}{r} 327 \\ \times\, 347 \\ \hline \end{array}$$

$$= 326673$$

How is it done?

The first 3 digits of the answer are (327 − 1) i.e. 326.

The next 3 digits are the figures which added to 326 make 999, i.e. 673. Here is another example.

$$\begin{array}{r} 821 \\ \times\, 146 \\ \hline \end{array} \quad + \quad \begin{array}{r} 821 \\ \times\, 853 \\ \hline \end{array} \quad = \quad 820179$$

Try this trick on your friends and relatives and see if they can work out how you do it.

Note It is best if they give you three-digit numbers which are 'all jumbled up'. Try to discourage numbers like '444' or '777' because they are 'too easy for you'.

Exercise F

1. Place the following numbers in order of size, smallest first:
   0.085, 0.058, 0.11, 0.03, 0.07.

2. Reduce the cost of each of the following items by one tenth of its
   price: (a) T.V.: £300 (b) Car: £4500 (c) Book: £4.50

3. The average of three numbers is 11. If two of the numbers are 8 and
   12, what is the third number?

4. Write down the next two numbers in each sequence:
   (a) 1, 5, 9, 13, . . .
   (b) 11, 16, 22, 29, . . .
   (c) 48, 24, 12, 6, . . .
   (d) 1, 4, 9, 16, . . .

5. How many pieces of wire of length 7.2 cm can be cut from a reel of
   wire of length 5 m?

7·2 cm

5 m

6. A shopkeeper sells an average of 6 radios per day from Monday to
   Friday inclusive. On Saturday he sells 15 radios. What is the average
   number of radios sold per day over the six days, from Monday to
   Saturday?

7. Write in their simplest form:
   (a) $\frac{12}{16}$ (b) $\frac{30}{45}$ (c) $\frac{20}{32}$ (d) $\frac{24}{60}$.

8. Copy and complete the table.

Fraction	Decimal	Percentage
$\frac{1}{2}$		
	0.2	
		10%
$\frac{3}{8}$		
		90%

9. A manufacturer purchases materials to the value of £30 000 of which
   £5000 worth are zero-rated for V.A.T. and the rest carry V.A.T. at 15%.
   (a) Calculate the V.A.T. paid on these materials.
   (b) Write down the total cost of all materials and V.A.T.

10. A man drives a car at an average speed of 65 km/h and does an
    average of 10 km per litre of petrol.
    (a) How far does he drive in 4 hours?
    (b) How much petrol does he use?
    (c) How much does it cost, if the price of petrol is 42.5p/litre?

Project 7   ESTIMATING GAME

This is a game for two players. On squared paper draw out an answer grid with the numbers shown below.

Answer grid

1215	429	2475	1485	8415	275
315	975	1089	4050	750	2125
891	1050	165	2025	819	1701
585	3315	525	1950	231	3861
2079	6885	550	4950	375	1785
1275	1250	3159	8019	4250	935

The players now take turns to choose two numbers from the question grid below and multiply them on a calculator.

Question grid

11	25	81
15	39	85
21	50	99

The number obtained is crossed out on the answer grid using the player's own colour. The winner is the first player with four answers in a line (horizontal, vertical or diagonal).

Exercise G

Find the missing numbers.

1.

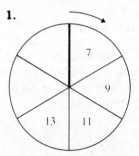

2.

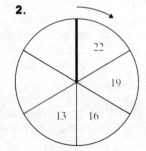

3.

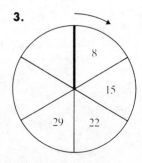

4.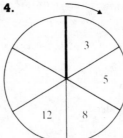

5.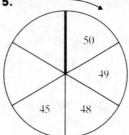

6.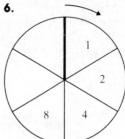

7.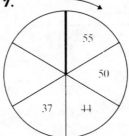

8.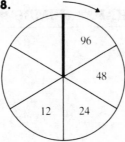

9.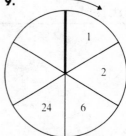

Write down the following sequences and work out the numbers indicated by ∗.

10. 1, 4, 7, ∗, ∗, 16.

11. 7, 6, 8, 7, 10, 9, ∗, ∗.

12. 11, 15, 21, 29, ∗, 51, ∗.

13. 1, 4, 9, 16, ∗, ∗, 49.

14. 144, 72, 36, ∗, 9, ∗.

15. 2, 1, $\frac{1}{2}$, ∗, $\frac{1}{8}$, ∗.

16. 1, 3, 5, ∗, ∗, 11.

17. 2, 4, 12, 48, ∗, ∗.

18. 60, 57, 51, 42, ∗, ∗.

19. 1, ∗, 27, 64, 125, ∗.

20. 20, 34, 49, 65, ∗, ∗.

21. (a) Write down the next two lines of the sequence:
$$3 \times 4 = 3 + 3^2$$
$$4 \times 5 = 4 + 4^2$$
$$5 \times 6 = 5 + 5^2$$
$$=$$
$$=$$

 (b) Complete the lines below
$$10 \times 11 =$$
$$30 \times 31 =$$

22. (a) Write down the next two lines of the sequence:
$$3^2 = 1^2 + 4 \times 1 + 4$$
$$4^2 = 2^2 + 4 \times 2 + 4$$
$$5^2 = 3^2 + 4 \times 3 + 4$$
$$6^2 = 4^2 + 4 \times 4 + 4$$
$$=$$
$$=$$

 (b) Complete the lines below
$$12^2 =$$
$$22^2 =$$

23. (a) Write down the next two lines of the sequence:

$1^2 = 1$
$2^2 = 1 + 3$
$3^2 = 1 + 3 + 5$
$4^2 = 1 + 3 + 5 + 7$
$ =$
$ =$

(b) Complete the lines below.
$10^2 =$
$15^2 =$

Project 8   HAPPY NUMBERS

(a)   32

3^2 2^2

$9 + 4 =$ 13

1^2 3^2

$1 + 9 =$ 10

1^2 0^2

$1 + 0 = 1$

32 is a so-called 'happy' number because it ends with 1.

(b) Try a different number: 70. This time we will simplify the working by doing the squaring without writing it down.

70

$49 + 0 =$ 49

$16 + 81 =$ 97

$81 + 49 =$ 130

$1 + 9 + 0 =$ 10

$1 + 0 = 1$

So 70 is also a 'happy' number.

(c) Find out whether the following numbers are 'happy' or 'unhappy':
23, 85, 49, 40, 44, 14, 15, 94
Hint: Write single digit numbers with a nought in front: $4 \rightarrow 04$
$6 \rightarrow 06$

This helps to maintain the pattern.

Look out for patterns of numbers which repeat themselves. This will save a lot of working.

(d) If 23 is happy, is 32 happy?
If 24 is unhappy, is 42 happy?
If 25 is unhappy, is 52 happy?

Project 9   **LARGEST PRODUCT**

(a) Take any whole number (say 25) and split it into three smaller whole numbers. The three numbers must add up to 25.
(We might choose 5, 8 and 12).
Now multiply the three numbers together.

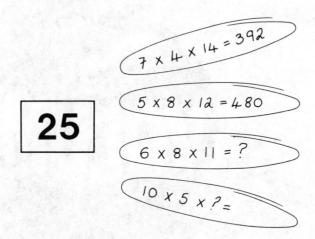

$$7 \times 4 \times 14 = 392$$

$$5 \times 8 \times 12 = 480$$

$$6 \times 8 \times 11 = ?$$

$$10 \times 5 \times ? =$$

25

Try a different combination of three numbers and again find their product. Which three numbers give the largest possible product?

(b) Now try different starting numbers and for each one find the combination of three numbers which gives the largest product.

Is there a general rule for finding the numbers which give the largest product?

(c) Now split the starting number into four (or five or even six) smaller numbers and find the combination which gives the greatest product.

Is there a rule for finding the numbers which give the largest product?

Part 4

4.1 AREA

Rectangle and triangle

Rectangle:
area = $l \times b$

Triangle:
area = $\dfrac{b \times h}{2}$

Exercise 1

Draw each diagram and work out the area.

1.

6 cm

4 cm

2.

7 cm

4 cm

3.

12 m

12 m

4.

5 cm

6 cm.

5.

11 m

3 m

6.

15 mm

10 mm

7.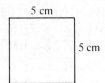
5 cm
5 cm

8.
8 cm
3 cm

9.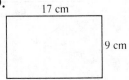
17 cm
9 cm

10.
5 m
8 m

11.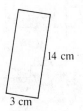
14 cm
3 cm

12.
3 cm
5 cm

13.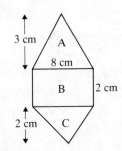
10 km
2 km

14.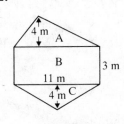
4 mm
12 mm

5.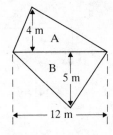
4 m
A
B
5 m
12 m

6.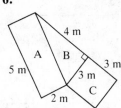
4 m
A B
3 m
5 m
3 m
C
2 m

7.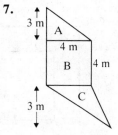
3 m
A
4 m
B
4 m
C
3 m

8.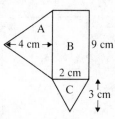
A
4 cm
B
9 cm
2 cm
C
3 cm

9.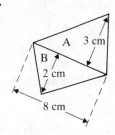
A 3 cm
B
2 cm
8 cm

10.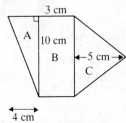
3 cm
A
10 cm
B
5 cm
C
4 cm

11.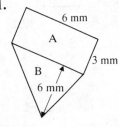
6 mm
A
3 mm
B
6 mm

12.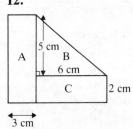
5 cm
A
B
6 cm
C
2 cm
3 cm

Exercise 2

Draw each diagram and then find the area.

1.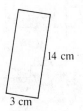
3 cm
A
8 cm
B
2 cm
2 cm
C

2.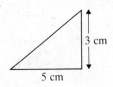
4 m
A
B
3 m
11 m
4 m C

3.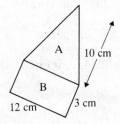
A
10 cm
B
3 cm
12 cm

4.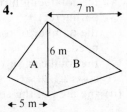
7 m
6 m
A B
5 m

Exercise 3

Find the area of each shape.
All lengths are in cm.

1.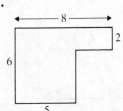
8
2
6
5

2.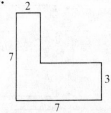
2
7
3
7

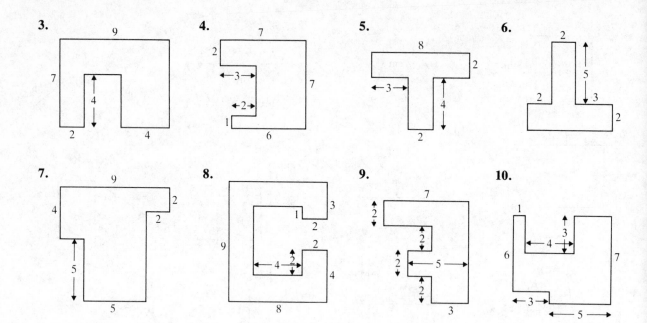

3. 9, 7, 4, 2, 4

4. 7, 2, 3, 2, 7, 1, 6

5. 8, 2, 3, 4, 2

6. 2, 5, 2, 2, 3, 2

7. 9, 4, 2, 2, 5, 5

8. 3, 2, 1, 9, 2, 4, 2, 8, 4

9. 7, 2, 2, 2, 5, 2, 3

10. 2, 1, 3, 4, 6, 7, 3, 5

Exercise 4

A decorator works out how many rolls of
wallpaper he needs for a room from the table
below.

Height from skirting	Measurement round walls (including doors and windows) in metres									
	8.6	9.8	11.0	12.2	13.4	14.6	15.8	17.0	18.2	19.4
2.20 m	4	4	5	5	6	6	7	7	8	8
2.35 m	4	4	5	5	6	6	7	8	8	9
2.50 m	4	5	5	6	6	7	7	8	8	9
2.65 m	4	5	5	6	6	7	8	8	9	9
2.80 m	4	5	6	6	7	7	8	9	9	10
2.95 m	5	5	6	7	7	8	9	9	10	10
3.10 m	5	5	6	7	8	8	9	10	10	11

1. A plan of one room is shown below

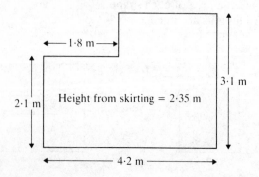

1·8 m
3·1 m
2·1 m   Height from skirting = 2·35 m
4·2 m

Work out
(a) the total length round the walls (the
    perimeter).
(b) the number of rolls of wallpaper he
    needs.
(c) the total cost of the wallpaper if one roll
    costs £3.20.
(d) the area of the ceiling of the room.

2. Work out the answers to parts (a), (b), (c) and (d) for each of the rooms shown below.

A.

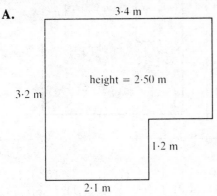

3·4 m

height = 2·50 m

3·2 m

1·2 m

2·1 m

B.

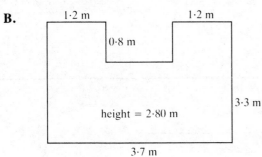

1·2 m   1·2 m

0·8 m

3·3 m

height = 2·80 m

3·7 m

C.

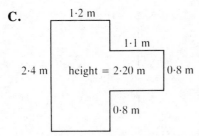

1·2 m

1·1 m

2·4 m   height = 2·20 m   0·8 m

0·8 m

D.

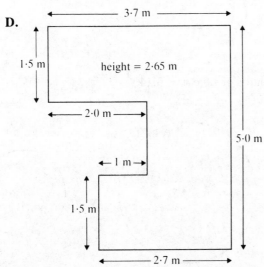

3·7 m

1·5 m   height = 2·65 m

2·0 m

5·0 m

1 m

1·5 m

2·7 m

Exercise 5

1. (a) Copy the diagram below.

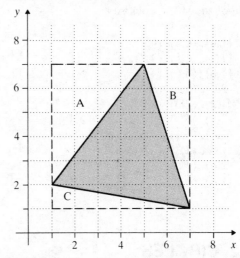

(b) Work out the areas of triangles A, B and C.

(c) Work out the area of the square enclosed by the broken lines.

(d) Hence work out the area of the shaded triangle. Give the answer in square units.

2. (a) Copy the diagram below.

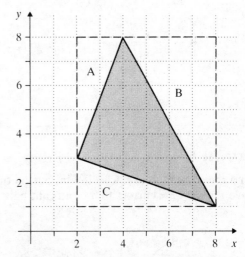

(b) Work out the areas of triangles A, B and C.

(c) Work out the area of the rectangle enclosed by the broken lines.

(d) Hence work out the area of the shaded triangle. Give the answer in square units.

For the remaining questions in this exercise draw a pair of axes similar to those in questions **1** and **2**. Plot the points in the order given and find the area of the shape enclosed.

3. (1,4), (6,8), (4,1)
4. (1,7), (8,5), (4,2)
5. (1,8), (8,6), (4,1)
6. (2,5), (6,2), (8,8)
7. (1,2), (7,3), (2,8)
8. (2,4), (6,1), (8,7), (4,8), (2,4)
9. (1,4), (5,1), (7,6), (4,8), (1,4)
10. (1,6), (2,2), (8,6), (6,8), (1,6)
11. (2,8), (4,5), (8,8), (4,1), (2,8)
12. (1,8), (8,5), (2,1), (4,5), (1,8)

13.

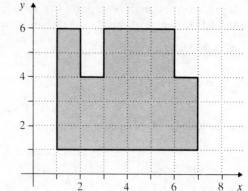

14. (1,8), (8,8), (8,6), (3,6), (3,5), (6,5), (6,4), (4,4), (4,2), (3,2), (3,1), (1,1), (1,8).

4.2 CIRCLES

Circumference of a circle

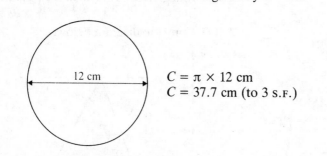

The circumference of the circle below is given by $C = \pi d$

$C = \pi \times 12$ cm
$C = 37.7$ cm (to 3 s.f.)

Exercise 6

Find the circumference. Use the 'π' button on a calculator or take $\pi = 3.14$. Give the answers correct to 3 significant figures.

1.

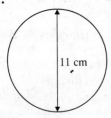

11 cm

2.

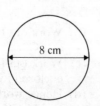

8 cm

3.

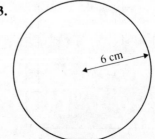

6 cm

4.

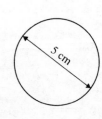

5 cm

5.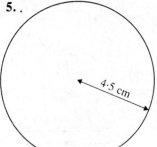
4·5 cm

6.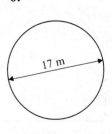
17 m

7.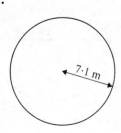
7·1 m

8.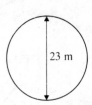
23 m

9.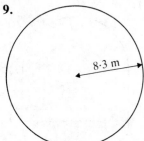
8·3 m

10.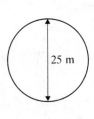
25 m

11.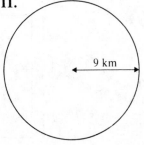
9 km

12.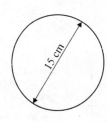
15 cm

13.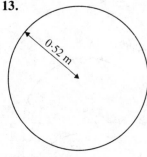
0·52 m

14.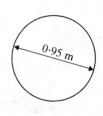
0·95 m

15.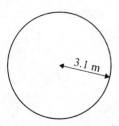
3.1 m

16. Diameter = 8.2 km   **17.** Radius = 0.84 mm   **18.** Diameter = 3.74 cm
19. Diameter = 18.2 m   **20.** Radius = 3.1 mm   **21.** Radius = 2.4 miles
22. Diameter = 8.3 feet   **23.** Radius = 3.9 km   **24.** Diameter = 0.092 m
25. Radius = 1.43 cm

Exercise 7

Find the perimeter of the shapes. Use the 'π' button on a calculator or take
π = 3.14. Give the answers correct to 3 significant figures.

1.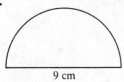
9 cm

2.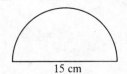
15 cm

3.
8 m

4.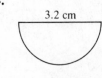
3.2 cm

5.

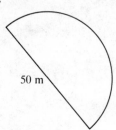

50 m

6.

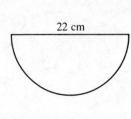

22 cm

7.

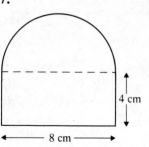

4 cm

8 cm

8.

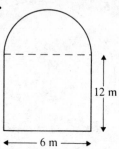

12 m

6 m

9.

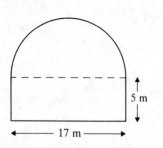

5 m

17 m

10.

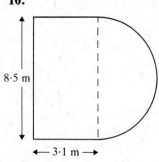

8·5 m

3·1 m

11.

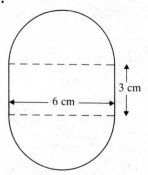

3 cm

6 cm

12.

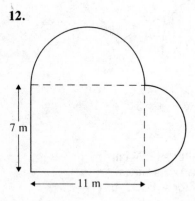

7 m

11 m

13.

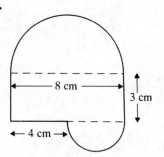

8 cm

3 cm

4 cm

14.

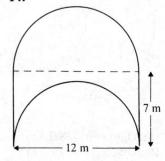

7 m

12 m

Area of a circle

Find the area of the circle shown.

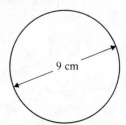

9 cm

The area of a circle of radius r is given by
$A = \pi r^2$
In this circle $r = 4.5$ cm
$\therefore$ Area of circle $= \pi \times 4.5^2$
$\qquad\qquad\quad = 63.6$ cm^2 (to 3 s.f.)
[Here we have used the 'π' button on a calculator.]

Exercise 8

In questions **1** to **20** find the area of the circle. Use the 'π' button on a calculator or use $\pi = 3.14$. Give the answers correct to three significant figures.

1.

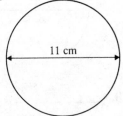

11 cm

2.

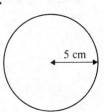

5 cm

3.

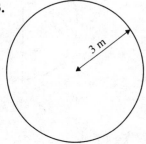

3 m

4.

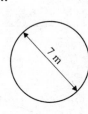

7 m

5.

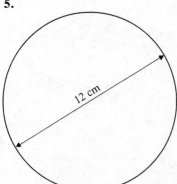

12 cm

6.

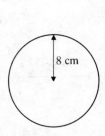

8 cm

7.

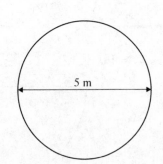

5 m

8.

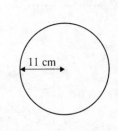

11 cm

9.

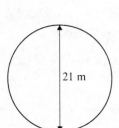

21 m

10.

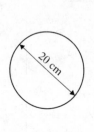

20 cm

11.

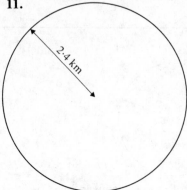

2.4 km

12.

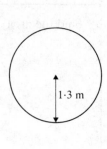

1·3 m

13. Radius = 9.7 cm   **14.** Diameter = 19 km   **15.** Diameter = 8.2 cm
16. Radius = 0.2 m   **17.** Diameter = 11.6 m   **18.** Radius = 1.8 cm
19. Radius = 0.85 m   **20.** Diameter = 3.9 km

Exercise 9

Find the area of each shape. Use the 'π' button on a calculator or use
π = 3.14. Give the answers correct to three significant figures.

1.

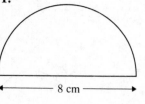

8 cm

2.

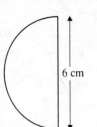

6 cm

3.

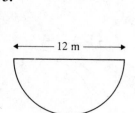

12 m

4.

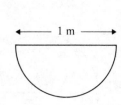

1 m

5.

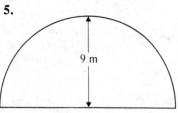

9 m

6.

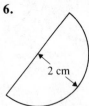

2 cm

7.

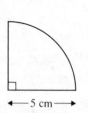

5 cm

8.

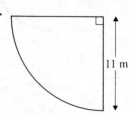

11 m

9.

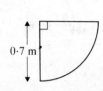

0·7 m

10.

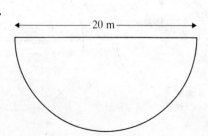

20 m

11.

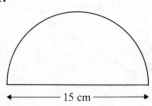

15 cm

Exercise 10

Find the area of each shape. Use the 'π' button on a calculator or take π = 3.14. Give the answers correct to three significant figures. All lengths are in cm.

1.

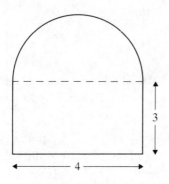

2.

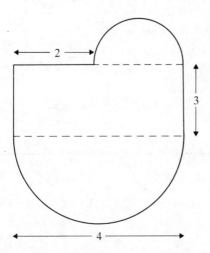

3.

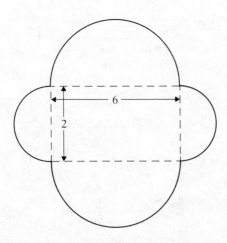

4.

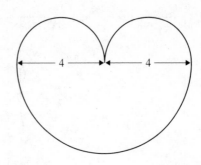

In questions **5** to **8** find the shaded area.

5.

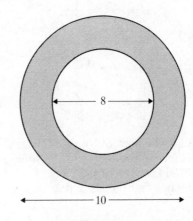

6.

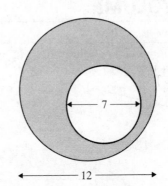

7.

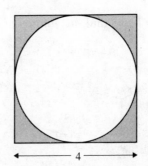

8.

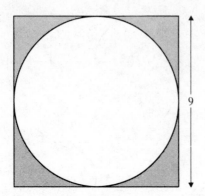

9.

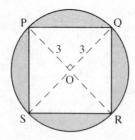

(a) Find the area of triangle OPQ.
(b) Hence find the area of the square PQRS.
(c) Find the area of the circle.
(d) Hence find the shaded area.

10.

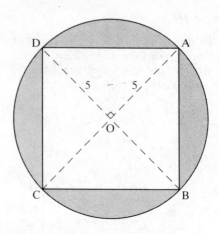

(a) Find the area of triangle OAD.
(b) Hence find the area of the square ABCD.
(c) Find the area of the circle.
(d) Hence find the shaded area.

4.3   VOLUME

The volume of a cuboid is given by the formula $V = l \times b \times h$.

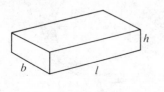

Exercise 11

In questions **1** to **8** find the volume of each cuboid.

1.

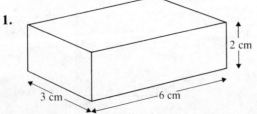

2.

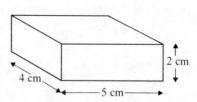

3.

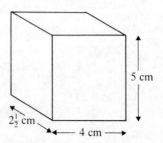

4. length = 7 m, breadth = 4 m, height = 3 m.
5. length = 10 cm, breadth = 5 cm, height = 100 cm.
6. length = 2 cm, breadth = 0.1 cm, height = 0.5 cm.
7. length = 3.1 cm, breadth = 3 cm, height = 10 cm.
8. length = 8.4 cm, breadth = 10 cm, height = 0.01 cm.

In questions **9** to **12** find the length of the side marked with a letter.

9.

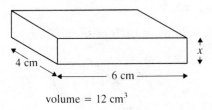

4 cm
6 cm
volume = 12 cm^3

10.

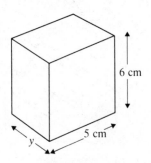

6 cm
5 cm
y
volume = 105 cm^3

11.

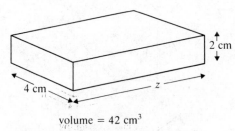

2 cm
4 cm
z
volume = 42 cm^3

12.

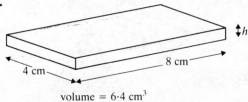

h
4 cm
8 cm
volume = 6·4 cm^3

For questions **13** to **19** find the volume of each solid. Each cube has a volume of 1 cm^3. Start each question by drawing a careful diagram.

13.

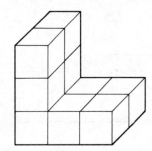

14.

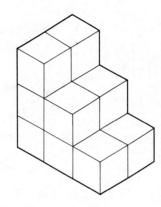

15.

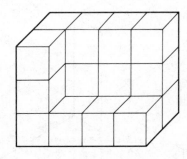

16.

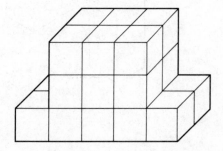

17.

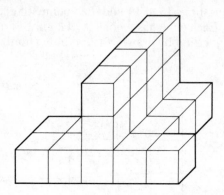

Prisms

A prism is an object with a uniform cross section

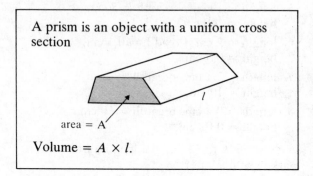

area = A

Volume = $A \times l$.

Exercise 12

Find the volume of each prism.

18.

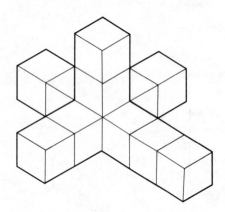

1.   Area of end = 15 cm²

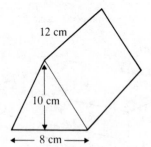

10 cm

2.   Area of end = 5 m²

12 m

19.

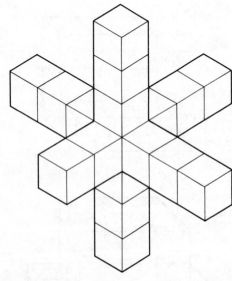

3.

12 cm

10 cm

← 8 cm →

4.

20 m

2 m

← 3 m →

5.

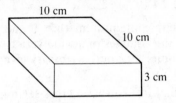

6.

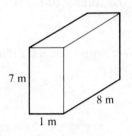

7.

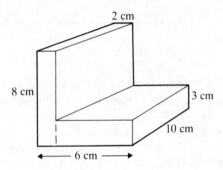

8.

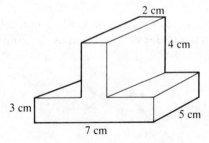

9.

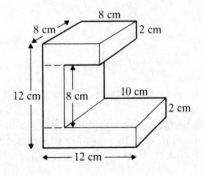

10.

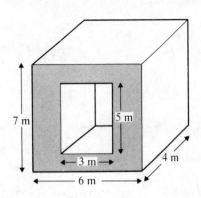

Cylinders

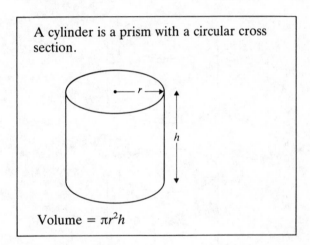

A cylinder is a prism with a circular cross section.

Volume = $\pi r^2 h$

Exercise 13

Find the volume of each cylinder. Use the 'π' button on a calculator or use π = 3.14. Give the answers correct to 3 s.f.

1.   **2.**

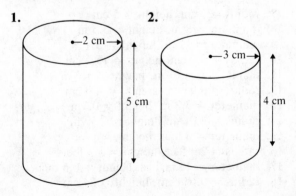

3.

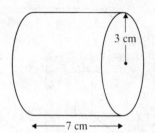

3 cm

←— 7 cm —→

4.

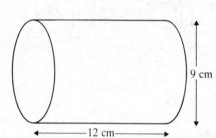

9 cm

←——— 12 cm ———→

5.

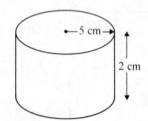

←—5 cm—→

2 cm

6.

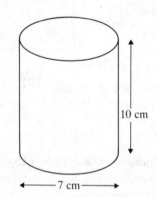

10 cm

←——— 7 cm ———→

7. radius = 7 cm, height = 5 cm
8. diameter = 8 m, height = 3.5 m
9. diameter = 11 m, height = 2.4 m
10. radius = 3.2 cm, height = 15.1 cm
11. diameter = 0.84 m, height = 1.2 m
12. radius = 0.95 cm, height = 6.2 cm
13. diameter = 3.3 m, height = 0.7 m
14. radius = 4.01 m, height = 0.59 m
15. diameter = 5 feet, height = 6 feet
16. radius = 2.4 feet, height = 5.5 feet
17. diameter = 13 inches, height = 6.6 inches
18. radius = 0.658 cm, height = 24 cm

Exercise 14

This exercise contains a mixture of questions involving the volumes of a wide variety of different objects. Where necessary give answers correct to 3 s.f.

1. A cylindrical bar has a cross-sectional area of 12 cm^2 and a length of two metres. Calculate the volume of the bar
    (a) in cm^3,
    (b) in m^3.

2. The diagram represents a building.

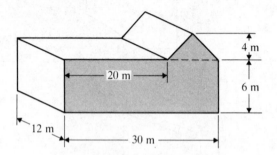

4 m

20 m

6 m

12 m

30 m

(a) Calculate the area of the shaded end.
(b) Calculate the volume of the building.

3. A rectangular block has dimensions 20 cm × 7 cm × 7 cm. Find the volume of the largest solid cylinder which can be cut from this block.

4. Brass washers are to be made 2 mm thick with a circular cross section as shown below.

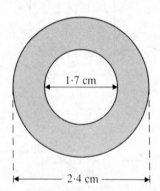

1·7 cm

2·4 cm

(a) Find the area of the flat surface of the washer.
(b) Calculate the volume of the washer.
(c) Find in cm^3 the volume of brass needed to make 10 000 of these washers.

5. A cylindrical water tank has internal diameter 40 cm and height 50 cm and a cylindrical mug has internal diameter 8 cm and height 10 cm. If the tank is initially full, how many mugs can be filled from the tank?

6. The diagram shows the cross section of a steel girder which is 4 m long.

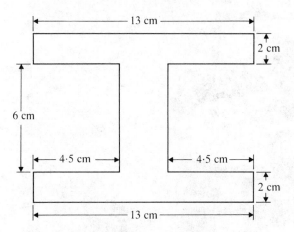

(a) Calculate the cross-sectional area in cm^2.
(b) Calculate the volume of the girder in cm^3.
(c) If 1 cm^3 of steel weighs 7.8 g find the weight of the girder in kg.
(d) How many girders can be carried on a lorry if its total load must not be more than 8 tonnes? (1 tonne = 1000 kg).

7. In the diagram all the angles are right angles and the lengths are in cm. Find the volume.

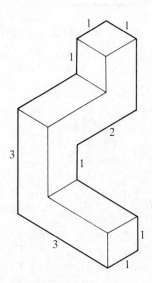

8. Mr Morton builds a fence at the end of his garden. The planks for the fence measure 1 m by 12 cm by 1 cm. The posts to which the planks are nailed are 10 cm square in cross section and 1.40 m long.

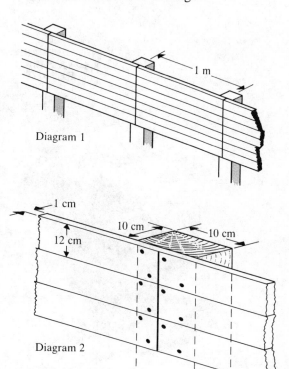

Diagram 1 shows a part of the fence and diagram 2 shows details of its construction.
(a) How many planks are there between each pair of posts?
(b) If the fence is 5 m long,
   (i) how many planks are needed?
   (ii) how many posts are needed? (There is a post at each end of the fence).
(c) Calculate the volume in cm^3 of
   (i) each plank
   (ii) each post
(d) Wood of the required quality costs 4p per 100 cm^3, irrespective of the thickness. Calculate the cost of
   (i) each plank
   (ii) each post
   (iii) all the wood for the whole fence.
(e) Each end of a plank is nailed to a post with two nails. How many nails are needed for the whole fence?

Part 5

5.1 NEGATIVE NUMBERS

You are used to working with negative numbers when recording low temperatures. On a very cold day the temperature might be −4 °C. This means 4 °C *below freezing*. If the temperature falls by a further 3° the new temperature will be −7 °C.

Exercise 1

1. The temperature in a room is 6 °C. What is the new temperature after a fall of 10°?

2. The temperature in a store is −2 °C. What is the new temperature after a fall of 4°?

3. The temperature in a barn is −3 °C. What is the new temperature after a rise of 8°?

4. Copy and complete the table below.

original temperature	change in temperature	final temperature
(a) 10 °C	fall of 6°	4 °C
(b) 7 °C	fall of 10°	*
(c) −3 °C	rise of 8°	*
(d) −14 °C	rise of 6°	*
(e) 5 °C	−3°	*
(f) 8 °C	−11°	*
(g) 16 °C	−20°	*
(h) −7 °C	+8°	*
(i) −3 °C	+5°	*
(j) −15 °C	+10°	*
(k) −9 °C	+21°	*

original temperature	change in temperature	final temperature
(l) 4 °C	−7°	*
(m) 6 °C	*	10 °C
(n) −3 °C	*	2 °C
(o) 4 °C	*	−2 °C
(p) −2 °C	*	4 °C
(q) −8 °C	*	−5 °C
(r) −7 °C	*	1 °C
(s) *	−3°	7 °C
(t) *	−2°	1 °C
(u) *	−5°	−2 °C
(v) *	−8°	3 °C
(w) *	+4°	7 °C
(x) *	+6°	1 °C
(y) *	+5°	−1 °C
(z) *	+7°	−3 °C

Exercise 2

In questions **1** to **20** state whether true or false.

1. $3 < 4$ **2.** $10 > 7$ **3.** $-2 < 4$
4. $-2 > 1$ **5.** $4 < -3$ **6.** $-3 > -6$
7. $3 < -5$ **8.** $6 > -2$ **9.** $-4 < -7$
10. $-6 > -10$ **11.** $8 < -7$ **12.** $-3 > -1$
13. $-4 < 6$ **14.** $-7 > -8$ **15.** $2 > -2$
16. $16 > -3$ **17.** $-3 > 0$ **18.** $2 < 0$
19. $-7 < -1$ **20.** $10 < -12$

In questions **21** to **40** insert $>$ or $<$ to make a true statement.

21. -2 4 **22.** 3 -5 **23.** -2 -6
24. 3 -1 **25.** 0 4 **26.** -3 0
27. -3 -8 **28.** 9 -7 **29.** -2 1
30. 0 -4 **31.** 8 -8 **32.** 7 -6
33. -3 0 **34.** 1 -1 **35.** -5 $-\frac{1}{2}$
36. $-\frac{1}{2}$ 1 **37.** 0 -8 **38.** -10 -11
39. -3 -7 **40.** 5 -2

In questions **41** to **60** put the numbers in order of size with the smallest first.

41. $2, -3, -4$ **42.** $-3, 7, -5$
43. $0, 5, -5$ **44.** $1, -3, -8$
45. $-4, -1, -2$ **46.** $6, -3, 2, -4$
47. $-1, 3, -2, 1$ **48.** $-3, 0, -2, 4$
49. $-3, 1, -5, 4$ **50.** $-3, 7, -7, 2$
51. $-1, 0, 4, -4$ **52.** $-6, 2, -1, -2$
53. $-4, 5, -1, 6$ **54.** $-8, -1, 10, -4$
55. $-8, 7, -3, 1, 0$ **56.** $-6, 0, -5, -9, 1$
57. $-1, -3, 5, 4, -2$ **58.** $8, -9, -1, 6, -2$
59. $-3, 5, -4, 1, 4$ **60.** $-6, -60, 17, 2, -20$

In questions **61** to **80** find the next two numbers in each sequence.

61. $10, 8, 6, 4$ **62.** $12, 9, 6$
63. $3, 2, 1, 0, -1$ **64.** $4, 2, 0, -2$
65. $12, 6, 0$ **66.** $-3, -2, -1$
67. $-8, -6, -4$ **68.** $10, 6, 2$
69. $15, 5, -5$ **70.** $-10, -6, -2$

71. $-7, -4, -1$ **72.** $6, 2, -2$
73. $2, 3, 5, 8$ **74.** $12, 11, 9, 6$
75. $0, 1, 3, 6$ **76.** $4, 3, 1, -2$
77. $-10, -9, -7, -4$ **78.** $5, 2, -1, -4$
79. $24, 10, -4$ **80.** $-11, -7, -3$

Adding and subtracting with negative numbers

$$-6 + 4 = -2 \qquad -3 - 6 = -9$$
$$10 - 16 = -6 \qquad -8 + 14 = 6$$
$$-2 - 10 = -12 \qquad 3 - 8 = -5$$

Exercise 3

1. $-2 + 6$ **2.** $7 - 10$ **3.** $-2 + 8$
4. $8 - 12$ **5.** $-3 + 10$ **6.** $-3 + 8$
7. $6 - 12$ **8.** $8 - 14$ **9.** $-3 + 1$
10. $-5 + 6$ **11.** $-5 + 5$ **12.** $7 - 20$
13. $4 - 20$ **14.** $7 - 6$ **15.** $-8 + 8$
16. $-8 + 11$ **17.** $17 - 27$ **18.** $-6 + 1$
19. $-3 + 2$ **20.** $10 - 12$ **21.** $-6 - 4$

22. $-7 + 3$ **23.** $-8 - 5$ **24.** $-6 - 14$
25. $-7 - 3$ **26.** $-8 - 1$ **27.** $-8 + 1$
28. $-7 + 2$ **29.** $8 - 6$ **30.** $4 - 3$
31. $-6 - 5$ **32.** $10 - 24$ **33.** $-7 - 6$
34. $10 - 15$ **35.** $-8 + 6$ **36.** $12 - 24$
37. $-8 - 15$ **38.** $-7 - 16$ **39.** $8 - 30$
40. $-7 + 10$ **41.** $-4 - 14$ **42.** $20 - 31$

43. $7 - 100$ **44.** $-8 - 82$ **45.** $-6 + 30$
46. $4 - 50$ **47.** $-7 - 13$ **48.** $-9 - 9$
49. $8 - 18$ **50.** $-11 + 11$ **51.** $-5 - 6$
52. $21 - 32$ **53.** $7 - 60$ **54.** $-100 + 1$
55. $-8 + 38$ **56.** $-17 - 3$ **57.** $10 - 51$
58. $17 - 18$ **59.** $-4 - 17$ **60.** $6 - 4$

$$\begin{array}{ll} 5 - -6 & -8 - +4 \\ = 5 + 6 & = -8 - 4 \\ = 11 & = -12 \end{array}$$

Exercise 4

1. $5 + (-4)$
2. $7 + (-3)$
3. $8 + (-4)$
4. $9 - (-5)$
5. $7 - (-3)$
6. $6 - (+4)$
7. $-4 - (-5)$
8. $-10 + (-4)$
9. $-4 - (+4)$
10. $-7 - (-2)$
11. $6 + (-10)$
12. $8 + (-9)$
13. $3 - (-4)$
14. $10 + (-5)$
15. $-3 - (-5)$
16. $6 - (+11)$
17. $-8 + (-12)$
18. $-8 - (+7)$
19. $9 - (+11)$
20. $7 - (-9)$

21. $-5 + (-6)$
22. $-7 - (-13)$
23. $-6 + (-2)$
24. $-8 - (-2)$
25. $7 - (+9)$
26. $3 - (+20)$
27. $-6 + (+6)$
28. $-8 + (-8)$
29. $-2 + (+8)$
30. $7 - (-8)$
31. $19 - (+3)$
32. $6 - (+9)$
33. $-11 - (-3)$
34. $7 + (-14)$
35. $-6 + (-4)$
36. $8 + (+9)$
37. $-7 + (-5)$
38. $-11 - (-11)$
39. $17 - (+15)$
40. $80 - (-15)$

Multiplying and dividing with negative numbers

(a) When the signs are the same, the answer is positive.
(b) When the signs are different, the answer is negative.

$$\begin{array}{ll} -3 \times (+4) = -12 & -6 \times (-3) = 18 \\ -12 \div (2) = -6 & -4 \div (-1) = 4 \end{array}$$

Exercise 5

1. $-3 \times (+2)$
2. $-4 \times (+1)$
3. $+5 \times (-3)$
4. $-3 \times (-3)$
5. $-4 \times (2)$
6. $-5 \times (3)$
7. $6 \times (-4)$
8. $3 \times (2)$
9. $-3 \times (-4)$
10. $6 \times (-3)$
11. $-7 \times (3)$
12. $-5 \times (-5)$
13. $6 \times (-10)$
14. $-3 \times (-7)$
15. $8 \times (6)$
16. $-8 \times (2)$

17. $-7 \times (6)$
18. $-5 \times (-4)$
19. $-6 \times (7)$
20. $11 \times (-6)$
21. $8 \div (-2)$
22. $-9 \div (3)$
23. $-6 \div (-2)$
24. $10 \div (-2)$
25. $-12 \div (-3)$
26. $-16 \div (4)$
27. $4 \div (-1)$
28. $8 \div (-8)$
29. $16 \div (-8)$
30. $-20 \div (-5)$

31. $-16 \div (1)$
32. $18 \div (-9)$
33. $36 \div (-9)$
34. $-45 \div (-9)$
35. $-70 \div (7)$
36. $-11 \div (-1)$
37. $-16 \div (-1)$
38. $1 \div (-\frac{1}{2})$
39. $-2 \div (\frac{1}{2})$
40. $50 \div (-10)$
41. $-8 \times (-8)$
42. $-9 \times (3)$
43. $10 \times (-60)$
44. $-8 \times (-5)$
45. $-12 \div (-6)$
46. $-18 \times (-2)$
47. $-8 \div (4)$
48. $-80 \div (10)$
49. $-16 \times (-10)$
50. $32 \div (-16)$

Exercise 6

1. $-7 + 3$
2. -3×4
3. $-3 - (-4)$
4. $8 \div (-2)$
5. $-4 \times (-4)$
6. $-8 - 5$
7. $4 + (-2)$
8. -3×1
9. $6 - 12$
10. $0 \times (-7)$
11. $-8 - 4$
12. $-1 \times (-8)$
13. $12 \div (-3)$
14. $10 \times (-10)$
15. $18 - 30$
16. $3 - (+8)$
17. $-16 \div 8$
18. $-7 - 4$
19. -4×5
20. $-8 + 13$

21. $-8 + 2$
22. $3 \times (-3)$
23. $8 \div (-8)$
24. $6 - (-3)$
25. $-6 \times (-1)$
26. -3×0
27. $-6 + 1$
28. $-8 - 7$
29. $-30 + 42$
30. $-2 + (-2)$

Exercise 7

1. -3×9
2. $10 - 23$
3. $-6 - 4$
4. $-7 - (-8)$
5. $12 \div (-6)$
6. -3×0
7. $-3 - (-3)$
8. $4 \times (-100)$
9. $-4 + 20$
10. $-6 \times (-7)$
11. $8 + (-9)$
12. $-3 \times (-11)$
13. $-30 \div (-2)$
14. $10 \times (-6)$
15. $-7 - 6$
16. $20 - 31$
17. 10×20
18. $-8 + 60$
19. $-4 - 40$
20. $0 \div (-8)$

21. $0 + (-9)$
22. $7 \times (-7)$
23. $14 - 24$
24. $-14 - 24$
25. $100 \div (-5)$
26. $-1 \times (-501)$

Exercise 8

1. Copy and complete the addition square below. The numbers inside the square are found by adding together the numbers across the top and down the side.

add	−2	1	4	0	−3	6	−1	5
−3		−2						
2								
4								
−2								
−1						5		
5								
−4								
1								

2. Copy and complete the multiplication square below. The numbers inside the square are found by multiplying together the numbers across the top and down the side.

multiply	−2	5	2	6	−4	0	−3	3
3	−6							
−1								
−2				8				
4								
5								
−4								
1								
−3								

5.2 USING LETTERS FOR NUMBERS

A large number of everyday problems can be solved using ordinary arithmetic with ordinary numbers. For example: 'work out 25% of £75'; 'take £8.85 away from £12.60'; 'divide 12.6 kg into ten equal parts'.

There are, however, an even larger number of mathematical problems which are much easier to solve when letters are used instead of numbers. Computer programs make use of algebra in statements like 'LET X = 2' or 'IF Y > 10 GO TO 70'.

Find what number I am left with.
(a) I start with x, multiply it by 7 and then add 10.
(b) I start with t, subtract 3 and then multiply the result by 5.

    (a) $x \to 7x \to 7x + 10$
    (b) $t \to t - 3 \to 5(t - 3)$

Exercise 9

In each question, find what number I am left with.

1. I start with x, multiply it by 3 and then add 6
2. I start with x, multiply it by 5 and then add 7
3. I start with x, double it and then subtract 4
4. I start with x, treble it and then add 10
5. I start with y, multiply it by 6 and then add 3
6. I start with y, double it and then subtract 7
7. I start with m, multiply it by 5 and then subtract 8
8. I start with x, multiply it by 6 and then subtract y
9. I start with y, treble it and then add t
10. I start with p, multiply it by 6 and then subtract a
11. I start with x, add 4 and then multiply the result by 3 [Hint: use brackets].
12. I start with x, add 3 and then multiply the result by 5

13. I start with y, add 11 and then multiply the result by 6

14. I start with m, subtract 5 and then multiply the result by 9

15. I start with t, multiply by 5 and then subtract 7

16. I start with x, subtract 6 and then multiply the result by 4

17. I start with x, add 3 and then divide the result by 4. [Hint: If you divide m by 5, write $\frac{m}{5}$ rather than $m \div 5$].

18. I start with x, subtract 7 and then divide the result by 3

19. I start with y, subtract 8 and then divide the result by 5

20. I start with x, add m and then divide the result by 7

21. I start with $2x$, add 7 and then multiply the result by 3

22. I start with $3x$, subtract y and then divide the result by 5

23. I start with $4a$, add 3, multiply the result by 2 and then divide the final result by 5

24. I start with m, subtract 6, multiply the result by 3 and then divide the final result by 4

25. I start with t, add x, multiply the result by 4 and then divide the final result by 5

26. I start with x, square it and then add 4

27. I start with x, square it and then subtract 6

28. I start with x, square it, add 3 and then divide the result by 4.

29. I start with n, add 2 and then square the result. [Use brackets]

30. I start with w, subtract x and then square the result

31. I start with y, add t and then square the result

32. I start with x, square it, subtract 7 and then divide the result by 3

33. I start with x, square it, multiply by 3 and then add 4.

34. I start with y, square it, add 4 and then multiply the result by 2

35. I start with a, cube it, subtract 3 and then divide the result by 7.

36. I start with z, cube it, add 6 and then divide the result by 8

37. I start with p, square it, subtract x and then multiply the result by 4

38. I start with x, subtract 9, square the result and then add 10

39. I start with y, add 7, square the result and then divide by x

40. I start with a, subtract x, cube the result and then divide by y.

Exercise 10

1. A plant is x cm tall at the beginning of the summer. During the summer it grows a further y cm and then the gardener prunes off 7 cm. How tall is it now?

2. When a man buys a small tree it is l cm tall. During the year it grows a further t cm and then he prunes off 10 cm. How tall is it now?

3. A piece of wood is l cm long. If I cut off a piece 3 cm long, how much wood remains?

4. A piece of string is 15 cm long. How much remains after I cut off a piece of length x cm?

5. A car in a showroom costs £c. The price goes up by £200 but is then reduced in a sale by £5. What is the cost in the sale?

6. The price of a book is x pence. The price goes up by 25p but is then reduced in a sale by y pence. What is the cost of the book?

7. On Thursday there are n people in a cinema. On Friday there are three times as many plus another 55. How many people are there in the cinema on Friday?

8. A soldier on an exercise crawls a distance of c metres, then walks a distance of w metres and finally runs a distance of 2000 metres. How far does he go?

9. A slug walks a distance of y cm, crawls a further d cm and finally runs x cm. How far does it go?

10. An athlete runs t km on Monday. On Tuesday she runs twice as far plus another 3 km. How far does she run (a) on Tuesday, (b) altogether on Monday and Tuesday?

11. A car dealer buys a car at an auction for £x. He puts it on sale at twice the price plus another £100. What is the price of the car?

12. A delivery van weighs l kg. At a depot it picks up goods weighing 200 kg and later delivers goods weighing m kg. How much does it weigh after making the delivery?

13. A box usually contains n chocolates. The shopkeeper puts an extra 2 chocolates into each box. A girl buys 4 boxes. How many chocolates does she have?

14. A brick weighs w kg. How much do six bricks weigh?

15. A sack weighs l kg. How much do x sacks weigh?

16. A man shares a sum of n pence equally between six children. How much does each child receive?

17. A sum of £p is shared equally between you and four others. How much does each person receive?

18. A cake weighing 12 kg is cut into n equal pieces. How much does each piece weigh?

19. A pie weighing m kg is shared equally between you and three others. How much does each person receive?

20. A small bag of sweets contains x sweets. A large bag contains three times as many sweets. John buys a large bag and then eats 11 sweets. How many sweets are left?

5.3 SUBSTITUTING FOR LETTERS

Exercise 11

1. $a = 3, b = 4, c = -1, d = -2, e = 5,$
   $v = -2, w = -3, x = 6, y = 0, z = 2$

   Copy and complete the table below. The number in each square is found by adding the numbers represented by the two letters in each square, for example $a + v = 1$.

a v	b v	d z	c x	d w
1				
b y	c z	a z	e z	e x
e v	a w	b w	d y	c y
c w	d x	e w	a x	b x
d v	e y	c v	b z	a y

2. $f = 4, g = -2, h = 5, i = -1, j = 3,$
   $p = -1, q = 3, r = -2, s = 4, t = -3$

   Copy and complete the table below. The number in each square is found by subtracting the second letter from the first letter in each square, for example $f - p = 5$.

f p	h s	g r	i r	j s
5				
g q	j q	i p	f s	h t
i q	f q	h q	g t	i t
h r	i s	j t	j r	f t
j f	g p	f r	h p	g s

3. Use the values for a, b, c, d, e, v, w, x, y, z given in question **1**. Complete the table given in question **1**, but this time multiply together the two letters in each square, for example $av = -6$.

If $l = 5$, $m = -2$, $x = 3$, work out (a) $4x$, (b) lm

(a) $4x = 4 \times 3$ (b) $lm = 5 \times -2$
    $= 12$ $= -10$

Exercise 14

If $a = 4$, $b = -2$, $c = -3$, $d = 2$, $x = 3$, $y = -1$ work out

1. $3c$	**2.** ab	**3.** $2a$	**4.** $4d$
5. $6a$	**6.** $3d$	**7.** xc	**8.** $9c$
9. ya	**10.** $6c$	**11.** $8b$	**12.** $4y$
13. $6y$	**14.** bc	**15.** $5c$	**16.** $10d$
17. cd	**18.** $7a$	**19.** da	**20.** $2x$
21. $4c$	**22.** $9a$	**23.** $10b$	**24.** $4b$
25. $3a$	**26.** $2c$	**27.** bx	**28.** ax
29. $5b$	**30.** xd	**31.** $3y$	**32.** $11b$
33. ac	**34.** $5a$	**35.** $9b$	**36.** $7c$
37. $2b$	**38.** $10a$	**39.** $5x$	**40.** $9x$
41. $8d$	**42.** db	**43.** $4a$	**44.** $3b$
45. $11y$	**46.** $8y$	**47.** $2d$	**48.** yb
49. $3x$	**50.** $11x$	**51.** yc	**52.** $10c$
53. $10x$	**54.** $7x$	**55.** $10y$	**56.** $11a$
57. xy	**58.** $2y$	**59.** $4x$	**60.** dy

Exercise 15

Work out the answers to questions **1** to **60** of Exercise 14 with $a = 2$, $b = -4$, $c = 5$, $d = -3$, $x = -7$, $y = -6$.

If $x = 3$, $y = -4$, work out
(a) $2x + y$ (b) $xy - y$

(a) $2x + y$ (b) $xy - y$
    $= 6 + -4$ $= -12 - -4$
    $= 6 - 4$ $= -12 + 4$
    $= 2$ $= -8$

Do some of the working in your head

Exercise 16

If $a = -4$, $b = 5$, $c = -2$, work out

1. $2a + 3$	**2.** $3b - 7$
3. $4a - 1$	**4.** $2b + c$
5. $5c - 2a$	**6.** $6a - 3$
7. $2c + b$	**8.** $3a - 2b$
9. $6c - 2b$	**10.** $3c + 4a$
11. $3c - 4$	**12.** $2a - 3c$

If $m = 3$, $n = -2$ and $t = 4$ find the value of (a) $m + n$,   (b) $n - t$

(a) $m + n$ (b) $n - t$
    $= 3 + -2$ $= -2 - 4$
    $= 3 - 2$ $= -6$
    $= 1$

Work down the page. It is easier to follow.

Exercise 12

If $a = 3$, $b = 5$, $c = 1$, $d = 7$, work out

1. $a + c$	**2.** $a - d$
3. $b - c$	**4.** $b + d$
5. $c + d$	**6.** $a - 8$
7. $b + 2$	**8.** $d - 4$
9. $c + 5$	**10.** $5 + d$
11. $a - b$	**12.** $a + 11$
13. $d - a$	**14.** $8 + d$
15. $c - 3$	**16.** $d - 10$
17. $c + 6$	**18.** $c - b$
19. $7 - b$	**20.** $d + a$

If $n = 5$, $t = 2$, $x = 0$, $y = 4$, work out

21. $x + n$	**22.** $y - t$
23. $x - y$	**24.** $5 + n$
25. $y + n$	**26.** $x - t$
27. $t - 10$	**28.** $t + x$
29. $4 - y$	**30.** $n + 10$
31. $x + y - t$	**32.** $t - n - 5$
33. $y - t + 2$	**34.** $y + t + n$
35. $x - 10 - y$	**36.** $x - t - 13$
37. $7 + t - n$	**38.** $n - 9 + y$
39. $3 + t - x$	**40.** $2 - y - t$

Exercise 13

Work out the answers to questions **1** to **20** of Exercise 12 with $a = 2$, $b = -3$, $c = 0$, $d = 5$.

Work out the answers to questions **21** to **40** of Exercise 12 with $n = -1$, $t = 3$, $x = 2$, $y = -2$.

13. $7b + 3a$ **14.** $8a + 6c$
15. $2b - 4a$ **16.** $4b + 5$
17. $3a + 8$ **18.** $2c - a$
19. $5a - 2c$ **20.** $3b + 7$

If $n = 3$, $x = -1$, $y = 6$, work out
21. $2x - 3$ **22.** $3y + 4n$
23. $5n + 2x$ **24.** $4y - x$
25. $7y - 2$ **26.** $3x + 2n$
27. $10x + 5$ **28.** $6x - y$
29. $4x - 5y$ **30.** $2y - 10$
31. $8n - 2y$ **32.** $7n + 3y$
33. $6y + 4$ **34.** $4n + 5x$
35. $2n + 3x$ **36.** $5y - 20$
37. $9y - n$ **38.** $8x + 2n$
39. $5x + 6$ **40.** $3n - 2x$

If $m = 3$, $h = -2$, $k = 4$, $t = -3$, work out
41. $2m + h - 2t$ **42.** $3k + 7 + 6t$
43. $hk - m + 3t$ **44.** $mt + 2h - 8$
45. $5k + 2 + 3h$ **46.** $2t - 3k - 2h$
47. $th - 2k - m$ **48.** $tk - m + 5h$
49. $3h + 10t - 9$ **50.** $6 - 8k - t$

Exercise 17

Work out the answers to questions **1** to **20** of Exercise 16 with $a = 3$, $b = -2$, $c = 4$.

Work out the answers to questions **21** to **40** of Exercise 16 with $n = -3$, $x = 2$, $y = -1$.

Work out the answers to questions **41** to **50** of Exercise 16 with $m = -2$, $h = 7$, $k = -1$, $t = -5$.

$a^2 = a \times a$

$a^3 = a \times a \times a$

$2a^2 = 2(a^2)$

$(2a)^2 = 2a \times 2a$

$a(b - c)$:   Work out the term in brackets first

$\dfrac{a + b}{c}$:   The division line works like a bracket, so workout $a + b$ first.

If $x = 2$, $y = -3$, work out

(a) y^2,   (b) $3x^2$

(a) $y^2 = -3 \times -3$ (b) $3x^2 = 3 \times 4$
    $= 9$ $= 12$

Exercise 18

If $m = 2$, $t = -2$, $x = -3$, $y = 4$, work out
1. m^2 **2.** t^2
3. x^2 **4.** y^2
5. m^3 **6.** t^3
7. x^3 **8.** y^3
9. $2m^2$ **10.** $(2m)^2$
11. $2t^2$ **12.** $(2t)^2$
13. $2x^2$ **14.** $(2x)^2$
15. $3y^2$ **16.** $4m^2$
17. $5t^2$ **18.** $6x^2$
19. $(3y)^2$ **20.** $3m^3$

21. $x^2 + 4$ **22.** $y^2 - 6$
23. $t^2 - 3$ **24.** $m^3 + 10$
25. $x^2 + t^2$ **26.** $2x^2 + 1$
27. $m^2 + xt$ **28.** my^2
29. $(mt)^2$ **30.** $(xy)^2$
31. $(xt)^2$ **32.** yx^2
33. $m - t$ **34.** $t - x$
35. $y - m$ **36.** $m - y^2$
37. $t + x$ **38.** $2m + 3x$
39. $3t - y$ **40.** $xt + y$

41. $3(m + t)$ **42.** $4(x + y)$
43. $5(m + 2y)$ **44.** $2(y - m)$
45. $m(t + x)$ **46.** $y(m + x)$
47. $x(y - m)$ **48.** $t(2m + y)$
49. $m^2(y - x)$ **50.** $t^2(x^2 + m)$

51. $\dfrac{2y + t}{3}$ **52.** $\dfrac{2t + m}{2}$

53. $\dfrac{x + t}{5}$ **54.** $\dfrac{y - t}{m}$

55. $\dfrac{y - m}{t^2}$ **56.** $\dfrac{x^2 + m}{11}$

Exercise 19

Work out the answers to questions **1** to **56** of Exercise 18 with $m = -1$, $t = -4$, $x = 3$, $y = -5$.

74

5.4 COLLECTING LIKE TERMS

$7x + 3 + 3x + 5 + x = 11x + 8$

$3a + 2b - 2 + 4a + 7 = 7a + 2b + 5$

$x^2 + 3x + 9 + 4x + 3x^2 = 4x^2 + 7x + 9$

$2x - 3y + 2xy + 5x + 3xy = 7x - 3y + 5xy$

Exercise 20

Collect like terms together.
1. $2x + 3 + 3x + 5$
2. $4x + 8 + 5x - 3$
3. $5x - 3 + 2x + 7$
4. $6x + 1 + x + 3$
5. $4x - 3 + 2x + 10 + x$
6. $5x + 8 + x + 4 + 2x$
7. $7x - 9 + 2x + 3 + 3x$
8. $5x + 7 - 3x - 2$
9. $4x - 6 - 2x + 1$
10. $10x + 5 - 9x - 10 + x$

11. $6x - 3 + 2x - 5 + x - 1$
12. $3x + 2 - x - 7 + x$
13. $10x - 7 - 4x + 8 + 3x + 5$
14. $11x + 4 - x - 4 + 3x$
15. $6x - 5 - 5x + 10 - x + 1$
16. $5y - 6 + 2y + 4$
17. $3y + 4 + 6y - 6 + y$
18. $2y + 10 - y - 10 + 3y$
19. $5y - 6 - 4y - 2 - y$
20. $11y + 3 - 8y + 5 + y$

21. $4a + 6b + 3 + 9a - 3b - 4$
22. $8m - 3n + 1 + 6n + 2m + 7$
23. $6p - 4 + 5q - 3p - 4 - 7q$
24. $12s - 3t + 2 - 10s - 4t + 12$
25. $a - 2b - 7 + a + 2b + 8$
26. $3x + 2y + 5z - 2x - y + 2z$
27. $6x - 5y + 3z - x + y + z$
28. $2k - 3m + n + 3k - m - n$
29. $12a - 3 + 2b - 6 - 8a + 3b$
30. $3a + x + e - 2a - 5x - 6e$

Remember: You cannot add x^2 to $3x$

You cannot add y^2 to $5y$

You cannot add xy to $4x$

Exercise 21

Collect like terms together.
1. $x^2 + 3x + 2 + 4x + 1$
2. $x^2 + 4x + 3 + 3x + 5$
3. $x^2 + 5x + 2 - 2x + 1$
4. $x^2 + 2x + 2x^2 + 4x + 5$
5. $x^2 + 5x + x^2 + x - 7$
6. $2x^2 - 3x + 8 + x^2 + 4x + 4$
7. $3x^2 + 4x + 6 - x^2 - 3x - 3$
8. $5x^2 - 3x + 2 - 3x^2 + 2x - 2$
9. $2x^2 - 2x + 3 - x^2 - 2x - 5$
10. $6x^2 - 7x + 8 - 3x^2 + 5x - 10$

11. $3a^2 + 2a + 4 - 3a^2 + 6a + 5$
12. $m^2 + 6m - 7 + m^2 + 2m - 3$
13. $8 - 3x - x^2 + 2 + 4x - 2x^2$
14. $10 + 2x + x^2 - 8 - 6x - 4x^2$
15. $17 - 2t + 2t^2 + 4t + 5 + 2t$
16. $18 + t^2 - 3t + 5 + t^2 + 3t - 2t^2$
17. $n^2 - 2n + 3 + 2n^2 + 1 + 2n - 3n^2$
18. $3x^2 + 10 - 6x + 19 - x + x^2$
19. $5 - 2x - 3x^2 - 1 + x + x^2$
20. $2x^2 + 10x - 5 - 5 + x - 2x^2 + 10$

21. $x^2 + 2xy + 3x + 2x + 3xy$
22. $3x^2 + 4xy - 2x + x^2 + 2xy$
23. $5x^2 - 3x + 2xy + 2x^2 + 4x + 6xy$
24. $4x^2 + 6x + 4xy + x^2 - 5x - 2xy$
25. $x^2 - 5x - 2xy + 6x + 3x^2 + 5xy$
26. $m^2 + 4m + 2mn + 3m^2 - 2m + mn$
27. $a^2 - 3a + 2ab + 7a^2 - 2a + 2ab$
28. $c^2 + 3c + 4cd - c^2 - 3c + 2cd$
29. $z^2 - 3z + 2xz + 2z^2 + 8z + 8xz$
30. $5p^2 - 7p + 2pq - p^2 - 3p - 2pq$

31. $3y^2 - 6x + y^2 + x^2 + 7x + 4x^2$
32. $8 - 5x - 2x^2 + 4 + 6x + 2x^2$
33. $5 + 2y + 3y^2 - 8y - 6 + 2y^2 + 3$
34. $ab + a^2 - 3b + 2ab - a^2$
35. $3c^2 - d^2 + 2cd - 3c^2 - d^2$
36. $ab + 2a^2 + 3ab - 4a^2 + 2a$
37. $x^3 + 2x^2 - x + 3x^2 + x^3 + x$
38. $5 - x^2 - 2x^3 + 6 + 2x^2 + 3x^3$
39. $xy + ab - cd + 2xy - ab + dc$
40. $pq - 3qp + p^2 + 2qp - q^2$

Exercise 22

Find the perimeter of each of the following shapes. All the lengths are given in cm. Give the answers in the simplest form.

1.

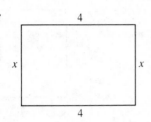

2.

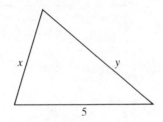

3.

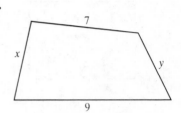

4.

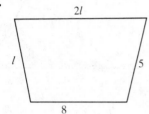

5.

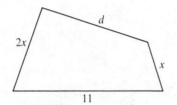

6.

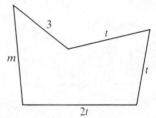

7.

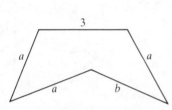

8.

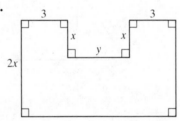

9.

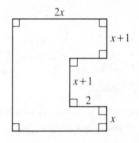

5.5   SIMPLIFYING TERMS AND BRACKETS

$$3 \times 4x = 12x$$
$$8 \times 6y = 48y$$
$$-3 \times 2x = -6x$$

$$x \times 3x = 3x^2$$
$$2z \times 4z = 8z^2$$
$$4(2x \times 3x) = 24x^2$$

Exercise 23

Write in a more simple form.

1. $2 \times 3x$	**2.** $4 \times 2x$	**3.** $3 \times 2x$
4. $5 \times 3x$	**5.** $3 \times 2y$	**6.** $4 \times 5y$
7. $7 \times 3x$	**8.** $-2 \times 3x$	**9.** $-5 \times 4x$
10. $-2 \times 5x$	**11.** $7 \times 4a$	**12.** $5 \times 3a$
13. $2x \times 3$	**14.** $3y \times 4$	**15.** $5y \times 5$
16. $x \times 2x$	**17.** $x \times 4x$	**18.** $x \times 6x$

19. $y \times 3y$	**20.** $y \times 10y$	**21.** $x \times 7x$
22. $a \times 5a$	**23.** $2x \times 3x$	**24.** $3x \times 4x$
25. $2x \times 5x$	**26.** $4x \times 2x$	**27.** $7x \times 2x$
28. $6x \times 3x$	**29.** $5y \times 2y$	**30.** $4t \times 6t$
31. $x \times 2x^2$	**32.** $2x \times 3x^2$	**33.** $4y \times y^2$
34. $3a \times 2a^2$	**35.** $3y \times 3y^2$	**36.** $5x^2 \times x$
37. $7p \times 3p$	**38.** $2(3x \times 2x)$	**39.** $4(3x \times 5x)$
40. $5(2x \times 3x)$	**41.** $3(2x \times 5x^2)$	**42.** $2(x \times 6x^2)$
43. $4(x \times x^2)$	**44.** $3(2y \times 2y)$	**45.** $6(a \times 2a^2)$
46. $x \times 3x^3$	**47.** $y \times 2x$	**48.** $2a \times 3a^2$
49. $2a \times 3b$	**50.** $2p \times 5q$	**51.** $3x \times 5y$
52. $6x \times 3x^2$	**53.** $3a \times 8a^3$	**54.** $3(3x \times 4x^2)$
55. $ab \times 2a$	**56.** $xy \times 3y$	**57.** $cd \times 5c$
58. $ab \times ab$	**59.** $2xy \times xy$	**60.** $3d \times 2c$

Exercise 24

Write down the area of each shape in its simplest form. All lengths are in cm.

1.
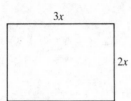
3x
2x

2.
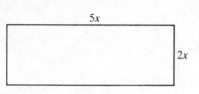
5x
2x

3.
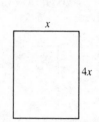
x
4x

4.
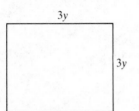
3y
3y

5.
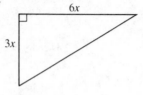
6x
3x

6.
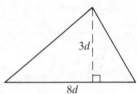
3d
8d

7.
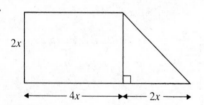
2x
4x   2x

8.
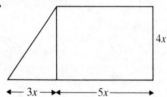
4x
3x   5x

9.
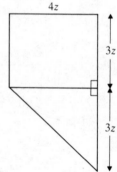
4z
3z
3z

Remove the brackets

$3(x - 2) = 3x - 6$

$4(2x + 3) = 8x + 12$

$x(2x - 3) = 2x^2 - 3x$

$- 2x(x - 4) = - 2x^2 + 8x$

Exercise 25

Remove the brackets

1. $2(x + 3)$
2. $3(x + 5)$
3. $4(x + 6)$
4. $2(2x + 1)$
5. $5(2x + 3)$
6. $4(3x - 1)$
7. $6(2x - 2)$
8. $3(5x - 2)$
9. $5(3x - 4)$
10. $7(2x - 3)$

11. $2(2x + 3)$
12. $3(2x + 1)$
13. $5(x + 4)$
14. $6(2x + 2)$
15. $4(x + 3)$
16. $12(x + 7)$
17. $3(2x - 3)$
18. $10(x + 4)$
19. $9(2x + 5)$
20. $8(3x - 6)$

21. $- 2(2x + 3)$
22. $- 4(2x + 1)$
23. $- 3(x + 2)$
24. $- 2(3x + 4)$
25. $- 2(4x - 1)$
26. $- 5(2x - 2)$
27. $- 3(2x + 1)$
28. $- (2x + 1)$
29. $- (3x + 2)$
30. $- (4x - 5)$

31. $x(x + 3)$
32. $x(x + 5)$
33. $x(x - 2)$
34. $x(x - 3)$
35. $x(2x + 1)$
36. $x(3x - 2)$
37. $x(3x + 5)$
38. $2x(x - 1)$
39. $2x(x + 2)$
40. $3x(2x + 3)$

Exercise 26

1. Three rods A, B and C have lengths of x, $(x + 1)$ and $(x - 2)$ cm respectively, as shown

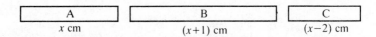

In the diagrams below express the length l in terms of x.
Give your answers in their simplest form.

(a)

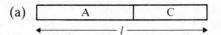

(b)

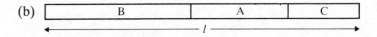

(c)

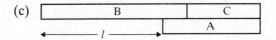

(d)

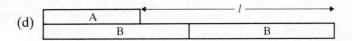

(e)

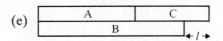

(f)

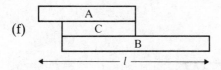

(g)

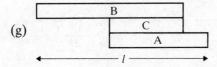

2. Four rods A, B, C and D have lengths as shown below.

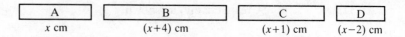

In the diagrams below express the length *l* in terms of *x*.
Give your answers in their simplest form.

(a)
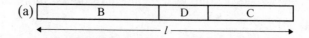

(b)
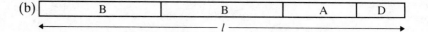

(c)
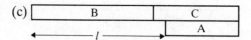

(d)
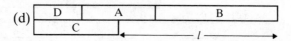

(e)
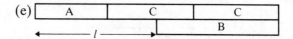

(f)
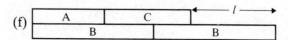

(g)
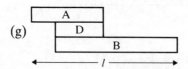

(h)
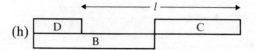

(i)
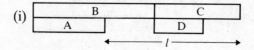

Part 6

6.1 SOLVING EQUATIONS

(a) $x - 3 = 8$	(b) $7 + y = 2$
$x = 8 + 3$	$y = 2 - 7$
$x = \mathbf{11}$	$y = \mathbf{-5}$

Exercise 1

Solve the equations.

1. $x - 3 = 5$ **2.** $x - 4 = 6$
3. $x - 2 = 11$ **4.** $x + 5 = 8$
5. $x + 7 = 12$ **6.** $x + 15 = 21$
7. $x - 3 = 1$ **8.** $x + 4 = 5$
9. $x - 8 = 0$ **10.** $x + 4 = 2$
11. $x + 6 = 3$ **12.** $x + 8 = 3$

13. $y - 7 = -5$ **14.** $y - 8 = -10$
15. $y + 10 = 20$ **16.** $y + 9 = 4$
17. $y - 7 = -6$ **18.** $y + 25 = 15$
19. $4 + x = 9$ **20.** $5 + x = 7$
21. $8 + x = 24$ **22.** $a + 6 = -2$
23. $a - 7 = -3$ **24.** $a + 6 = 0$

25. $7 = x + 2$ **26.** $9 = x - 3$
27. $15 = x + 4$ **28.** $12 = x - 7$
29. $5 = x + 11$ **30.** $16 = x - 7$
31. $18 = 9 + x$ **32.** $23 = 11 + x$
33. $-10 = x + 6$ **34.** $7 = 6 + x$
35. $18 = 13 + x$ **36.** $-5 = 7 + x$

(a) $3x = 15$	(b) $4x = 3$
$x = \dfrac{15}{3}$	$x = \dfrac{3}{4}$
$x = 5$	

Exercise 2

Solve the equations.

1. $3x = 9$ **2.** $2x = 12$
3. $4x = 28$ **4.** $5x = 30$

5. $7x = 56$

6. $4x = 36$

7. $9x = 81$

8. $9x = 90$

9. $6x = 180$

10. $12x = 60$

11. $10x = 1000$

12. $8x = 96$

13. $5x = 2$

14. $7x = 5$

15. $8x = 3$

16. $4x = 1$

17. $2x = 1$

18. $9x = 5$

19. $3x = 5$

20. $4x = 7$

21. $3x = 7$

22. $2x = 9$

23. $3x = 10$

24. $5x = 11$

25. $5x = -4$

26. $6x = -24$

27. $5x = -10$

28. $4x = -36$

29. $3x = -2$

30. $12x = -1$

31. $7x = -10$

32. $5x = 1$

33. $4x = -9$

34. $10x = -10$

35. $18x = -18$

36. $17x = -68$

37. $8 = 4x$

38. $10 = 2x$

39. $12 = 3y$

40. $72 = 9a$

41. $6 = 5a$

42. $15 = 2z$

43. $-8 = 2y$

44. $-7 = 2x$

45. $9 = -3m$

46. $15 = -5n$

47. $-20 = -2x$

48. $-40 = -4y$

15. $\dfrac{a}{7} = 10$

16. $7 = \dfrac{x}{5}$

17. $9 = \dfrac{x}{4}$

18. $7 = \dfrac{x}{11}$

19. $-3 = \dfrac{x}{3}$

20. $-1 = \dfrac{x}{8}$

21. $\dfrac{x}{10} = -\dfrac{1}{2}$

22. $\dfrac{x}{8} = -10$

23. $-2 = \dfrac{a}{80}$

24. $\dfrac{x}{2} = \dfrac{1}{4}$

25. $3x = 60$

26. $4x = 28$

27. $\dfrac{x}{2} = 8$

28. $\dfrac{x}{3} = 15$

(a) $2x - 1 = 7$
$2x = 7 + 1$
$2x = 8$
$x = \dfrac{8}{2}$
$x = 4$

(b) $3x + 4 = 6$
$3x = 6 - 4$
$3x = 2$
$x = \dfrac{2}{3}$

(a) $\dfrac{x}{2} = 4$

(b) $\dfrac{x}{5} = -3$

$x = 4 \times 2$
$x = 8$

$x = -3 \times 5$
$x = -15$

Exercise 3

Solve the equations.

1. $\dfrac{x}{3} = 4$

2. $\dfrac{x}{4} = 5$

3. $\dfrac{x}{5} = 4$

4. $\dfrac{x}{4} = 7$

5. $\dfrac{x}{8} = 9$

6. $\dfrac{x}{6} = -2$

7. $\dfrac{x}{2} = -2$

8. $\dfrac{x}{5} = 0$

9. $\dfrac{x}{10} = 0.1$

10. $\dfrac{x}{6} = 60$

11. $\dfrac{x}{2} = \dfrac{1}{2}$

12. $\dfrac{x}{6} = \dfrac{1}{3}$

13. $\dfrac{a}{7} = \dfrac{1}{2}$

14. $\dfrac{a}{8} = \dfrac{1}{4}$

Exercise 4

1. $2x - 3 = 3$

2. $3x - 1 = 5$

3. $4x - 3 = 5$

4. $3x - 5 = 13$

5. $5x - 7 = 3$

6. $7x - 1 = 27$

7. $2x - 1 = 4$

8. $3x + 1 = 13$

9. $4x + 2 = 5$

10. $5x + 1 = 7$

11. $5x - 3 = 10$

12. $3x + 1 = 2$

13. $2y + 10 = 11$

14. $3y - 6 = -3$

15. $2y + 10 = 9$

16. $3y + 10 = 7$

17. $4y + 10 = 10$

18. $3y - 6 = -4$

19. $5a + 6 = 10$

20. $7a + 4 = 0$

21. $9a - 7 = 0$

22. $10a - 3 = 0$

23. $5n - 3 = 11$

24. $6n + 3 = -2$

25. $3x + 4 = -3$

26. $8x - 2 = 10$

27. $4t + 10 = 0$

28. $6 + 3x = 12$

29. $5 + 2x = 13$

30. $7 + 4x = 20$

31. $5 + 8x = 10$

32. $8 + 5x = 2$

33. $3 + 7x = 2$

34. $8 + 5x = 0$

35. $9 + 3x = 0$

36. $5 + 3x = -1$

37. $10 = 2x + 3$

38. $2 = 3x - 4$

39. $7 = 4x - 5$

40. $4 = 5x - 1$

41. $7 = 3x + 6$

42. $-11 = 3x - 5$

43. $6 = 3x - 4$

44. $-2 = 2x + 1$

45. $0 = 10x - 1$

46. $0 = 11x + 2$

47. $19 = 6x - 5$

48. $7 = 3x + 7$

Solve the equations

(a) $5x + 1 = 3x + 8$ (b) $4x - 2 = x - 6$

$5x - 3x = 8 - 1$ $4x - x = -6 + 2$

$2x = 7$ $3x = -4$

$x = \dfrac{7}{2}$ $x = -\dfrac{4}{3}$

$x = 3\tfrac{1}{2}$ $x = -1\tfrac{1}{3}$

Exercise 5
Solve the equations.
1. $3x + 1 = 2x + 3$
2. $5x + 3 = 2x + 12$
3. $4x - 1 = x + 2$
4. $6x - 2 = 2x + 6$
5. $5x + 7 = 4x + 11$
6. $3x - 3 = x + 3$
7. $10x + 1 = 4x + 4$
8. $7x - 8 = x - 2$
9. $5x - 7 = 3x - 3$
10. $11x - 20 = 6x + 5$

11. $4x + 2 = 17 - x$
12. $5x - 3 = 11 - 2x$
13. $6x + 1 = 33 - 2x$
14. $3x - 7 = 1 - 5x$
15. $4x - 1 = 5 - 2x$
16. $8x + 2 = 7 - 2x$
17. $6x - 7 = 2 - 4x$
18. $3x + 9 = 17 + 2x$
19. $10x - 8 = 20 + 6x$
20. $3x - 12 = 4 - 3x$

21. $5x - 2 = 6 + 4x$
22. $10x + 7 = 12 - 2x$

23. $3x + 5 = 8 - x$
24. $7x = 8 - 2x$
25. $3x = 10 + x$
26. $4x - 12 = 2x$
27. $7x + 1 = 5x$
28. $2x + 1 = x - 6$
29. $3x - 2 = 2x - 10$
30. $5x - 4 = 2x - 10$

Exercise 6
Solve the equations.
1. $2(x - 1) = 3$
2. $3(x + 1) = 4$
3. $4(x - 2) = 1$
4. $5(x - 3) = 10$
5. $3(2x - 1) = 6$
6. $2(3x + 3) = 12$
7. $5(3x - 2) = 5$
8. $2(3x - 5) = 6$
9. $10(x - 2) = 1$
10. $6(4x + 1) = 18$

11. $3(x - 1) = 2x - 2$
12. $4(x + 2) = 3x + 10$
13. $2(2x - 1) = x + 4$
14. $3(x - 1) = 2(x + 1) - 2$
15. $4(2x - 1) = 3(x + 1) - 2$
16. $5 + 2(x + 1) = 5(x - 1)$
17. $6 + 3(x + 2) = 2(x + 5) + 4$
18. $5(x + 1) = 2x + 3 + x$
19. $4(2x - 2) = 5x - 17$
20. $x + 2(x + 4) = -4$

21. $3x + 2(x + 1) = 3x + 12$
22. $4x - 2(x + 4) = x + 1$
23. $2x - 3(x + 2) = 2x + 1$
24. $5x - 2(x - 2) = 6 - 2x$
25. $3(x + 1) + 2(x + 2) = 10$
26. $4(x + 3) + 2(x - 1) = 4$
27. $3(x - 2) - 2(x + 1) = 5$
28. $5(x - 3) + 3(x + 2) = 7x$
29. $3(2x + 1) - 2(2x + 1) = 10$
30. $4(3x - 1) - 3(3x + 2) = 0$

6.2   SOLVING PROBLEMS WITH EQUATIONS

If I multiply a 'mystery' number by 2 and then add 3 the answer is 14. Find the 'mystery' number.

Let the mystery number be x.
Then $2x + 3 = 14$
$2x\quad = 11$
$x\quad = 5\tfrac{1}{2}$

The 'mystery' number is $5\tfrac{1}{2}$

Exercise 7

Find the 'mystery' number in each question by forming an equation and then solving it.

1. If I multiply the number by 3 and then add 4, the answer is 13.
2. If I multiply the number by 4 and then add 5, the answer is 8.
3. If I multiply the number by 2 and then subtract 5, the answer is 4.

82   **Part 6**

4. If I multiply the number by 5 and then subtract 7, the answer is 3.

5. If I double the number and then add 9, the answer is 20.

6. If I treble the number and then subtract 5, the answer is 2.

7. If I multiply the number by 8 and then add 7, the answer is 10.

8. If I treble the number and then subtract 11, the answer is 10.

9. If I multiply the number by 7 and then add 6, the answer is 3.

10. If I multiply the number by 10 and then add 19, the answer is 16.

11. If I add 3 to the number and then multiply the result by 4, the answer is 10.

12. If I add 4 to the number and then multiply the result by 3, the answer is 15.

13. If I subtract 3 from the number and then double the result, the answer is 4.

14. If I add 5 to the number and then multiply the result by 3, the answer is 20.

15. If I treble the number and then subtract 7, the answer is 2.

16. If I multiply the number by 6 and then add 5, the answer is 8.

17. If I subtract 4 from the number and then multiply the result by 5, the answer is 3.

18. If I add 11 to the number and then double the result, the answer is 31.

19. If I multiply the number by 7 and then subtract 6, the answer is 11.

20. If I add 8 to the number and then treble the result, the answer is 16.

If I add 3 to a 'mystery' number and then treble the result, I get the same answer as when I multiply the number by 2 and then subtract 7. Find the 'mystery' number.

Let the mystery number be x

Then $3(x + 3) = 2x - 7$

$$3x + 9 = 2x - 7$$
$$3x - 2x = -7 - 9$$
$$x = -16$$

The mystery number is -16

Exercise 8

Find the 'mystery' number in each question by forming an equation and then solving it.

1. If I double the number and then add 7, I get the same answer as when I add 10 to the number.

2. If I multiply the number by 4 and then add 5, I get the same answer as when I double the number and then add 8.

3. If I treble the number and then add 11, I get the same answer as when I double the number and then add 15.

4. If I multiply the number by 4 and then subtract 1, I get the same answer as when I double the number and then add 9.

5. If I multiply the number by 5 and then subtract 12, I get the same answer as when I treble the number and then subtract 8.

6. If I multiply the number by 7 and then subtract 1, I get the same answer as when I multiply the number by 4 and then add 1.

7. If I multiply the number by 5 and then subtract 12, I get the same answer as when I double the number and then subtract 9.

8. If I treble the number, add 1 and then multiply the result by 2, the answer is 6.

9. If I multiply the number by 4, subtract 1 and then multiply the result by 3, the answer is 9.

10. If I double the number, add 3 and then multiply the result by 5, the answer is 20.

11. If I treble the number, subtract 4 and then multiply the result by 4, the answer is 8.

12. If I multiply the number by 5, subtract 1 and then multiply the result by 6, the answer is 18.

13. If I multiply the number by 4 and then add 1, I get the same answer as when I double the number and then add 7.

14. If I add 2 to the number and then multiply the result by 3, I get the same answer as when I add 4 to the number and then double the result.

15. If I add 5 to the number and then multiply the result by 4, I get the same answer as when I add 1 to the number and then multiply the result by 2.

16. If I subtract 3 from the number and then multiply the result by 6, I get the same answer as when I add 2 to the number and then multiply the result by 4.

17. If I treble the number, subtract 7 and then multiply the result by 5, the answer is 20.

18. If I multiply the number by 4, add 5 and then multiply the result by 7, the answer is 21.

19. If I multiply the number by 6 and then subtract 1, I get the same answer as when I multiply by 3 and then add 8.

20. If I subtract 4 from the number and then multiply the result by 7, I get the same answer as when I add 1 to the number and then multiply the result by 4.

Exercise 9

Answer these questions by forming an equation and then solving it.

1. Find x if the perimeter is 7 cm

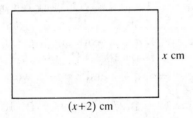

x cm

$(x+2)$ cm

2. Find x if the perimeter is 5 cm.

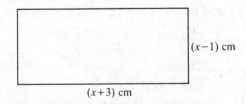

$(x-1)$ cm

$(x+3)$ cm

3. Find y if the perimeter is 7 cm.

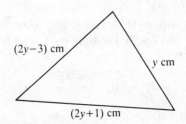

$(2y-3)$ cm

y cm

$(2y+1)$ cm

4. Find t if the perimeter is 6 cm.

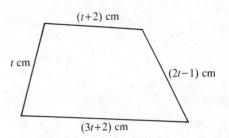

$(t+2)$ cm

t cm

$(2t-1)$ cm

$(3t+2)$ cm

5. The length of a rectangle is 3 times its width. If the perimeter of the rectangle is 11 cm, find its width. Hint: Let the width be x cm.

6. The length of a rectangle is 4 cm more than its width. If its perimeter is 13 cm, find its width.

7. The width of a rectangle is 5 cm less than its length. If the perimeter of the rectangle is 18 cm, find its length.

8. Find x in the following rectangles:

(a)   (b)

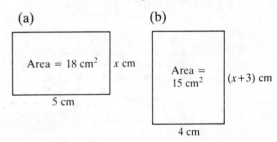

Area = 18 cm^2 x cm

5 cm

Area = 15 cm^2 $(x+3)$ cm

4 cm

9. Find y in the following triangles:

(a)   (b)

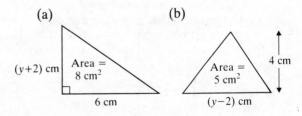

$(y+2)$ cm   Area = 8 cm^2

6 cm

Area = 5 cm^2 4 cm

$(y-2)$ cm

10. The length of a rectangle is 5 cm more than its width. The perimeter of the rectangle is 38 cm. Find the width of the rectangle and hence the area of the rectangle.

11. Find x in the following triangles:

(a)   (b)

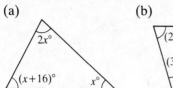 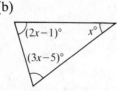

12. The angles of a triangle are $32°$, $x°$ and $(4x + 3)°$. Find the value of x.

13. Find a in the diagrams below

(a)   (b)

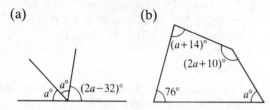

14. Kathryn has some money saved in her piggy bank. On her birthday her father doubles the money she has and then her mother gives her another 75p. She now has 185p. How much did she have to start with?

15. Each diagram in the sequence below consists of a number of dots.

Diagram number	1	2	3
	•• ••	••• •• • •••	•••• • • • • ••••

(a) Draw diagram number 4 and diagram number 5.

(b) Copy and complete the table below:

Diagram number	Number of dots
1	4
2	8
3	
4	
5	
6	

(c) Without drawing the diagrams, state the number of dots in
  (i) diagram number 8

(ii) diagram number 14
(iii) diagram number 52

(d) State the number of the diagram which has 64 dots.

(e) If we write x for the diagram number and n for the number of dots, write down a formula involving x and n.

Exercise 10

Multiple choice exercise.

1. What is the value of $-7 + (-7)$?
  A. 0   **B.** 14   **C.** -14 **D.** 49

2. What is the value of $-8 \div (-2)$?
  A. -4 **B.** 4   **C.** 16   **D.** $\frac{1}{4}$

3. What is the value of $-9 + 200$?
  A. -209 **B.** -191 **C.** 191
  D. -1800

4. If $a = -3$ and $b = 5$, work out $2a - b$.
  A. -1 **B.** 1   **C.** 11   **D.** -11

5. If $x = 4$ and $y = -3$, work out $3x - 2y$.
  A. 6   **B.** -6 **C.** 18   **D.** -18

6. If $m = -1$ and $n = -2$, work out $m^2 + n^2$
  A. -5 **B.** 5   **C.** -3 **D.** 4

7. If $c = -4$, $d = 2$, work out $3(d - c)$.
  A. 6   **B.** -18 **C.** 18   **D.** -6

8. If $p = -3$, $q = 2$ and $r = -2$, work out $2q + pr$.
  A. -2 **B.** 7   **C.** 9   **D.** 10

9. If $x = -6$ and $y = 3$, work out $2x^2 + y$
  A. 75   **B.** 69   **C.** 147   **D.** -141

10. I start with x then add 7, double the result and finally divide by 3. The final result is
  A. $\dfrac{2(x + 7)}{3}$ **B.** $2x + \dfrac{7}{3}$
  C. $\dfrac{2x + 7}{3}$ **D.** $3(2x + 7)$

11. I start with x, then square it, multiply by 3 and finally subtract 4. The final result is
  A. $(3x)^2 - 4$ **B.** $(3x - 4)^2$ **C.** $3x^2 - 4$
  D. $3(x - 4)^2$

12. I start with n, then add 4, then square the result and finally multiply by 3. The final result is
  A. $3(n^2 + 4)$ **B.** $\dfrac{(n + 4)^2}{3}$ **C.** $3n^2 + 4$
  D. $3(n + 4)^2$

13. Solve the equation $3x - 7 = 23$.
    A. $x = 5\frac{1}{3}$ **B.** $x = 10$ **C.** $x = 30$
    D. $x = 27$

14. Solve the equation $4x + 5 = 3$.
    A. $x = \frac{1}{2}$ **B.** $x = 2$ **C.** $x = -\frac{1}{2}$
    D. $x = -2$

15. Solve the equation $3x - 1 = 2x + 8$.
    A. $x = 9$ **B.** $x = 7$ **C.** $x = 1\frac{4}{5}$
    D. $x = 1\frac{2}{5}$

16. Remove the brackets and simplify
    $2(x + 7) + 3(x - 1)$.
    A. $5x - 11$ **B.** $5x + 17$ **C.** $5x + 11$
    D. $6x + 14$

17. Remove the brackets and simplify
    $4(x - 2) - 3(x + 1)$.
    A. $x - 5$ **B.** $x - 11$ **C.** $7x - 5$
    D. $7x - 11$

18. Solve the equation $4(2x - 1) = 3x + 5$.
    A. $x = \frac{5}{9}$ **B.** $x = 1\frac{4}{5}$ **C.** $x = \frac{9}{11}$
    D. $x = -\frac{3}{8}$

19. If I add 7 to a certain number and then
    multiply the result by 5, the answer is 10.
    What is the number?
    A. -20 **B.** 5 **C.** -5 **D.** $1\frac{3}{5}$

20. If I multiply a certain number by 4 and then
    subtract 11, the answer is 2. What is the
    number?
    A. $11\frac{1}{2}$ **B.** $-2\frac{1}{4}$ **C.** $4\frac{1}{4}$ **D.** $3\frac{1}{4}$

6.3   CHANGING THE SUBJECT

Make x the subject.

(a) $x - e = t$

$x = t + e$

(b) $mx = c$

$x = \dfrac{c}{m}$

(c) $B + n = x + a$

$B + n - a = x$

(d) $p + q = Ax$

$\dfrac{p + q}{A} = x$

Exercise 11

Make x the subject

1. $x + a = c$
2. $x + d = m$
3. $x + h = m$
4. $x + e = t$
5. $x - m = q$
6. $x - k = m$
7. $x - n = a + b$
8. $x + B = c + b$
9. $x + D = a + d$
10. $x - M = m + t$
11. $x - v = u - w$
12. $x + T = t - s$
13. $B + x = n$
14. $M + x = m$
15. $N + x = a - b$
16. $R + x = v - n$
17. $x + K = y^2$
18. $x - a^2 = b^2$
19. $x - n^2 = N^2$
20. $x + p = -a$

21. $a = x - n$
22. $mn = x + r$
23. $c = x + m$
24. $B = x - b$
25. $x + b - c = a$
26. $x + c - d = e$
27. $x + a^2 - b^2 = c^2$
28. $x - v^2 = m^2 - mn$
29. $b = x - a - t$
30. $f + g = x - h$
31. $x - B = b + B^2$
32. $x + A - a = a$

33. $x - t = T^2 + t$
34. $w = x + w^3$
35. $uv = x + w^2$
36. $t^3 + x = T^3$
37. $x - abc = a^3$
38. $mn^2 = m^3 + x$
39. $a + bc = x - cb$
40. $4pq = pq + x$

Exercise 12

Make y the subject.
1. $3y = 12$
2. $5y = 30$
3. $ay = c$
4. $my = t$
5. $My = m$
6. $ty = a$
7. $ym = n$
8. $yx = L$
9. $ym^2 = n^2$
10. $yq = h$
11. $aby = A$
12. $m^2y = M^2$
13. $c = ay$
14. $x = ty$
15. $v = dy$
16. $u^2 = yv^2$
17. $b = t^2y$
18. $B = by$
19. $c = ye$
20. $k^2y = a$

21. $xy = a + b$
22. $my = e - f$
23. $ny = s + t$
24. $Hy = p + q$
25. $zy = ab + c$
26. $vy = a^2 - b^2$
27. $pq = My$
28. $km - m^2 = ny$
29. $yx^2 = c - k$
30. $yp = a - b - A$

31. $zy = \dfrac{A}{x}$
32. $vy = \dfrac{B}{w}$

33. $ky = \dfrac{Ba}{d}$
34. $m^2y = \dfrac{1}{n^2}$

35. $xy = \dfrac{m}{x}$
36. $py = \dfrac{A}{p}$

37. $\dfrac{N}{n} = yn$

38. $Ly = \dfrac{A}{B}$

39. $Py = \dfrac{a+b}{c}$

40. $Qy = \dfrac{e+t}{k}$

41. $y + t = a$

42. $y - m^2 = v$

43. $b = y + k$

44. $e + y = x$

45. $y + mn = n^2$

46. $ab = y - b^2$

47. $zy = n - a$

48. $py = x - z$

49. $y - t^2 = T^2$

50. $ny = \dfrac{C}{d}$

Make a the subject.
(a) $am - d = f$
$$am = f + d$$
$$a = \frac{f+d}{m}$$

(b) $c(a - x) = y$
$$ca - cx = y$$
$$ca = y + cx$$
$$a = \frac{y+cx}{c}$$

Exercise 13

Make a the subject.

1. $2a + 1 = 10$

2. $3a - 2 = 19$

3. $na + b = t$

4. $ma + v = q$

5. $pa - A = B$

6. $na - q = A$

7. $ka - w = n^2$

8. $ma + m = n$

9. $at + m = e$

10. $aB - w^2 = v^2$

11. $L + pa = d$

12. $M = ma - n$

13. $x = xa + y$

14. $v^2 = xa - t$

15. $sa - s^2 = z^2$

16. $pq + ra = x^2$

17. $lm + ab = h^2$

18. $t + .ae = d + b$

19. $p^2 = m + n + Ba$

20. $km = ma - n^2$

21. $m(a - n) = t$

22. $u(a + x) = x$

23. $p(a + w) = y$

24. $A(a - u) = q$

25. $L(x + a) = m$

26. $n(x^2 + a) = x^3$

27. $r(a - r) = s^2$

28. $x(a - x) = y^2$

29. $3(a - 4) = 1$

30. $5(a + 2) = 8$

31. $T = n(a - t)$

32. $V = w(a - y)$

33. $w + q = m(a - w)$

34. $x^2 - y^2 = z(a - z)$

35. $ut + at = v^2$

36. $MN + ma = L^2$

37. $z(x + a) = x$

38. $y^2 = w(a - w)$

39. $q(a - q) = x^2 + q^2$

40. $k(m + a) = km + n$

Formulae involving fractions

Make k the
subject
(a) $\dfrac{k}{m} = n$
$$k = mn$$

(b) $\dfrac{k}{a} + b = e$
$$\frac{k}{a} = e - b$$
$$k = a(e - b)$$

Exercise 14

Make k the subject.

1. $\dfrac{k}{n} = a$

2. $\dfrac{k}{t} = A$

3. $\dfrac{k}{x} = x$

4. $z = \dfrac{k}{p}$

5. $v = \dfrac{k}{w}$

6. $\dfrac{k}{n} = n^2$

7. $\dfrac{k}{m} = -e$

8. $\dfrac{k}{t} = (a - b)$

9. $\dfrac{k}{h} = x + y$

10. $\dfrac{k}{m} = -m$

11. $\dfrac{k}{(a+b)} = z$

12. $\dfrac{k}{m-n} = B$

13. $D = \dfrac{k}{m-p}$

14. $\dfrac{mk}{n} = a$

15. $\dfrac{nk}{x} = y$

16. $\dfrac{ak}{e} = y$

17. $\dfrac{vk}{a} = z$

18. $\dfrac{km}{a} = a$

19. $\dfrac{kz}{x} = y$

20. $\dfrac{kq}{v} = w$

21. $\dfrac{x}{a} = \dfrac{mk}{b}$

22. $\dfrac{xk}{c} = \dfrac{A}{m}$

23. $\dfrac{kz}{v} = \dfrac{v}{b}$

24. $\dfrac{ke}{t} = \dfrac{t}{n}$

25. $\dfrac{mk}{(x+y)} = a$

26. $\dfrac{nk}{(p+q)} = d$

27. $\dfrac{Ak}{q} = (x + t)$

28. $\dfrac{k}{n} = \dfrac{1}{a + d^2}$

29. $\dfrac{w}{B} = \dfrac{Bk}{w}$

30. $\dfrac{kz}{v} = \dfrac{v}{z}$

Think about it 2

CROSS NUMBERS

Here we have five cross number puzzles with a difference. There are no clues, only answers, and it is your task to find where the answers go.
(a) Copy out the cross number pattern
(b) Fit all the given numbers into the correct spaces. Tick off the numbers from the lists as you write them in the square.

1.

| 4 | 2 | 1 | 5 | 3 | | | 6 |

2 digits	3 digits	4 digits	5 digits	6 digits
11	315	2131	14708	137866
13	415	9176	33057	
16	438	5341	42153	
50	578	3726	54780	
79	806	4156		
93	459	3204		
	755	6197		
	619			
	862			
	638			

2.

| 4 | 2 | 1 | 4 | | | | | |

2 digits	3 digits	4 digits	5 digits	6 digits
26	215	5841	21862	134953
41	427	9217	83642	727542
19	106	9131	21362	
71	872	1624	57320	
63	725	1506		
76	385	4214		
	156	5216		
	263	4734		
	234	2007		
	180	2637		

3.

2 digits	3 digits	4 digits	5 digits	6 digits
64	756	8234	31492	There is one
61	725	3938	67052	but I cannot
29	205	5375	69127	tell you what
52	157	7166		it is.
87	852	5781		
78	927	2336		
85	135	1827		
	603	9062		
	846			
	738			

4.

2 digits	3 digits	4 digits	5 digits	6 digits
99	571	9603	24715	387566
25	918	8072	72180	338472
52	131	4210	54073	414725
26	328	3824	71436	198264
42	906	8916	82125	
57	249			
30	653			7 digits
53	609			8592070
14	111			
61	127			
	276			

5. This one is much more difficult but it *is* possible! Don't give up.

2 digits	3 digits	4 digits	5 digits	6 digits
26	306	3654	38975	582778
28	457	3735	49561	585778
32	504	3751	56073	728468
47	827	3755	56315	
49	917	3819	56435	7 digits
52	951	6426	57435	8677056
70		7214	58535	
74		7315	58835	
		7618	66430	
		7643	77435	
		9847	77543	

Exercise A

1. A machine fills 690 oil drums in one hour. How many oil drums will it fill in 20 minutes?

2. Thirty books cost £75 and weigh 6000 g. Find (a) the cost and (b) the weight of 12 of these books.

3. The entire surface area of the solid object shown is covered with paint, the thickness of paint being 1 mm.

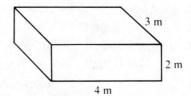

(a) Find the total surface area of the object.
(b) Find the volume of paint used in m³.

4. The average length of a boy's pace is 70 cm. How many steps would he take in walking a distance of 350 m?

5. Copy and complete

	Fraction	Decimal
(a)	$\frac{1}{4}$	0.25
(b)	$\frac{1}{5}$	
(c)		0.5
(d)	$\frac{3}{4}$	
(e)		0.6
(f)	$\frac{5}{8}$	

6. What change do you receive from £20 after buying 11 tins at 32p, 16 cans at 19p and 14 apples at 6p?

7. Work out, without using a calculator.

(a) 2.42 × 6   (b) 0.072 × 9
(c) 17 − 3.6   (d) 8.1 + 9.95
(e) 17.92 ÷ 7   (f) 210.6 ÷ 6

8. A car dealer offers a discount of 5% when a car is paid for with cash. Find the cost of a £800 car after the discount.

9. Which would cost less and by how much: 40 pencils at 8p each or 15 biros at 22p each?

10. 6, 7, 8, 13, 15, 17, 23, 27, 39, 41, 54.
Which of the above numbers are:

(a) even numbers   (b) divisible by 3
(c) prime numbers   (d) divisible by 9?

Project 2   CALCULATOR WORDS

'LEEDS

If we work out $25 \times 503 \times 4 + 37$ on a calculator we should obtain the number 50337. If we turn the calculator upside down (and use a little imagination) we see the word 'LEEDS'.

Find the words given by the clues below.

1. $83 \times 85 + 50$ (Lots of this in the garden)
2. $211 \times 251 + 790$ (Tropical or Scilly)
3. $19 \times 20 \times 14 - 2.66$ (Not an upstanding man)
4. $(84 + 17) \times 5$ (Dotty message)
5. $0.01443 \times 7 \times 4$ (Three times as funny)
6. $79 \times 9 - 0.9447$ (Greasy letters)
7. $50.19 - (5 \times 0.0039)$ (Not much space inside)
8. $2 \div 0.5 - 3.295$ (Rather lonely)
9. $0.034 \times 11 - 0.00292; 9^4 - (8 \times 71)$ (two words) (Nice for breakfast)
10. $7420 \times 7422 + 118^2 - 30$ (Big Chief)
11. $(13 \times 3 \times 25 \times 8 \times 5) + 7$ (Dwelling for masons)
12. $71^2 - 11^2 - 5$ (Sad gasp)
13. $904^2 + 89621818$ (Prickly customer)
14. $(559 \times 6) + (21 \times 55)$ (What a surprise!)
15. $566 \times 711 - 23617$ (Bolt it down)
16. $\dfrac{9999 + 319}{8.47 + 2.53}$ (Sit up and plead)
17. $\dfrac{2601 \times 6}{4^2 + 1^2}; (401 - 78) \times 5^2$ (two words) (Not a great man)
18. $0.4^2 - 0.1^2$ (Little Sidney)
19. $\dfrac{(27 \times 2000 - 2)}{(0.63 \div 0.09)}$ (Not quite a mountain)
20. $(5^2 - 1^2)^4 - 14239$ (Just a name)
21. $48^4 + 102^2 - 4^2$ (Pursuits)
22. $615^2 + (7 \times 242)$ (Almost a goggle)
23. $14^4 - 627 + 29$ (Good book, by God!)
24. $6.2 \times 0.987 \times 1\,000\,000 - 860^2 + 118$ (Flying ace)
25. $(426 \times 474) + (318 \times 487) + 22018$ (Close to a bubble)
26. $\dfrac{36^3}{4} - 1530$ (Foreign-sounding girl's name)
27. $(594 \times 571) - (154 \times 132) - 38$ (Female Bobby)
28. $(7^2 \times 100) + (7 \times 2)$ (Lofty)
29. $240^2 + 134; 241^2 - 7^3$ (two words) (Devil of a chime)
30. $1384.5 \times 40 - 1.991$ (Say this after sneezing)
31. $(2 \times 2 \times 2 \times 2 \times 3)^4 + 1929$ (Unhappy ending)
32. $141918 + 83^3$ (Hot stuff in France)

Exercise B

1. Seven books cost £24.15. How many of these books could be bought for £34.50?

2. Write the following correct to the nearest penny:
   (a) £6.537 (b) £15.708 (c) £11.6241
   (d) £8.029 (e) £0.6267 (f) £1.071

3. A maths teacher bought 40 calculators at £7.20 each and a number of other calculators costing £3.95 each. In all he spent £367. How many of the less expensive calculators did he buy?

4. In the diagram below calculate
   (a) the area of rectangle ABCD
   (b) the area of the shaded trapezium XBCY
   (c) the percentage of the rectangle ABCD which is shaded.

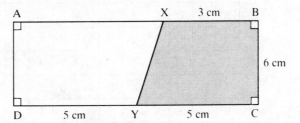

5. Mrs Alexander's salary is £8500 per year. She pays no tax on the first £2100 of her salary but pays 30% on each remaining £.
   (a) How much tax does she pay?
   (b) How much does she earn after tax?

6. A machine produces 120 articles per hour. How many articles does it produce in $2\frac{1}{4}$ hours?

7. What change do you receive from £10 after buying 6 pens at 25p, 3 rubbers at 18p and 4 pencils at 21p?

8. A slimmer's calorie guide shows how many calories are contained in various foods:

   Bread 1.2 calories per g
   Cheese 2.5 calories per g
   Meat 1.6 calories per g
   Butter 6 calories per g

   Calculate the number of calories in the following meals:

   (a) 50 g bread, 40 g cheese, 100 g meat, 15 g butter.
   (b) 150 g bread, 85 g cheese, 120 g meat, 20 g butter.

9. Write as a single number.
   (a) 8^2 (b) 1^4 (c) 10^2
   (d) 3×10^3 (e) 2^5 (f) 3^4

10. A cylinder has a volume of 200 cm^3 and a height of 10 cm. Calculate the area of its base.

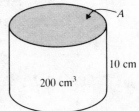

Project 3   MATHEMATICAL WORDSEARCH

These words are hidden in the square shown below.

rectangle, isosceles, multiply, subtract, parallel, infinity, square, number, figure, obtuse, circle, divide, index, power, acute.

They may appear written forwards, backwards or diagonally. Find as many of them as you can.

P	X	Q	E	D	U	B	B	V	K	J	N	O	B	N
B	Q	M	V	N	S	G	A	L	I	Z	G	J	Q	Y
W	I	L	G	R	Y	E	P	K	S	N	J	D	Y	T
O	E	E	V	B	B	L	L	M	V	I	D	W	T	C
E	M	L	E	X	E	F	P	E	R	K	W	W	I	A
S	Q	L	J	V	L	O	E	I	C	G	V	J	N	R
U	G	A	K	T	C	I	T	I	T	S	Y	L	I	T
T	Z	R	T	N	R	Q	U	V	V	L	O	W	F	B
B	O	A	N	R	I	W	C	R	L	R	U	S	N	U
O	F	P	R	E	C	T	A	N	G	L	E	M	I	S
I	K	I	P	O	W	E	R	D	U	O	E	V	N	Q
R	L	B	G	P	A	N	Q	Y	G	M	W	O	D	U
J	A	J	Y	U	D	I	V	I	D	E	B	Y	E	A
N	J	Z	B	D	R	Y	Q	G	R	Z	F	E	X	R
S	E	T	A	L	V	E	Y	N	X	C	J	M	R	E

Exercise C   OPERATOR SQUARES

Each empty square contains either a number or a mathematical symbol ($+$, $-$, $\times$, $\div$). Copy each square and fill in the missing details.

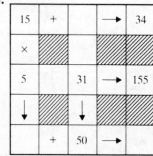

4.

38			→	52
×		+		
		1	→	3
↓		↓		
	−	15	→	99

5.

	×	10	→	90
+		÷		
			→	$5\frac{1}{2}$
↓		↓		
20	×		→	100

6.

	×		→	42
÷		÷		
	−	3	→	11
↓		↓		
$\frac{1}{2}$		2	→	1

7.

	×	2	→	34
−				
	×		→	36
↓		↓		
8	−		→	$7\frac{1}{2}$

8.

	−		→	83
÷		×		
	÷	8	→	$\frac{1}{4}$
↓		↓		
	+	56	→	101

9.

9			→	45
×		−		
		2	→	2
↓		↓		
9	×		→	27

10.

25	×		→	250
−		÷		
	÷		→	
↓		↓		
9	−	0·1	→	

11.

0·1	×	20	→	
		+		
6	−		→	
↓		↓		
0·6	+		→	20·8

12.

	×	100	→	50
−		×		
		2	→	2·1
↓		↓		
0·4	×		→	

13.

	×	0·1	→	0·7
÷		×		
	÷	0·2	→	10
↓		↓		
	+		→	

14.

	+	6	→	7·2
+				
	÷	5	→	
↓		↓		
8·2		30	→	38·2

15.

	×		→	20
−				
	+	10	→	11·2
↓		↓		
98·8	+	2	→	

16.

4	×	$\frac{1}{2}$	→	
	░	+	░	░
1	−		→	
↓	░	↓	░	░
?	×	$\frac{3}{4}$	→	3

17.

	−	$\frac{1}{8}$	→	$\frac{1}{8}$
×	░	×	░	░
$\frac{1}{2}$	÷	4	→	
↓	░	↓	░	░
$\frac{1}{8}$	+		→	

18.

0·4	−	0·01	→	
	░	×	░	░
		×	→	36
↓	░	↓	░	░
4	÷	0·1	→	

Project 4 — DESIGNING SQUARE PATTERNS

The object is to design square patterns of different sizes. The patterns are all to be made from smaller tiles all of which are themselves square.

Designs for a 4 × 4 square:

(a)

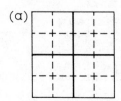

This design consists of four tiles each 2 × 2.
The pattern is rather dull.

(b) Suppose we say that the design must contain at least one 1 × 1 square.

This design is more interesting and consists of seven tiles.

1. Try the 5 × 5 square. Design a pattern which divides the 5 × 5 square into eight smaller squares.

2. Try the 6 × 6 square. Here you must include at least one 1 × 1 square. Design a pattern which divides the 6 × 6 square into nine smaller squares. Colour in the final design to make it look interesting.

3. The 7 × 7 square is more difficult. With no restrictions, design a pattern which divides the 7 × 7 square into nine smaller squares.

4. Design a pattern which divides an 8 × 8 square into ten smaller squares. You must not use a 4 × 4 square.

5. Design a pattern which divides a 9 × 9 square into ten smaller squares. You can use only one 3 × 3 square.

6. Design a pattern which divides a 10 × 10 square into eleven smaller squares. You must include a 3 × 3 square.

7. Design a pattern which divides an 11 × 11 square into eleven smaller squares. You must include a 6 × 6 square.

Exercise D

1. Copy and complete the following bill.

$6\frac{1}{2}$ lb of potatoes at 12p per lb　　= £

　4 lb of beef at　　　　per lb　　= £7.20

　　jars of coffee at 95p per jar　= £6.65

　　　　　　　　　Total　= £

2. In a sale, discount at the rate of 10p in the £ is allowed on all articles. What is the sale price of an article for which the normal price is £7?

3. Calculate the area of the shape below. Take $\pi = 3$.

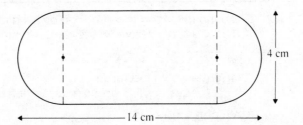

4 cm

14 cm

4. 12 pints of milk will feed 5 babies for 2 days. Copy and complete the following:
   (a) 6 pints of milk will feed 5 babies for　　days.
   (b) 12 pints of milk will feed 1 baby for　　days.
   (c) 12 pints of milk will feed 2 babies for　　days.
   (d)　　pints of milk will feed 5 babies for 8 days.

5. (a) A man changed £100 into Italian lire when the exchange rate was 2145 lire = £1. Calculate the number of lire he received.
   (b) A woman changed £50 into French francs when the exchange rate was F11.60 = £1. Calculate the number of francs she received.

6. A map uses a scale of 1 cm = 100 m.
   (a) Calculate the actual length, in km, of a railway line which is 4 cm long on the map.
   (b) A road is 200 m long. Calculate, in cm, the length this would be on the map.

7. Jane is six years old and Sarah is eighteen. In how many years will Sarah be exactly twice as old as Jane?

8. Work out $2\frac{1}{4} \times 3\frac{1}{2}$, giving your answer in its simplest form.

9. Find the missing digits.

(a)

1		4
+		3	8
6	8	

(b)

8		7
−	3	5	
	8	1

10. How many triangles can you see in the diagram below?

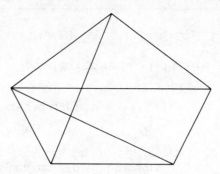

Project 5   CONVERGING SEQUENCES

1. Do the following investigation on a calculator.
   1. Take any positive whole number (say 9)
   2. Divide by 5
   3. Add 1 to the answer
   4. Write down the result
   5. Repeat steps 2, 3 and 4 a further ten or twenty times.

What is happening?

A flow chart for the operation is shown below.

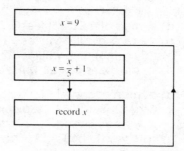

Try the sequence using a different starting number, say 7 or 20.
How about decimal numbers?
How about negative numbers?

2. Now see what happens with a different sequence.

Take any number (say 7) and work through the flow chart below.

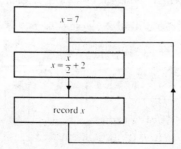

What is happening this time?
Try the sequence using different starting numbers.

3. This one is more difficult.
Take any number (say 7) and work through the flow chart below.

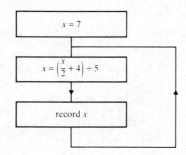

4. Investigate what happens with other flow charts.

Exercise E

Plot the points and join them up in order. You should produce a picture in each case.

1. Draw axes with both x and y from 0 to 10.

A: (3,2), (4,2), (5,3), (3,5), (3,6), (2,7), (1,6), (1,8), (2,9), (3,9), (5,7), (4,6), (4,5), (6,4), (8,4), (8,5), (6,7), (5,7).
B: (7,4), (9,2), (8,1), (7,3), (5,3).
C: (1,6), (2,8), (2,9), (2,7).
D: Draw a dot at (3,8).

2. Draw axes with both x and y from 0 to 10.

A: (6,5), (7,6), (9,5), (10,3), (9,1), (1,1), (3,3), (3,4), (4,5), (5,4), (4,3), (6,4), (8,4), (9,3).
B: (8,3), (8,2), (7,1).
C: (6,3), (6,2), (5,1).
D: (5,2), (4,1).
E: Draw a dot at (3,2).

3. Draw axes with both x and y from 0 to 8.

A: (6,6), (1,6), (2,7), (7,7), (6,6), (6,1), (7,2), (7,7).
B: (1,6), (1,1), (6,1).
C: (3,5), (3,3), (2,2), (2,5), (5,5), (5,2), (2,2), (3,3), (5,3).

4. Draw axes with x from 0 to 8 and y from 0 to 4.

A: (7,1), (8,1), (7,2), (6,2), (5,3), (3,3), (2,2), (6,2), (1,2), (1,1), (2,1).
B: (3,1), (6,1).
C: (3,3), (3,2).
D: (4,3), (4,2).
E: (5,3), (5,2).
F: Draw a circle of radius $\frac{1}{2}$ unit with centre at $(2\frac{1}{2},1)$.
G: Draw a circle of radius $\frac{1}{2}$ unit with centre at $(6\frac{1}{2},1)$.

5. Draw axes with *x* from −4 to +4 and *y* from 0 to 10.

A: (3,5), (2,7), (0,8), (−1,8), (−2,7), (−3,7), (−4,8), (−2,9), (0,9), (2,8), (3,7), (3,2), (1,1), (0,3), (−2,2), (−2,4), (−3,4), (−2,6), (−1,6), (−1,5), (−2,6), (−2,7).
B: (−1,3), (−2,3).
C: (1,3), (0,3).

6. Draw axes with *x* from 0 to 17 and *y* from 0 to 22.

A: (13,4), (12,4), (14,3), (16,3), (14,4), (13,4), (11,5), (9,4), (10,4), (14,2), (13,1), (14,2), (17,3), (16,3). Draw a dot at $(10\frac{1}{2},4\frac{1}{2})$.
B: (12,6), (12,7), (15,8), (13,8), (14,9), (12,10), (11,9), (9,10), (7,9), (8,9), (12,7). Draw a dot at $(8\frac{1}{2},9\frac{1}{2})$.
C: (11,11), (10,12), (6,14), (5,14), (7,15), (9,14), (10,16), (13,15), (10,14), (12,13), (13,13), (10,12). Draw a dot at $(6\frac{1}{2},14\frac{1}{2})$.
D: (10,17), (9,17), (5,19), (4,19), (6,20), (8,19), (8,21), (10,22), (11,22), (9,19), (11,18), (12,18), (9,17). Draw a dot at $(5\frac{1}{2},19\frac{1}{2})$.

7. Draw axes with both *x* and *y* from 0 to 14.
A: (1,3), (9,3), (7,7), (6,5), (8,5), (7,7), (8,9), (12,1), (2,1), (1,3), (6,13), (8,13), (4,5), (6,5).
B: (8,13), (13,3), (12,1).

8. Draw axes with *x* from 0 to 16 and *y* from 0 to 10.
A: (2,1), (2,2), (8,10), (16,10), (16,9), (10,1), (2,1), (8,9), (14,9), (10,3), (10,2), (16,10).
B: (8,9), (8,8), (4,2), (10,2), (10,3), $(4\frac{2}{3},3)$.
C: (8,8), $(13\frac{1}{3},8)$.

Project 6   **KNOCKOUT COMPETITION**

1. Eight players entered for a spelling competition organised on a 'knock-out' basis. The results are shown below.

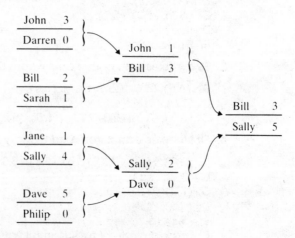

John	3		
Darren	0	John	1
		Bill	3
Bill	2		
Sarah	1		Bill	3
			Sally	5
Jane	1		
Sally	4	Sally	2
		Dave	0
Dave	5		
Philip	0		

Quarter-finals   *Semi-finals*   *Final*

(a) Who was the winner?
(b) Who were the beaten semi-finalists?
(c) Who scored most points in the quarter-finals?
(d) How many matches were played altogether in the whole competition?

2. The diagram below shows a K.O. competition for which 10 players were entered. This time we need a preliminary round involving players W, X, Y and Z.

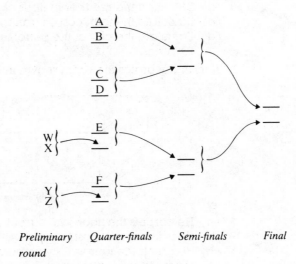

Preliminary round   *Quarter-finals*   *Semi-finals*   *Final*

(a) How many players had to play in the preliminary round?
(b) How many matches were played altogether in the whole competition?

3. Draw diagrams similar to those above to show the procedure for organising a knock-out competition for
(a) 20 players
(b) 23 players
(c) 32 players
(d) 43 players
In each case, calculate the total number of matches played up to and including the final.

4. Can you find a rule connecting the number of players p and the number of matches m?

5. In a major tournament like Wimbledon, the better players are seeded from 1 to 16. Can you organise a tournament for 32 players so that, if they win all their games,
(a) seeds 1 and 2 can reach the final,
(b) seeds 1, 2, 3 and 4 can reach the semi-finals,
(c) seeds 1, 2, 3, 4, 5, 6, 7 and 8 can reach the quarter-finals?

Exercise F

1. A group of four adults are planning a holiday in France. The ferry costs, for the return journey, are:

Adult	£25
Car	£62

Travel around France is estimated at 2000 km and petrol costs 5 francs per litre. The car travels 10 km on one litre of petrol.

(a) Calculate the total cost of the return journey on the ferry.
(b) Calculate the number of litres of petrol to be used.
(c) Calculate the total cost, in francs, of the petrol.
(d) Calculate the cost of the petrol in pounds, if £1 is equivalent to 10 francs.

2. A man decorates the room shown in the diagram

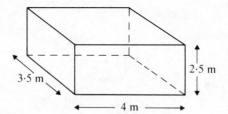

(a) He carpets the floor with carpet costing £8.20 per m². How much does the carpet cost?
(b) He paints the four walls with paint which costs 32p per m². How much does the paint cost?
(c) He covers the ceiling with tiles, which measure 25 cm by 25 cm. How many tiles does he need?

3. The table below gives details of the repayments on bank loans.

Amount of loan in £'s	12 monthly repayments in £'s	24 monthly repayments in £'s
10	0.93	0.50
30	2.75	1.53
50	4.61	2.52
80	7.40	4.04
400	37.10	20.20
600	55.60	30.50
700	64.70	35.60

(a) What is the monthly repayment on a loan of £80 taken over 24 months?
(b) What is the monthly repayment on a loan of £600 taken over 12 months?
(c) A loan of £400 is taken over 12 months.
   (i) Calculate the total repayment
   (ii) Calculate the interest paid on the loan.
(d) A loan of £730 is taken over 24 months.
   (i) Calculate the total repayment
   (ii) Calculate the interest paid on the loan.

Project 7

AN UNUSUAL SEQUENCE

This work is easier when a calculator is used.

(a) Take a number
  (i) If it is odd, multiply by 3 and then add 1.
  (ii) If it is even, divide by 2.
(b) Take the result and repeat either (i) or (ii) above.
(c) Carry on until you get stuck.
  For example $5 \rightarrow 16 \rightarrow 8 \rightarrow 4 \rightarrow 2 \rightarrow 1$

We will stop when we get to 1 because 1 leads to 4 and back to 1 and so on.

Try the following numbers: 6, 10, 12, 40, 52.

It appears that all the numbers eventually lead to 1. No one has ever found a number which did not produce a final result of 1. If you can find such a number, you will be famous.

Copy and complete the table below.

Number	3	5	13	11	14	17	32	19	23	33	39
Number of steps to reach 1											

Which two-digit number takes the most steps to reach 1?

(More difficult) Which three-digit number takes the most steps to reach 1?

Investigate what happens if you change the rules for the sequence (e.g. If the number is odd, multiply by 3 and subtract 1. If the number is even, divide by 2)

Exercise G

1. In 1986 the costs of running a car for the year were

Petrol	£648
Servicing	£144
Insurance	£ 85.50
Road licence	£105

(a) The cost of petrol was 45p per litre. How many litres were used?
(b) Average petrol consumption was 13 km per litre. What was the total distance travelled?
(c) What was the total cost of running a car in 1986?
(d) In 1987 the petrol costs and the insurance costs remain the same. The cost of servicing goes up by 10% and the cost of the road licence goes up by 20%. What was the total cost of running a car in 1987?

2. A washing machine has a listed price of £320. The machine can be bought in one of two ways:
   (i) On hire purchase, in which a deposit of 20% is paid and then a further 24 monthly payments of £13.60.
   (ii) A discount price for cash, in which the dealer offers a discount of 8% on the list price. Calculate
      (a) the deposit required if the machine is bought on hire purchase
      (b) the total amount of the 24 monthly payments
      (c) the total hire purchase price
      (d) the discount price if the machine is paid for with cash.

3. A shop offers a video recorder at £500 cash or credit terms. The credit terms are 12p in the £ added to the cash price and the whole repayable in 12 equal, monthly instalments. Calculate:
   (a) the price of the recorder on credit terms.
   (b) the amount of each monthly instalment, to the nearest penny.

4. Nine books cost £22.05. How many of these books could be bought for £36.75?

5. (a) Write down a three-digit number with all digits different   For example: 361

   (b) Reverse the order of the digits   163

   (c) Take away the smaller number from the larger number
$$\begin{array}{r} 361 \\ -163 \\ \hline 198 \end{array}$$

   (d) Reverse the digits of the answer   891

   (e) Add the last two numbers
$$\begin{array}{r} 198 \\ +891 \\ \hline 1089 \end{array}$$

   (f) Try this procedure with four other three-digit numbers. What do you always obtain?

Project 8   MATHEMATICAL SNOOKER

Here we have a rather strange snooker table. There are only four pockets and the base is divided into squares. We are going to play with only one ball. We always play the same shot, starting at the point (1,1)

and each time aiming along the diagonal. When the ball hits the cushion, it bounces off along the next diagonal.

For example the table here is 6 × 4 and there are three rebounds at the cushions before the ball goes into a pocket.

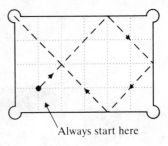

Always start here

This table is 8 × 6

Into which pocket will the ball go? How many rebounds were there at the cushions?

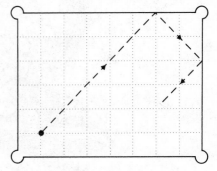

We are going to look at lots of different sizes of table to see if we can discover any rules which might enable us to predict, for any size table, the number of rebounds before the ball goes into a pocket.

Part A
Draw diagrams to show the following size tables and count the number of rebounds. Record the results in a table.
4 × 2, 3 × 2, 8 × 6, 6 × 3, 4 × 3, 6 × 4, 8 × 4, 12 × 9, 9 × 6, 16 × 12.

What do you notice about some of the results?

Part B
(a) Look at tables 8 × 7, 7 × 6, 6 × 5, 5 × 4, 4 × 3, 3 × 2 where the first number is one more than the second number. Is there a rule for the number of rebounds? If you find a rule write it down.
(b) Look at tables 11 × 9, 9 × 7, 7 × 5, 5 × 3 where the first number is two more than the second number.
(Why have we left out 10 × 8, 8 × 6, 6 × 4, 4 × 2? See Part A).
Is there a rule for the number of rebounds?
(c) Look at tables 10 × 7, 8 × 5, 7 × 4, 5 × 2. Is there a rule this time?
(d) Finally look at a mixture: 11 × 5, 12 × 7, 13 × 9, 11 × 2.

Part C
Can you now predict the number of rebounds for *any* size table? See if your predictions are correct.

Part D
So far we have only been looking at the number of rebounds. Is it possible to predict which pocket the ball will go into for any size table? Now you are on your own.

Part 7

7.1 ANGLES

The angles at a point add up to 360°.
The angles on a straight line add up to 180°.

(a)

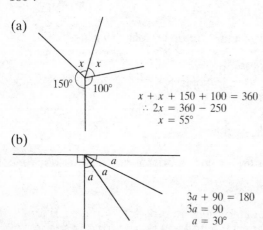

$x + x + 150 + 100 = 360$
$\therefore 2x = 360 - 250$
$x = 55°$

(b)

$3a + 90 = 180$
$3a = 90$
$a = 30°$

Exercise 1

Find the angles marked with letters. The lines AB and CD are straight.

1.

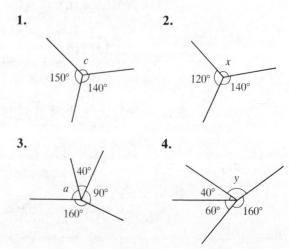

150° c 140°

2.

120° x 140°

3.

40° a 90°   160°

4.

y 40°   60°   160°

5.
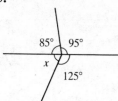

6.
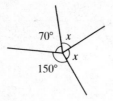

7.

8.
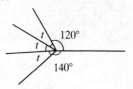

9.
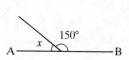

10.
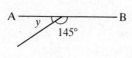

11.
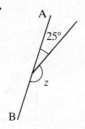

12.
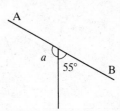

13.
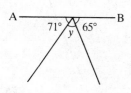

14.
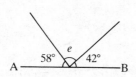

15.
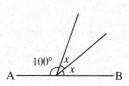

16.
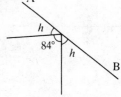

17.
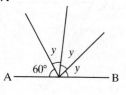

18.
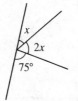

19.
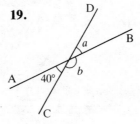

20.
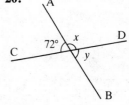

The angles in a triangle add up to 180°.

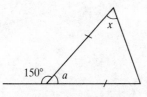

$a = 180 - 150° = 30°$

The triangle is isosceles ∴ $2x + 30 = 180$
$$2x = 150$$
$$x = 75°$$

Exercise 2

Find the angles marked with letters. For the more difficult questions (**9** to **26**) it is helpful to draw a diagram.

1.

2.
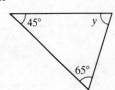

3.

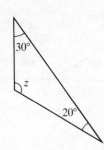

4.

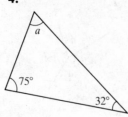

5.

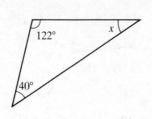

6.

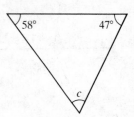

7.

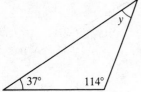

8.

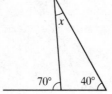

9.

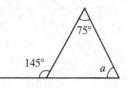

10.

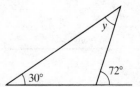

11.

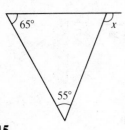

12.

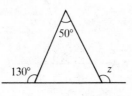

13.

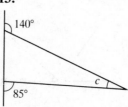

14.

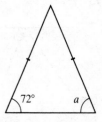

15.

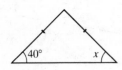

16.

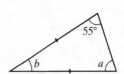

17.

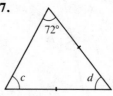

18.

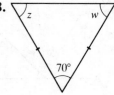

19.

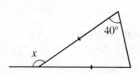

20.

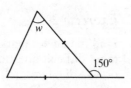

21.

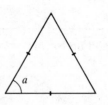

22.

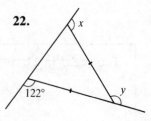

23.

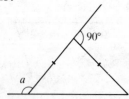

24.

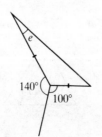

25.

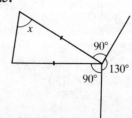

26.

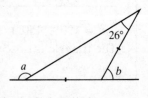

When a line cuts a pair of parallel lines all the acute angles are equal and
all the obtuse angles are equal.

(a)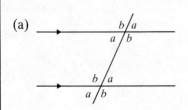

(b)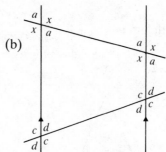

Exercise 3

Find the angles marked with letters.

1.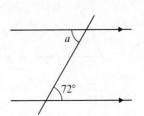

2.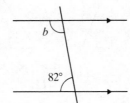

3.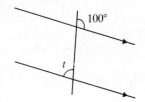

4.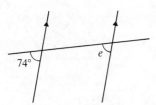

5.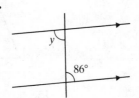

6.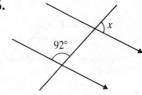

7.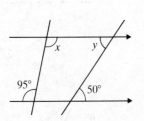

8.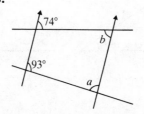

9.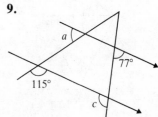

10.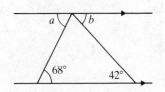

11.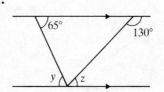

12.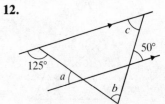

The next exercise contains questions which summarise the work of the last three exercises.

Exercise 4

Find the angles marked with letters.

1.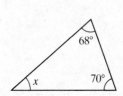

2.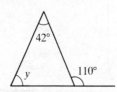

3.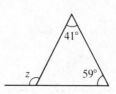

4.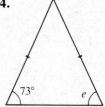

5.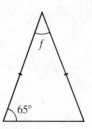

6.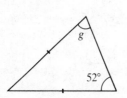

7.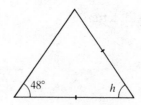

8.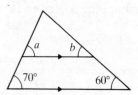

9.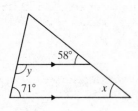

10.

11.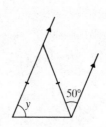

12.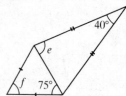

13.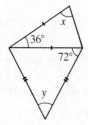

14.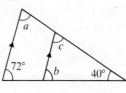

15.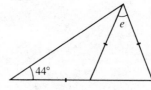

16.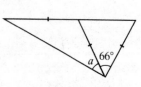

17.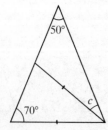

18.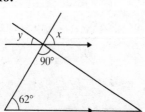

19.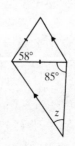

20.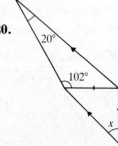

7.2 MENTAL ARITHMETIC

In each test the questions are read out by the teacher while all pupils' books are closed. Each question is repeated once and then the answer, and only the answer, is written down. All working is done 'in the head'.

Each test, including the recording of results, should take about 30 minutes.

The tests appear in the book so that pupils can check afterwards to see where they made mistakes.

Test 1

1. What number is seventeen more than eighty-two?
2. What is a half of a half of 80?
3. What number is twenty times as big as 30?
4. Write in figures the number two hundred and four thousand and twenty.
5. A television program lasting $2\frac{1}{2}$ hours starts at half-past six. When does it finish?
6. What number is 80 more than 230?
7. How many threes are there in ninety?
8. A record costs £3.20. How much change do I receive from a ten pound note?
9. Find the cost of nine tickets at 20 pence each.
10. What four coins make 44 pence?
11. Work out $\frac{1}{8}$ plus $\frac{3}{8}$ and give the answer as a decimal.
12. A beer crate holds twelve bottles. How many crates are needed for 40 bottles?
13. If the 9th of August is a Saturday, what day of the week is the 19th?
14. By how much is two metres more than 40 cm?
15. Write down 207 pence in pounds and pence.
16. The sides of a square measure 16 cm. Find the total distance around the outside of the square.
17. A television costing £270 is reduced by £58. What is the new price?
18. A lottery prize of £32 000 is shared equally between sixteen people. How much does each person receive?

19. Cold drinks cost twelve pence each. How many can I buy for one pound?
20. What are 19 threes?
21. How many inches are there in three feet?
22. A newsagent stacks 300 magazines into 15 equal piles. How many magazines are in each pile?
23. Add together 37 and 45.
24. What is 10% of £50?
25. Lemons cost eleven pence each. How much do I have to pay for a dozen lemons?
26. A cake costs 36 pence. Find the change from a five pound note.
27. A woman smokes ten cigarettes a day and cigarettes cost £1.30 for 20. How much does she spend in four days?
28. When playing darts you score double ten, double twelve and treble two. What is your total score?
29. What are six fifties?
30. Cheese costs 80 pence a pound. How much do I spend if I buy four ounces of cheese?

Test 2

1. A jacket costing £62 is reduced by £15. What is the new price?
2. Work out a half of a half and give the answer as a decimal.
3. How many sevens are there in sixty-three?
4. What number is ten times as big as 16.6?
5. A sum of £72 is divided equally between six people. How much does each person receive?
6. Find the cost of six bottles of wine at £2.50 each.
7. What four coins make thirty pence?
8. What number is 37 more than 55?
9. By how much is one metre more than 33 cm?
10. Write down 850 pence in pounds and pence.
11. A greengrocer's tray has room for eight melons. How many trays are needed for 30 melons?

12. A film lasting one hour and forty minutes starts at half past seven. When does it finish?

13. If the 14th of June is a Tuesday, what day of the week was the 5th of June?

14. Lemons cost seven pence each. How many can I buy for 60 pence?

15. If you score a treble 18 at darts, how many do you score?

16. What is a half of a half of 56?

17. Write in figures the number five hundred and ten thousand, two hundred and eighty.

18. What are 40 fives?

19. The sides of an equilateral triangle are 17 cm long. Write down the perimeter of the triangle.

20. A librarian stacks 180 books in nine equal piles. How many books are in each pile?

21. How many inches are there in one and a half feet?

22. Add together 9, 13 and 32.

23. A bag of sugar costs 43 pence. Find the change from a five pound note if I buy two bags of sugar.

24. When playing darts you score double five, double ten and treble twenty. What is your total score?

25. A man smokes 60 cigarettes a day and cigarettes cost £1.20 for 20. How much does he spend in two days?

26. Add together 85 and 110.

27. What is 50% of £2000?

28. What are seven 20's?

29. An expensive foreign cheese costs £3.60 a pound. How much does a man pay for eight ounces of cheese?

30. What is the date exactly a fortnight after the 3rd of January?

Test 3

1. Find the cost of seven packets of sweets at nine pence each.

2. What number is 26 more than 25?

3. Write down one thousand pence in pounds.

4. Oranges cost 11 pence each. How many can I buy for 50p?

5. What are eighteen twos?

6. If the 14th of May is a Wednesday, what day of the week is the 19th?

7. A cake weighing 108 ounces is shared equally between nine children. How much does each child receive?

8. A quiz programme on television lasts for an hour and a quarter and starts at ten past six. When does it finish?

9. What four coins make twenty pence?

10. Work out $\frac{1}{10}$ plus $\frac{1}{5}$ and give the answer as a decimal.

11. What is a half of a half of 1000?

12. By how much is 3 metres more than 30 cm?

13. How many fours are there in a hundred?

14. What number is five times as big as forty?

15. An egg box holds six eggs. How many boxes are needed for 15 eggs?

16. Write in figures the number seventeen thousand and nine.

17. How many feet are there in a yard?

18. A car costing £3400 is reduced by £260. What is the new price?

19. If you score a treble fifteen at darts, how many do you score?

20. How many ounces are there in a quarter of a pound?

21. A teacher stacks 1000 books into twenty equal piles. How many books are in each pile?

22. A square has an area of 400 cm². How long is each side of the square?

23. Add together 7, 18 and 54.

24. A ball-point pen costs 22 pence. Find the change from a ten pound note.

25. Pencils cost five pence each. How much will two dozen pencils cost?

26. A man drinks three pints of beer a day and beer costs 80 pence a pint. How much does he spend in two days?

27. Add together 38 and 39.

28. What is 15% of £200?

29. A darts player scores double fifteen, double five and treble one. What is his total score?

30. What are fifteen 30's?

Test 4

1. Add together 27 and 32.
2. How many sixes are there in 54?
3. A drink costs 75p. Find the change from a £5 note.
4. What number is twice as big as 59?
5. What four coins make 77 pence?
6. Find the cost of seven ice creams at 12p each.
7. A film lasting $1\frac{1}{2}$ hours starts at ten minutes to nine. When does it finish?
8. If the 6th of January is a Monday, what day of the week is the 12th?
9. Write one fifth as a decimal.
10. Work out $\frac{1}{2}$ plus $\frac{1}{4}$ and give the answer as a decimal.
11. How many inches are there in two feet?
12. How many centimetres are there in 2 m?
13. Apples cost 9 pence each. How many can I buy for 40p?
14. What number is twice as big as 115?
15. A builder stacks 80 blocks into 10 equal piles. How many blocks are in each pile?
16. A coat costing £49 is reduced by £17. What is the new price?
17. What are 17 twos?
18. An egg box holds 6 eggs. How many boxes are needed for 20 eggs?
19. What number is 28 more than 63?
20. Add together 11, 8 and 15.
21. A shopkeeper has 100 footballs. How many are left after he sells two dozen?
22. How many ounces are there in a pound?
23. By how much is 2 metres more than 20 cm?
24. What number is a hundred times as big as 30?
25. Write down 328 pence in pounds and pence.
26. Add together 65 and 165.
27. Work out 20% of £10.
28. A shopkeeper buys a gross of melons. How many is this?
29. A man smokes 40 cigarettes a day and cigarettes cost £1.20 for 20. How much does he spend in three days?
30. A bottle of wine costs £1.95. Find the change from a ten pound note.

Test 5

1. How many ten pence coins are needed to make two pounds?
2. Add three to 9 fours.
3. How many cakes costing 30 pence can be bought for £1.50?
4. Which is the larger: 0.12 or 0.2?
5. How many minutes are there between 9.15 a.m. and 11.15 a.m.?
6. A car does 30 miles per gallon of petrol. How much petrol is used on a journey of 180 miles?
7. I go shopping with three pounds and buy three cakes at twenty pence each. How much money have I left?
8. An escaped prisoner is free for 72 hours. How many days is this?
9. A cake weighing 852 grams is cut in half. How heavy is each piece?
10. What is a half of a half of 30?
11. Find the average of 7 and 23.
12. How many nines are there in one hundred and eighty?
13. What number is twice as big as one hundred and sixty?
14. What four coins make 65 pence?
15. A quarter of a man's wages are taken in deductions. What percentage does he have left?
16. A fishing rod costing £24 is reduced by £5.50. What is the new price?
17. How many minutes are there in three hours?
18. Write in figures the number 'two hundred and two thousand and four'.
19. Write three hundredths as a decimal.
20. A packet of peanuts costs 64 pence. Find the change from a ten pound note.
21. What is 4.30 a.m. on the 24 hour clock?
22. What is 20% of £50?
23. Add together £1.75 and 55 pence.
24. Large eggs cost seven pence each. How many can I buy for sixty pence?

25. Large brown eggs cost nine pence each. How much will a dozen eggs cost?

26. Which is the larger: 0.3 or 0.23?

27. Add together 5, 16 and 22.

28. A pint of milk costs 20 pence and Mrs Green buys two pints a day. What is her bill for seven days?

29. A train took 3 hours to travel 186 miles. What was the average speed of the train?

30. What four coins make 65 pence? Give a different answer to that given in question 14.

Test 6

1. What number divided by 7 gives an answer of 12?

2. Add together four 50 pences and three 20 pences and give the answer in pounds.

3. Which is the larger fraction: $\frac{1}{2}$ or $\frac{1}{3}$?

4. What number multiplied by itself gives an answer of 144?

5. If I change £4 into 20 pence coins, how many will I get?

6. What is the angle between the hands of a clock at 6 o'clock?

7. What is the biggest number that can be made from the figures 5, 9 and 2?

8. Find the difference between $8\frac{1}{2}$ and 20.

9. Rewrite as an ordinary number 2×10^4.

10. Write one centimetre as a fraction of one metre.

11. If meat costs £3.40 per kilo, how much will I pay for 500 g?

12. The profit on a magazine is 10 pence. How many must be sold to make a profit of £35?

13. What number equals ten dozen?

14. What is the smallest number which must be added to 40 to make it exactly divisible by 6?

15. How many 100 ml glasses can be filled from a two-litre bottle?

16. Write in figures the number 'two hundred and seven thousand, eight hundred and twenty'.

17. A ruler costs 5 pence. How many can be bought for £3?

18. The difference between two numbers is 13. One of the numbers is 18. What is the other number?

19. If plastic tube is 20p for 50 cm, how much will 4 m of tube cost?

20. A pile of 12 bricks is 1.2 metres high. What is the thickness of each brick?

21. In a class of 20 children, $\frac{3}{4}$ were girls. What was the number of boys?

22. A car tyre costs £14. How much does a set of five tyres cost?

23. A rectangular pane of glass is 5 feet long and 2 feet wide. Glass costs £1.40 per square foot. How much will the pane cost?

24. The single fare for a journey is £8 and a day return is £13.50. How much is saved by buying a day return rather than two singles?

25. The monthly rental for a television is £6.50. Six months rent must be paid in advance. How much is that?

26. How many 30 pence rulers can be bought for £2?

27. Gas costs 5 pence per unit. How much would you pay for 200 units?

28. How many weeks is 91 days?

29. How long is it between 6.25 p.m. and 8.10 p.m.?

30. A quarter of my wages are taken in deductions. What percentage have I got left?

Test 7

1. Find the average of 8 and 20.

2. If a man earns £4.50 per hour, how much does he earn in 4 hours?

3. How many eights are there in seventy-two?

4. What number is twice as big as thirty-nine?

5. Write in figures the number 'sixty thousand and eleven'.

6. A man stays awake for five days. How many hours is this?

7. What is 8.15 p.m. on the 24-hour clock?

8. How many five pence coins are needed to make one pound?

9. Write four-fifths as a decimal.

10. A video recorder costing £450 is reduced by £55. What is the new price?

11. I go shopping with ten pounds and buy two items at eighty pence each. How much money have I left?

12. A packet of twenty sweets costs 50 pence. How much does each sweet cost?

13. A car consumes one gallon of petrol for every 25 miles travelled. How much petrol is used on a journey of 200 miles?

14. How many seconds are there in $2\frac{1}{2}$ minutes?

15. On a sunny day one-tenth of the water in a pool evaporates. What percentage is left?

16. Add together £4.80 and 50 pence.

17. Add eleven to 8 sixes.

18. What is 50% of £800?

19. How many 25 pence rubbers can be bought for £10?

20. Bananas cost eight pence each. How many can I buy for one pound?

21. A rod of length 188 cm is cut in half. How long is each piece?

22. How many minutes are there between 20.30 and 21.15?

23. Add together 6, 14 and 32.

24. How many half-litre glasses can be filled from a large bowl containing sixteen litres?

25. If a man earns £3.50 per hour, how much does he earn in three hours?

26. A packet of crisps costs 12 pence and a boy eats two packets every day. How much does he spend in five days?

27. An aircraft took four hours to fly a distance of 2000 miles. What was the average speed of the aircraft?

28. The road tax for a car is £100. About how much is this per month?

29. A man died in 1975 aged 68. In what year was he born?

30. By how much is three metres longer than three centimetres?

Test 8

1. Work out 50% of £70.

2. By how much is one kilometre more than one metre?

3. A film lasting an hour and a half starts at a quarter-past seven. When does it finish?

4. There are 20 children in a class and 15 of them are girls. What percentage is this?

5. What number is twice as big as two hundred and sixty?

6. Between midnight and noon the temperature rises by 18°. If the temperature is minus 4 °C at midnight, what is it at noon?

7. From seven times five, take away ten.

8. What four coins make fourteen pence?

9. What is a half of a half of 90?

10. What number is a hundred times fifty-four?

11. A shop assistant is paid £50 a week. About how much is that in a year?

12. Add together £3.75 and 40 pence.

13. How many millimetres are there in one metre?

14. A woman died in 1968 aged 70. In what year was she born?

15. Six pounds of parsnips cost 84 pence. How much do they cost per pound?

16. The maths homework consists of questions 10 to 20. How many questions is that?

17. How many days are there in twenty weeks?

18. Write down ten thousand pence in pounds.

19. If I have £1.40 change from a five pound note, how much have I spent?

20. The time by the school clock is five-past nine. The clock is ten minutes fast. What is the correct time?

21. Spell the word 'isosceles'.

22. The single fare for a journey is £6.50 and a day return is £11. How much is saved by buying a day return rather than two singles?

23. What number is 29 less than 85?

24. There are 50 people on a bus and 30 of them are men. What percentage is this?

25. An egg box holds a dozen eggs. How many boxes are needed for forty eggs?

26. Two angles of a triangle are 60° and 62°. What is the third angle?

27. A car travels at 80 miles per hour for an hour and a quarter. How far does it go?

28. How many two pence coins are needed to make ten pounds?

29. What number is twenty times as big as forty?

30. A ship sails at 25 kilometres per hour for four hours. At what speed is it sailing?

Test 9

1. What number is twice as big as 65?

2. Add together £2.20 and 95 pence.

3. A man died in 1965 aged 70. In what year was he born?

4. Eight pounds of potatoes cost 96 pence. How much do they cost per pound?

5. How many days are there in twelve weeks?

6. By how much is one kilogram more than 50 grams?

7. Write down six pence in pounds and pence.

8. Work out 25% of £800.

9. From four times nine take away seven.

10. How many centimetres are there in 300 millimetres?

11. The time by my watch is a quarter-past eight. My watch is ten minutes slow. What is the correct time?

12. If I have 27 pence change from a one pound note, how much have I spent?

13. A film lasting $2\frac{1}{2}$ hours starts at a quarter to six. When does it finish?

14. Add together 4, 26 and 21.

15. Spell the word 'parallel'.

16. What five coins make 37 pence?

17. What is the date exactly a fortnight after the 8th of June?

18. How many centimetres are there in 30 metres?

19. A teacher sets questions 50 to 100 for homework. How many questions is that?

20. Grapefruit cost twelve pence each. Find the cost of a dozen grapefruit.

21. How many inches are there in a yard?

22. How much less than 140 is 14?

23. Between noon and midnight the temperature falls by 15°. If the temperature is 8 °C at noon, what is the temperature at midnight?

24. There are 24 people in a room. Six are men. What percentage is this?

25. The single fare for a journey is £6 and a day return is £9.50. How much is saved by buying a day return rather than two singles?

26. Two angles of a triangle are 55° and 60°. What is the third angle?

27. A car costing £4000 is reduced by £140. What is the new price?

28. A television programme lasting 45 minutes finished at ten past seven. When did it start?

29. A ship was due to arrive at noon on Wednesday, but arrived at 10 00 on Thursday. How many hours late was it?

30. Write in figures the number 'two hundred million and forty thousand'.

Test 10

1. How many minutes are there in 5 hours?

2. Add together £8.60 and 55 pence.

3. Find the average of 7, 11 and 12.

4. A packet of 20 sweets costs 90 pence. How much is each sweet?

5. The time by my watch is twenty past nine. What is the correct time if my watch is 10 minutes slow?

6. A ship was due at noon on Sunday but arrived at 3.00 p.m. on Monday. How many hours late was the ship?

7. How many days are there in 15 weeks?

8. From nine times eight take away eleven.

9. Thirty-one out of fifty people are men. What percentage is this?

10. Electric cable costs 60 pence per foot. How much do I pay for 3 inches of cable?

11. Spell the word 'equation'.

12. Two angles of a triangle are 55° and 40°. What is the third angle?

13. How many 5 pence coins are needed to make 90 pence?

14. If a man earns £3.20 per hour, how much does he earn in 5 hours?

15. A T.V. programme lasting 35 minutes starts at 12 minutes to 6. When does it finish?

16. How much less than 180 is 34?

17. Nine oranges costing twelve pence each are bought with a £5 note. What is the change?

18. Add 13 to twelve 7's.

19. How many millimetres are there in $3\frac{1}{2}$ cm?

20. A car travels at an average speed of 50 m.p.h. How far does it travel in $2\frac{1}{2}$ hours?

21. What is the perimeter of a square of area 25 cm^2?

22. A rod of length 318 cm is cut in half. How long is each piece?

23. A half is a third of a certain number. What is the number?

24. About how much does a man earn in a week if he is paid £5000 a year?

25. Between midnight and 3.00 a.m. the temperature falls by 7°. If the temperature at midnight was 5 °C, what was the temperature at 3.00 a.m.?

26. An egg box holds 6 eggs. How many boxes are needed for 40 eggs?

27. A car costing £8400 is reduced in price by £270. What is the new price?

28. A man smokes 60 cigarettes a day and cigarettes cost £1.20 for 20. How much does he spend in 3 days?

29. By how much is 1 metre longer than 1 mm? (answer in mm).

30. Write in figures the number 'ten million, forty-two thousand and eleven'.

Test 11

1. A tape cost 95 pence. Find the change from five pounds.

2. The floor of a rectangular room is 8 m by 6 m. What is the distance around the room?

3. Write the number 788 to the nearest ten.

4. By how many does a quarter of 60 exceed 10?

5. Two tapes cost eight pounds. How much will seven tapes cost?

6. What number divided by nine gives five as the answer?

7. What number is ten times as big as 0.3?

8. Write one gram as a fraction of one kilogram.

9. How many 5p coins are there in a bag worth £3?

10. I spend 86 pence and pay with a pound coin. My change consists of three coins. What are they?

11. What fraction must be added to $1\frac{3}{4}$ to make $2\frac{1}{8}$?

12. Twenty per cent of the pupils cycle to school, eight per cent walk, and the rest go by bus. What percentage go by bus?

13. Of the 28 children in a class, a quarter were boys. How many girls were there?

14. Find the cost in pounds of five pens at 25 pence each.

15. I arrive at the docks at 7.25 a.m. and my ferry is due to leave at 8.20 a.m. How long do I have to wait?

16. Find the average of 13 and 27.

17. By how much is 17 greater than $11\frac{1}{2}$?

18. Add together £3.85 and 60 pence.

19. Spell the word 'diagonal'.

20. How many half centimetre lengths can be cut from a piece of string which is 40 centimetres long?

21. A car travelling at 30 m.p.h. takes 20 minutes for a journey. How long will the journey take at 60 m.p.h.?

22. Five light bulbs costing forty pence each are bought with a ten pound note. What is the change?

23. The difference between two numbers is 12. One of the numbers is 20. What is the other?

24. A ruler costs 15 pence. How many can be bought for 90p?

25. How many 20p coins are worth the same as six 50p coins?

26. A certain number multiplied by itself gives 64 as the answer. What is a quarter of that number?

27. If string costs two pounds for one metre, how much will 25 cm cost?

28. After spending £2.35, what change have I from £5?

29. Add together four 50 pence coins and seven 20 pence coins and give the answer in pounds.

30. How many feet are there in ten yards?

7.3 SPEED, DISTANCE, TIME

Finding speed

> A lorry takes 5 hours to travel 310 km.
> Find the average speed of the lorry.
>
> Use the formula: speed = $\dfrac{\text{distance}}{\text{time}}$
>
> Speed of lorry = $\dfrac{310}{5}$ = 62 km/h.

Finding distance travelled

> How far will a bullet travel in 1.2 s if it is
> moving at a speed of 1200 m/s?
>
> Use the formula: distance = speed × time.
>
> Distance travelled = 1200 × 1.2
> = 1440 m.

Exercise 5

1. A car travelling at a steady speed takes 4 hours to travel 244 km. What is the speed of the car?

2. A man runs 750 m in a time of 100 s. At what speed does he run?

3. A train takes 6 hours to travel 498 km. What is the speed of the train?

4. After a meal an earthworm moves a distance of 45 cm in 90 s. At what speed does the worm move?

5. During the first month of her life a baby girl grows 4 cm in 28 days. What is the average speed at which she is growing?

6. In the rush-hour a double-decker bus takes 2 hours to travel a distance of 19 km. Find the average speed of the bus.

7. A small plane leaves London at 7.15 p.m. and arrives in Aberdeen, 800 km away, at 9.15 p.m. Find the average speed.

8. A car leaves Norwich at 10.00 a.m. and arrives at York, 290 km away, at 2.00 p.m. Find the average speed.

9. A car leaves Dover at 8.00 a.m. and arrives in London at 10.30 a.m. If the distance is 120 km, find the average speed.

10. A train leaves London at 5.00 a.m. and arrives in Glasgow at 10.15 a.m. If the distance is 630 km, find the average speed.

11. An albatross flies a distance of 470 km in 20 hours. How fast does it fly?

12. A drunken man leaves a public house at 11.15 p.m. and arrives home at midnight. At what average speed does he walk, if he lives 1½ miles from the public house?

Exercise 6

1. A car travels at a constant speed of 40 m.p.h. for three hours. How far does it go?

2. An athlete runs at a steady speed of 5 m/s for 100 s. How far does he run?

3. How far will a train travel in 15 s if it is going at a steady speed of 20 m/s?

4. A ball travels for 30 s at a speed of 12 m/s. Find the distance it covers.

5. An aircraft flies at a speed of 800 km/h for 2½ h. How far does it fly?

6. How far will a ship sail in half an hour if it is going at a steady speed of 24 km/h?

7. Calculate the distance from Edinburgh to Glasgow if it takes 12 h to walk between the two towns at a speed of 6 km/h.

8. A killer shark, attacking a fishing boat, swims at a speed of 13 m/s for half a minute. How far does it swim in this time?

9. A well-trained greyhound runs for 25 s at a speed of 22 m/s. How far does it run?

10. A rocket is flying at a speed of 1000 km/h. How far does it go in 15 minutes?

11. A car leaves London at 8.30 a.m. and arrives in Edinburgh at 5.30 p.m. If the car travels at an average speed of 75 km/h, how far is it from London to Edinburgh?

12. A lorry leaves Manchester at 10.00 a.m. and arrives in Dover at 3.30 p.m., having travelled at an average speed of 75 km/h. How far is it from Manchester to Dover?

The three formulae

As an aid to memory use the triangle

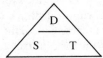

To find speed, cover S so that $S = \dfrac{D}{T}$

To find distance, cover D so that $D = S \times T$

To find time, cover T so that $T = \dfrac{D}{S}$

Exercise 7

Copy and complete the table below.

	Speed	Distance	Time
1.	8 m/s	16 m	s
2.	30 km/h	km	3 h
3.	m/s	24 m	2 s
4.	4 m/s	16 m	s
5.	10 km/h	km	5 h
6.	km/h	60 km	3 h
7.	2 m/s	22 m	s
8.	m/s	35 m	5 s
9.	8 km/h	km	4 h
10.	8 m/s	24 m	s
11.	15 km/h	km	3 h
12.	km/h	150 km	3 h
13.	7 m/s	m	8 s
14.	m/s	36 m	4 s
15.	10 m/s	50 m	s
16.	70 km/h	km	4 h
17.	m/s	27 m	9 s
18.	100 km/h	500 km	h
19.	55 km/h	55 km	h
20.	m/s	49 m	7 s
21.	20 m.p.h.	5 miles	h
22.	m.p.h.	8 miles	30 minutes
23.	km/h	4 km	15 minutes
24.	7 km/h	km	30 minutes
25.	22 km/h	km	15 minutes
26.	24 m.p.h.	12 miles	minutes
27.	36 km/h	18 km	minutes
28.	20 m/s	m	0.1 s
29.	300 m/s	m	0.02 s
30.	48 km/h	km	20 minutes

Exercise 8

1. Find the time taken:
   (a) 360 km at 20 km/h
   (b) 56 miles at 8 m.p.h.
   (c) 200 m at 40 m/s
   (d) 60 km at 120 km/h.

2. Find the distance travelled:
   (a) 55 m.p.h. for 2 hours
   (b) 17 m/s for 20 seconds
   (c) 63 km/h for 5 hours
   (d) 5 cm/day for 12 days.

3. Find the speed:
   (a) 98 miles in 7 hours
   (b) 364 km in 8 hours
   (c) 250 m in 10 seconds
   (d) 63 cm in 6 minutes.

The next three questions are more difficult because they involve fractions.
Be careful with the units.

4. Find the time taken:
   (a) 6 km at 24 km/h
   (b) 12 m at 60 m/s
   (c) 8 miles at 80 m.p.h.
   (d) 17 km at 51 km/h.

5. Find the distance travelled:
   (a) 17 km/h for $\frac{1}{2}$ hour
   (b) 26 m.p.h. for 30 minutes
   (c) 54 km/h for 15 minutes
   (d) 60 m.p.h. for 20 minutes.

6. Find the speed:
   (a) 16 miles in $\frac{1}{2}$ hour (in m.p.h.)
   (b) 24 km in 30 minutes (in km/h)
   (c) 21 miles in 15 minutes (in m.p.h.)
   (d) 15 km in 20 minutes (in km/h).

7. A lizard runs 18 m in 5 seconds. Find the speed.

8. A car takes 15 minutes to travel 22 miles. Find the speed in m.p.h.

9. An athlete runs at 9 km/h for 30 minutes. How far does he run?

10. A plane flies 80 miles at a speed of 240 m.p.h. How long does it take in minutes?

11. A killer ant runs at 3 m.p.h. for 30 minutes. How far does she run?

12. An Olympic swimmer takes 20 minutes to swim 2 km. At what speed does he swim in km/h?

13. A cyclist takes 12 minutes to travel 4 miles. At what speed does he cycle in m.p.h.?

14. A train travels at 100 m.p.h. for 6 minutes. How far does it go?

15. A rowing boat covers a distance of 4 miles at a speed of 12 m.p.h. How many minutes does it take?

16. A car goes at 60 m.p.h. for 1 hour 30 minutes. How far does it travel?

17. A horse runs for 2 hours 15 minutes at a speed of 8 m.p.h. How far does it run?

18. An octopus swims 7 km at a speed of 3 km/h. How long does it take in hours and minutes?

19. In a car race the winning car passed the finishing line 8 seconds ahead of the car which came second. If both cars were travelling at 72 m/s, what was the distance between the two cars at the end?

20. The distance from London to Penzance by rail is 420 km. At what average speed must a train travel to cover this distance in 4 hours?

21. In France the T.G.V. does the non-stop Paris to Lyon run, a distance of 448 km in 2 hours 40 minutes. Calculate the average speed in km/h for the journey.

22. The distance from London to Manchester is 295 km. Mr Simpson leaves London for Manchester and drives for 3h 30 min at an average speed of 74 km/h. How far will he be from Manchester after this time?

23. A sprinter runs 100 m in 10 s. Calculate his average speed in km/h.

24. A motorist averaged 50 km/h and 75 km/h over two consecutive 50 km stretches of road.
    (a) Calculate the times taken to cover these two distances.
    (b) Give the total time, in hours, taken to cover the whole distance of 100 km.
    (c) Calculate the motorist's average speed over the whole 100 km.

7.4 TRAVEL GRAPHS

Exercise 9

Make an accurate copy of each graph and then answer the questions which follow.

1. The graph shows a car journey in three stages.

   (a) How far has the car gone after 2 hours?
   (b) How far has the car gone after 2½ hours?
   (c) How long does the car take to go 5 km?
   (d) How long does the car take to go 25 km?
   (e) What is the speed
       (i) from O to A,
       (ii) from A to B,
       (iii) from B to C?

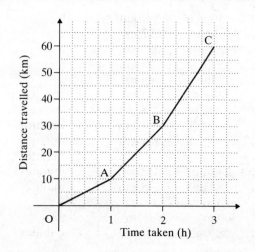

2. The graph shows a train journey in four stages.

  (a) How far has the train travelled after
       (i) 2 hours, (ii) $1\frac{1}{2}$ hours, (iii) $3\frac{1}{4}$ hours?
  (b) How long does the train take to travel
       (i) 5 km, (ii) 60 km, (iii) 20 km?
  (c) What is the speed
         (i) from O to A,   (ii) from A to B,
       (iii) from B to C,   (iv) from C to D?

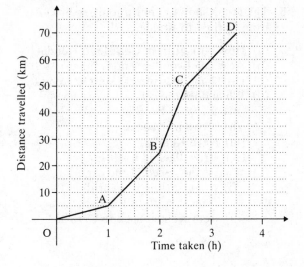

3. The graph shows a bus journey in four stages

  (a) How far has the bus travelled after
       (i) $1\frac{1}{2}$ hours, (ii) $3\frac{3}{4}$ hours, (iii) 1 hour?
  (b) What is the speed
         (i) from O to A,   (ii) from A to B,
       (iii) from B to C,   (iv) from C to D?

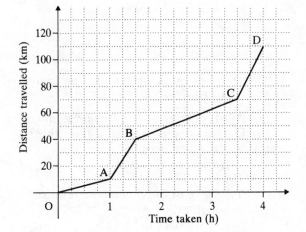

4. The graph shows a return journey by car from Leeds to Scarborough.

  (a) How far is it from Leeds to York?
  (b) How far is it from York to Scarborough?
  (c) At which two places does the car stop?
  (d) How long does the car stop at Scarborough?
  (e) When does the car
         (i) arrive in York,
        (ii) leave York,
       (iii) arrive in Scarborough,
        (iv) arrive back in Leeds?
  (f) What is the speed of the car
         (i) from Leeds to York,
        (ii) from York to Scarborough,
       (iii) from Scarborough to Leeds?

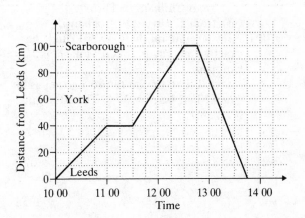

5. The graph shows a return journey by car from Carlisle to Kendal.

(a) How far is it from Carlisle to Kendal?
(b) At which two places does the car stop?
(c) How long does the car stop at Kendal?
(d) When does the car
    (i) arrive in Penrith,
    (ii) arrive in Kendal,
    (iii) leave Kendal,
    (iv) arrive back in Carlisle?
(e) What is the speed of the car
    (i) from Carlisle to Penrith,
    (ii) from Penrith to Kendal,
    (iii) from Kendal back to Carlisle?

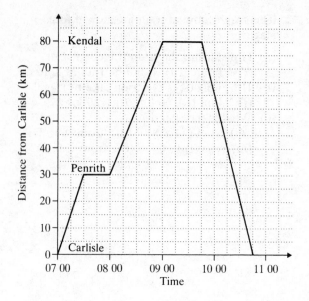

6. The graph shows an athlete on a run from Molash to Thruxted.

(a) At which three places does he stop?
(b) For how long does he stop altogether?
(c) At what time does he
    (i) arrive in Thruxted,
    (ii) leave Chilham,
    (iii) arrive in Bogham on the return journey,
    (iv) arrive back in Molash?
(d) At what speed does he run
    (i) from Molash to Chilham,
    (ii) from Chilham to Thruxted,
    (iii) from Thruxted to Bogham,
(e) At what time on the outward run is he exactly half way between Molash and Chilham?
(f) At what time on the return journey is he exactly half way between Thruxted and Bogham?

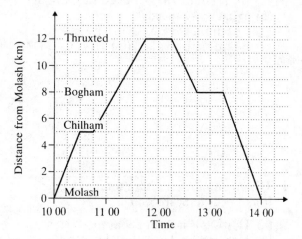

7. The graph shows a man's journey by train,
   boat and train from London to Paris.

   (a) At what time does he
       (i)   arrive at Dover,
       (ii) arrive in Paris,
       (iii) leave Calais,
       (iv) leave Dover?
   (b) How long does he stop at Dover?
   (c) At what speed does he travel
       (i)   from Calais to Paris,
       (ii) from London to Dover,
       (iii) from Dover to Calais?
   (d) At what time is he exactly half way
       between Calais and Paris?
   (e) Calculate the *average* speed for the
       whole journey from London to Paris
       (including stops).

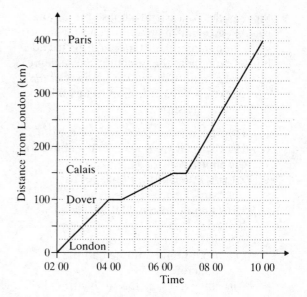

8. The graph shows a woman's journey by
   plane from London to Aberdeen.

   (a) At what time does she
       (i) arrive in Glasgow,
       (ii) leave Birmingham?
   (b) How far is she from Aberdeen at 12.15?
   (c) At what speed does she fly
       (i)   from London to Birmingham,
       (ii) from Birmingham to Glasgow,
       (iii) from Glasgow to Aberdeen?
   (d) At what time has she flown one third of
       the distance from Birmingham to
       Glasgow?
   (e) Calculate the average speed for the
       whole journey from London to
       Aberdeen (including stops).

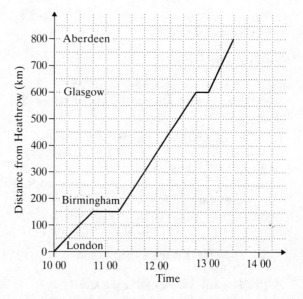

9. Steve cycles to a friend's house but on the way his bike gets a puncture, and he has to walk the remaining distance. At his friend's house, he repairs the puncture, has a game of snooker and then returns home. On the way back, he stops at a shop to buy a book on how to play snooker.

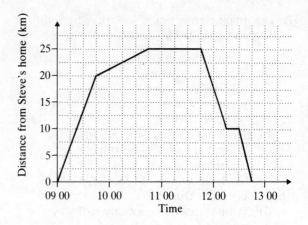

(a) How far is it to his friend's house?
(b) How far is it from his friend's house to the shop?
(c) At what time did his bike get a puncture?
(d) How long did he stay at his friend's house?
(e) At what speed did he travel
  (i) from home until he had the puncture,
  (ii) after the puncture to his friend's house,
  (iii) from his friend's house to the shop,
  (iv) from the shop back to his own home?

Exercise 10

In questions **1** to **4** make an accurate copy of each graph and then answer the questions which follow.

1. At the same time in the morning Susan leaves home in her car and her brother David leaves home on his bicycle and cycles along the same road as Susan. Susan stops at a garage during the journey but David cycles all the way without stopping. Susan and David arrive in Oxford at the same time.

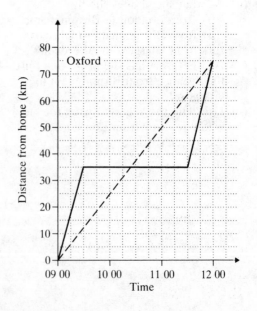

(a) How far is it from their home to Oxford?
(b) For how long does Susan stop?
(c) How far from Oxford is the garage?
(d) Estimate the time when David passes Susan.
(e) At what speed does
  (i) David cycle,
  (ii) Susan drive to the garage,
  (iii) Susan drive from the garage to Oxford?
(f) How far apart are Susan and David at 11 00 h?

2. The graph shows the journeys made by two trains A and B between London and Brighton.

(a) At what time did
(i) train A leave London,
(ii) train B leave Brighton?
(b) At what speed did train A travel?
(c) At what speed did train B travel?
(d) How far apart were the trains at these times?
(i) 08 30 h   (ii) 09 00 h
(iii) 09 30 h   (iv) 10 30 h
(e) Estimate how far from London the trains passed each other.
(f) At what time would train A arrive in Brighton if its speed was increased to 60 km/h?

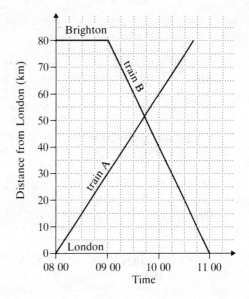

3. The graph shows the journeys of two boys as they travelled along the same road from Hastings.

(a) How long after John did Mark leave?
(b) Calculate the speed of
(i) John for the first two hours
(ii) Mark from Hastings to Tonbridge,
(iii) John for the second part of his journey,
(iv) Mark from Tonbridge to Dartford.
(c) When did Mark overtake John?
(d) When did John overtake Mark?
(e) When did John arrive in Dartford?
(f) How far apart were John and Mark at 15 15 h?

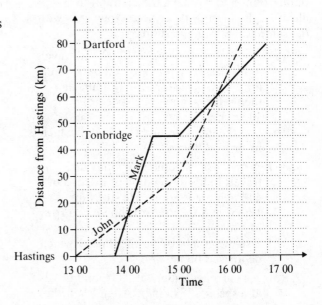

4. Mr Berol and Mr Hale use the same road to travel between Aston and Borton.

(a) At what time did
   (i) Mr Berol arrive in Borton,
   (ii) Mr Hale leave Aston?
(b) (i) When did Mr Berol and Mr Hale pass each other?
   (ii) In which direction was Mr Berol travelling?
(c) Find the following speeds:
   (i) Mr Hale from Aston to Stanley,
   (ii) Mr Berol from Aston to Borton,
   (iii) Mr Hale from Stanley to Borton,
   (iv) Mr Berol from Borton back to Aston.
(d) (More difficult) When did Mr Hale arrive in Borton?

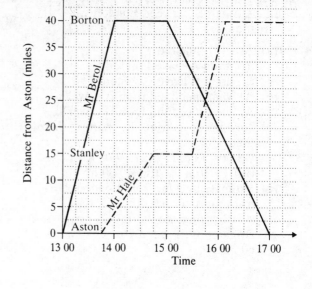

In questions **5** to **9** draw a travel graph to illustrate the journey described. Draw axes with the same scales as in question **3**.

5. (a) A man leaves home at 10 00 and travels to his destination at a speed of 60 km/h for 1 hour. He stops for $1\frac{1}{2}$ hours and then returns home at a speed of 40 km/h.
   (b) Use the graph to find the time at which he arrived home.

6. (a) A man leaves home at midday and travels to his destination at a speed of 40 km/h for $1\frac{1}{2}$ hours. He stops for 1 hour and then returns home at a speed of 60 km/h.
   (b) Use the graph to find the time at which he arrived home.

7. (a) A man leaves home at 08 00 and drives at a speed of 30 km/h. After 1 hour he increases his speed to 50 km/h and continues at this speed for a further 1 hour. He stops for $\frac{3}{4}$ hour and then returns home at a speed of 80 km/h.
   (b) Use the graph to find the time at which he arrived home.

8. (a) Mrs Begg leaves home at 09 00 and drives at a speed of 60 km/h. After $\frac{1}{2}$ hour she reduces her speed to 50 km/h and continues at this speed for a further 1 hour. She stops for 15 minutes and then returns home at a speed of 40 km/h.
   (b) Use the graph to find the time at which she arrives home.

9. (a) It is 40 km from Dundee to Perth and 40 km from Perth to Stirling. Mark Dundee, Perth and Stirling on your graph with Dundee at the bottom.
   (b) A man leaves Dundee at 13 00 and travels at a speed of 40 km/h for 1 hour. He stops for $\frac{1}{2}$ hour at Perth and then continues his journey to Stirling at a speed of 40 km/h. He stops at Stirling for $\frac{1}{2}$ hour and then returns to Dundee at a speed of 80 km/h.
   (c) Use the graph to find the time at which he returns to Dundee.

7.5 STRAIGHT LINE GRAPHS

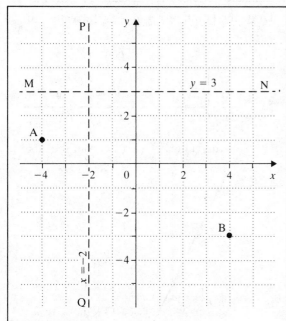

In the diagram above:
  A has coordinates $(-4,1)$.
  B has coordinates $(4,-3)$.
  Line MN has equation $y = 3$.
  Line PQ has equation $x = -2$.

Exercise 11

Draw a set of axes with x and y from -8 to $+8$. Plot and label the following points.

A(3,6), B(2,3), C(−2,4), D(−4,2), E(2,−2),

F(−3,−4), G(7,2), H(−6,−3), I(6,−4), J(−6,6),

K(7,7), L(3,−5), M(−5,−5), N(1,2), O(7,−2),

P(−6,4), Q(4,4), R(−4,4), S(1, 6), T(5,0),

U(0,−3), V(−7,−7), W(0,3).

In questions **1** to **10** list the points on the line given.
1. $y = 3$ **2.** $y = -5$
3. $y = 6$ **4.** $x = 7$
5. $x = -4$ **6.** $y = -2$
7. $x = 0$ **8.** $y = 7$
9. $y = x$ **10.** $y = 0$

In questions **11** to **26** write down the equation of the line on which the given points lie.
11. P, R, C, Q   **12.** H, U
13. B, E   **14.** F, I
15. R, D   **16.** M, L
17. W, U   **18.** M, Q, K
19. E, O   **20.** A, L
21. B, T. O   **22.** N, B
23. W, N   **24.** H, W, A
25. A, G   **26.** N, A

The next two exercises provide revision of negative numbers, which are used extensively in the rest of this section.

Exercise 12

1. $2 \times (-3)$ **2.** -3×3 **3.** $4 \times (-1)$
4. $-1 \times (-2)$ **5.** -3×4 **6.** $-2 \times (-2)$
7. $-3 \times (-4)$ **8.** $5 \times (-2)$ **9.** -1×6
10. $-6 \times (-2)$ **11.** $-3 \times (-5)$ **12.** -3×7
13. -3×1 **14.** $0 \times (-4)$ **15.** $5 \times (-6)$
16. -3×0 **17.** $-7 \times (-1)$ **18.** $-4 \times (-5)$
19. $3 \times (-6)$ **20.** -4×0 **21.** $8 \times (-1)$
22. -1×7 **23.** $0 \times (-3)$ **24.** $4 \times (-4)$

25. $-2 \times (-3)$ **26.** $7 \times (-5)$ **27.** $8 \times (-2)$
28. $(-2)^2$ **29.** $(-3)^2$ **30.** $(-1)^2$
31. $(0)^2$ **32.** -1×9 **33.** $9 \times (-1)$
34. $-9 \times (-1)$ **35.** -8×5 **36.** $(-4)^2$
37. $(2)^2$ **38.** $(-5)^2$ **39.** $0 \times (-7)$
40. $-6 \times (-9)$ **41.** $8 \times (-10)$ **42.** $(-10)^2$
43. $4 \times (-2)$ **44.** $6 \times (-3)$ **45.** $(-8)^2$
46. $0 \times (-10)$ **47.** $-9 \times (-3)$ **48.** $(-7)^2$

Exercise 13

Add together the numbers given.
1. $-4, 6$ **2.** $-2, -2$ **3.** $-6, -1$
4. $8, -5$ **5.** $4, -3$ **6.** $-3, -5$
7. $7, -2$ **8.** $-8, 2$ **9.** $-9, -4$
10. $-3, -3$ **11.** $9, -12$ **12.** $5, -1$
13. $-6, -2$ **14.** $4, -10$ **15.** $8, -11$
16. $-12, -10$ **17.** $-6, -7$ **18.** $-2, 5$
19. $5, 6$ **20.** $-7, 2$ **21.** $4, 13$
22. $-8, -5$ **23.** $-9, 15$ **24.** $9, -6$

25. $-7, -3, 2$ **26.** $8, -2, 1$
27. $-4, -5, 8$ **28.** $-1, 4, 3$
29. $-6, 2, 10$ **30.** $-2, -3, 6$
31. $-7, -2, 9$ **32.** $8, -2, 4$

Table of values

Work out a table of values for the graph of $y = 3x - 5$ for values of x from -3 to $+3$.

x	-3	-2	-1	0	1	2	3
$3x$	-9	-6	-3	0	3	6	9
-5	-5	-5	-5	-5	-5	-5	-5
y	-14	-11	-8	-5	-2	1	4

Exercise 14

Copy and complete the tables of values.

1. $y = 2x + 3$

x	-3	-2	-1	0	1	2	3
$2x$	-6	-4		0	2		
$+3$	3	3	3	3			
y				3			

2. $y = 4x - 2$

x	-3	-2	-1	0	1	2	3
$4x$			0		4		12
-2	-2	-2		-2	-2		
y				-2	2		

3. $y = 3x + 4$

x	-4	-3	-2	-1	0	1	2
$3x$							
$+4$							
y							

4. $y = x + 5$

x	-3	-2	-1	0	1	2	3
x	-3	-2					
$+5$	5	5					
y	2						

5. $y = 5x - 9$

x	-4	-3	-2	-1	0	1	2
$5x$							
-9							
y							

Drawing straight line graphs

Draw the graph of $y = 4 - 2x$ for values of x from -2 to $+3$

(a)

x	-2	-1	0	1	2	3
4	4	4	4	4	4	4
$-2x$	4	2	0	-2	-4	-6
y	8	6	4	2	0	-2

(b) Plot the values of x and y from the table

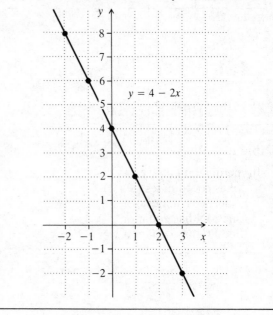

Exercise 15

For each question make a table of values and then draw the graph. Suggested scales: 1 cm to 1 unit on both axes, unless otherwise stated.

1. $y = 2x + 1$; x from -3 to $+3$.

x	-3	-2	-1	0	1	2	3
$2x$	-6	-4					
$+1$	1	1	1				
y	-5	-3					

2. $y = 3x - 5$; x from -2 to $+3$.
3. $y = x + 2$; x from -4 to $+4$.
4. $y = 2x - 7$; x from -2 to $+5$.
5. $y = 4x + 1$; x from -3 to $+3$.
   (Use scales of 1 cm to 1 unit on the x-axis and 1 cm to 2 units on the y-axis.)

6. $y = x - 3$; x from -2 to $+5$.
7. $y = 2x + 4$; x from -4 to $+2$.
8. $y = 3x + 2$; x from -3 to $+3$.
9. $y = x + 7$; x from -5 to $+3$.
10. $y = 4x - 3$; x from -3 to $+3$.

    (Use scales of 1 cm to 1 unit on the x-axis and 1 cm to 2 units on the y-axis.)

11. $y = 4 - 2x$; x from -3 to $+3$.

x	-3	-2	-1	0	1	2	3
4	4	4	4	4			4
$-2x$	6	4					-6
y	10	8					-2

12. $y = 8 - 2x$; x from -2 to $+4$.
13. $y = 5 - 3x$; x from -3 to $+3$.

14. $y = 2 - x$; x from -3 to $+3$.

x	-3	-2	-1	0	1	2	3
2	2	2	2	2			
$-x$	3	2					-3
y	5	4					

15. $y = 6 - x$; x from -1 to $+7$.
16. $y = 7 - 4x$; x from -2 to $+4$.
    (Use scales of 1 cm to 1 unit on the x-axis and 1 cm to 2 units on the y-axis.)
17. $y = -2 - 2x$; x from -3 to $+3$.
18. $y = -5 - x$; x from -2 to $+5$.
19. $y = 2x + 3$; x from -3 to $+3$.
20. $y = 10 - 2x$; x from 0 to $+6$.

7.6 CURVED GRAPHS

Table of values

Work out a table of values for the graph of $y = x^2 + 2x$ for values of x from -3 to $+3$

x	-3	-2	-1	0	1	2	3
x^2	9	4	1	0	1	4	9
$2x$	-6	-4	-2	0	2	4	6
y	3	0	-1	0	3	8	15

Exercise 16

Copy and complete the tables of values.

1. $y = x^2 + 3x$.

x	-4	-3	-2	-1	0	1	2
x^2	16	9	4				
$3x$	-12	-9	-6				
y	4	0	-2				

2. $y = x^2 + 5x$.

x	-4	-3	-2	-1	0	1	2
x^2	16						
$5x$	-20						
y	-4						

3. $y = x^2 + 4$.

x	-3	-2	-1	0	1	2	3
x^2							
$+4$	4	4	4	4			
y							

4. $y = x^2 - 7$.

x	-3	-2	-1	0	1	2	3
x^2	9						
-7	-7	-7					
y							

5. $y = x^2 - 2x$.

x	-3	-2	-1	0	1	2	3
x^2							9
$-2x$	6						-6
y							3

6. $y = x^2 - 4x$.

x	-2	-1	0	1	2	3	4
x^2							
$-4x$							
y							

7. $y = x^2 + 2x + 3$.

x	−3	−2	−1	0	1	2	3
x^2	9	4					
$+2x$	−6	−4					
$+3$	3	3	3	3			
y	6	3					

8. $y = x^2 + 3x − 2$.

x	−4	−3	−2	−1	0	1	2
x^2							
$+3x$							
$−2$	−2	−2					
y							

9. $y = x^2 + 4x − 5$.

x	−3	−2	−1	0	1	2	3
x^2							
$+4x$							
$−5$							
y							

10. $y = x^2 − 2x + 6$.

x	−3	−2	−1	0	1	2	3
x^2							
$−2x$							
$+6$							
y							

In questions **11** to **20** draw a table of values for the values of x given.

11. $y = x^2 + 4x$; x from −3 to +3.
12. $y = x^2 − 6x$; x from −4 to +2.
13. $y = x^2 + 8$; x from −3 to +3.
14. $y = x^2 + 3x + 1$; x from −4 to +2.
15. $y = x^2 − 5x + 3$; x from −3 to +3.
16. $y = x^2 − 3x − 5$; x from −2 to +4.
17. $y = x^2 − 3$; x from −5 to +1.
18. $y = 2x^2 + 1$; x from −3 to +3.
19. $y = 2x^2 + 3x$; x from −3 to +3.
20. $y = 3x^2 + 2x + 4$; x from −3 to +3.

Draw the graph of $y = x^2 + x − 2$ for values of x from −3 to +3.

(a)

x	−3	−2	−1	0	1	2	3
x^2	9	4	1	0	1	4	9
$+x$	−3	−2	−1	0	1	2	3
$−2$	−2	−2	−2	−2	−2	−2	−2
y	4	0	−2	−2	0	4	10

(b) Plot the x and y values from the table.

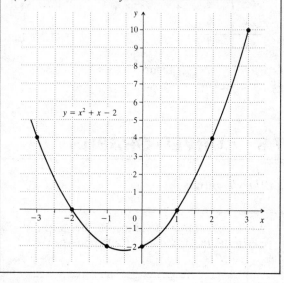

$y = x^2 + x − 2$

Exercise 17

For each question make a table of values and then draw the graph. Suggested scales: 2 cm to 1 unit on the x-axis and 1 cm to 1 unit on the y-axis.

1. $y = x^2 + 2$; x from −3 to +3.

x	−3	−2	−1	0	1	2	3
x^2	9	4	1	0	1		
$+2$	2	2	2				
y	11	6	3				

2. $y = x^2 + 5$; x from −3 to +3.
3. $y = x^2 − 4$; x from −3 to +3.
4. $y = x^2 − 8$; x from −3 to +3.
5. $y = x^2 + 2x$; x from −4 to +2.

x	−4	−3	−2	−1	0	1	2
x^2	16	9					4
$+2x$	−8	−6					4
y	8	3					8

6. $y = x^2 + 4x$; x from -5 to $+1$.
7. $y = x^2 + 3x$; x from -4 to $+2$.
8. $y = x^2 - 2x$; x from -3 to $+3$.
9. $y = x^2 - 5x$; x from -1 to $+6$.
10. $y = x^2 + 4x - 1$; x from -2 to $+4$.
11. $y = x^2 + 2x - 5$; x from -4 to $+2$
12. $y = x^2 + 3x + 1$; x from -4 to $+2$.
13. $y = x^2 + 4x - 1$; x from -5 to $+1$.
14. $y = x^2 + x - 2$; x from -3 to $+3$.
15. $y = x^2 - 4x + 1$; x from -1 to $+5$.

Exercise 18

These graphs are more difficult. For each question make a table of values and then draw the graph.

1. $y = x^3 + 1$; x from -3 to $+3$.
   Scales: 2 cm to 1 unit for x;
             1 cm to 5 units for y.

2. $y = \dfrac{12}{x}$; x from 1 to 12.

3. $y = 2x^2 + 3x - 1$; x from -4 to $+2$.
   Scales: 2 cm to 1 unit for x;
             1 cm to 1 unit for y.
   (Remember $2x^2 = 2(x^2)$. Work out x^2 and then multiply by 2).

4. $y = \dfrac{16}{x}$; x from 1 to 10.
   Scales: 1 cm to 1 unit for x;
             1 cm to 1 unit for y.

5. $y = x^3 + x^2 - 2$; x from -3 to $+3$.
   Scales: 2 cm to 1 unit for x;
             1 cm to 5 units for y.

6. $y = 3x^2 + 2x - 5$; x from -3 to $+3$.
   Scales: 2 cm to 1 unit for x;
             2 cm to 5 units for y.

7. $y = 2x^2 - 4x - 3$; x from -2 to $+4$.
   Scales: 2 cm to 1 unit for x;
             1 cm to 1 unit for y.

8. $y = x^3 + 1$; x from -3 to $+3$.
   Scales: 2 cm to 1 unit for x;
             1 cm to 5 units for y.

Intersecting line and curve

Draw the graphs of $y = x^2 - 2x$ and $y = x + 2$ and estimate the x-values of the two points where the graphs cut.

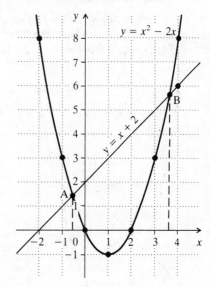

The graphs cut at the points marked A and B.
At A $x \approx -0.6$ (to 1 D.P.)
At B $x \approx 3.6$ (to 1 D.P.)

Exercise 19

In the following questions draw the graphs of the line and the curve and estimate the x-values at the points of intersection. Use scales of 1 cm to 1 unit on both axes.

1. (a) $y = x - 1$,
   (b) $y = x^2 - 3x$. Take values of x from -2 to $+4$.
   The tables of values are started below.

(a)

x	-2	-1	0	1	2	3	4
x	-2	-1	0	1			
-1	-1	-1	-1				
y	-3						

(b)

x	-2	-1	0	1	2	3	4
x^2	4					9	
$-3x$	6				-6		-12
y	10						

2. (a) $y = x - 3$,
  (b) $y = x^2 - 7$.
    Take values of x from -3 to $+3$.

3. (a) $y = 2x - 1$,
  (b) $y = x^2 + 2x - 3$.
    Take values of x from -4 to $+2$.

4. From the diagram below estimate the x-values at the two points where the line $y = x + 3$ cuts the curve $y = x^2 + 2x - 1$.

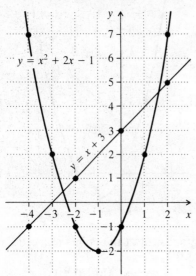

5. (a) $y = x^2 - 2x - 1$,
  (b) $y = 4 - x$.
    Take values of x from -2 to $+4$.
    The table of values for $y = 4 - x$ is started below.

x	-2	-1	0	1	2	3	4
4	4	4	4	4			
$-x$	2	1	0	-1			
y	6						

6. (a) $y = 2x - 8$,
  (b) $y = x^2 - 5x$.
    Take values of x from 0 to 6.

7. (a) $y = -x$,
  (b) $y = 4 - x^2$.
    Take values of x from -3 to $+3$.
    The line $y = -x$ passes through the points $(-3,3)$, $(-1,1)$, $(2,-2)$ etc.
    The table of values for $y = 4 - x^2$ is started below.

x	-3	-2	-1	0	1	2	3
4	4	4	4	4			
$-x^2$	-9	-4				-4	
y							

(Remember: $-x^2 = -(x^2)$.)

8. (a) $y = x$,
  (b) $y = x^2 - 2x - 3$.
    Take values of x from -2 to $+4$.

9. (a) $y = 7 - x$,
  (b) $y = \dfrac{8}{x}$. Take values of x from 0 to 8.

  Plot the points given in the tables below.

  (a) $y = 7 - x$:

x	0	2	4	6	7
y	7	5	3	1	0

  (b) $y = \dfrac{8}{x}$:

x	1	2	4	6	8
y	8	4	2	1.3	1

10. (a) $y = x$,
  (b) $y = \dfrac{12}{x}$. Take values of x from 1 to 12.

11. (a) $y = 9 - x$,
  (b) $y = \dfrac{10}{x}$. Take values of x from 1 to 10.

12. (a) $y = x$,
  (b) $y = 5 - x^2$.
    Take values of x from -3 to $+3$.

Part 8

8.1 REFLECTIONS

A′B′C′D′ is the image of ABCD after reflection in the broken line.

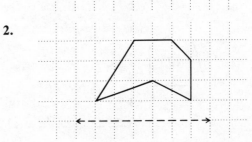

Exercise 1

On squared paper draw the object and its image after reflection in the broken line.

1.

2.

3.

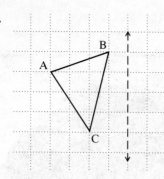

4.

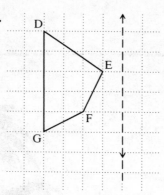

5.

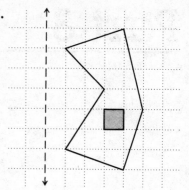

6.

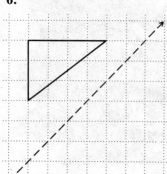

7.

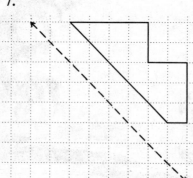

8.

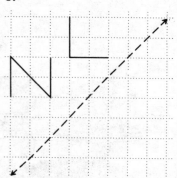

Exercise 2

Draw the image of the given shape after reflection in line AB and then reflect this new shape in line XY.

1.

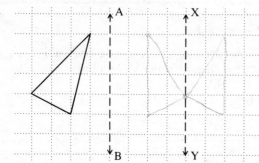

2.

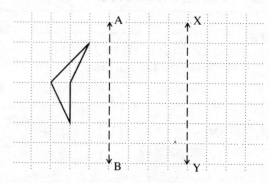

3.

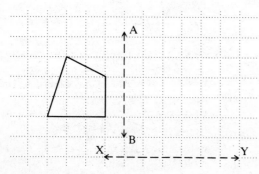

4.

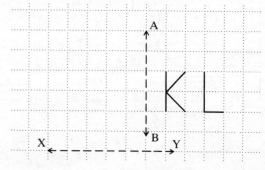

Exercise 3

1. Copy the diagram below.

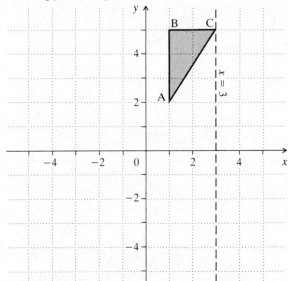

Draw the image of △ ABC after reflection in the lines indicated.
(a) the x-axis. Label it △1.
(b) the y-axis. Label it △2.
(c) the line $x = 3$. Label it △3.

For questions **2** to **5** draw a pair of axes so that both x and y can take values from -7 to $+7$.

2. (a) Plot and label D($-6,4$), E($-6,7$), F($-4,7$).
   (b) Draw the lines $y = 3$ and $x = -2$. [Use dotted lines.]
   (c) Draw the image of △ DEF after reflection in:
      (i) the x-axis. Label it △1.
      (ii) the y-axis. Label it △2.
      (iii) the line $y = 3$. Label it △3.
      (iv) the line $x = -2$. Label it △4.
   (d) Write down the coordinates of the image of point D in each case.

3. (a) Plot and label P($7,5$), Q($7,2$), R($5,2$).
   (b) Draw the lines $y = -1$, $x = 1$ and $y = x$. Use dotted lines.
   (c) Draw the image of △PQR after reflection in:
      (i) the line $y = -1$. Label it △1.
      (ii) the line $x = 1$. Label it △2.
      (iii) the line $y = x$. Label it △3.
   (d) Write down the coordinates of the image of point P in each case.

4. (a) Plot and label L($7,-5$), M($7,-1$), N($5,-1$).
   (b) Draw the lines $y = x$ and $y = -x$. Use dotted lines.
   (c) Draw the image of △LMN after reflection in:
      (i) the x-axis. Label it △1.
      (ii) the line $y = x$. Label it △2.
      (iii) the line $y = -x$. Label it △3.
   (d) Write down the coordinates of the image of point L in each case.

5. (a) Plot and label A($-7,-6$), B($-7,-2$), C($-4,-2$).
   (b) Draw the line $y = x$.
   (c) Reflect △ABC in the x-axis. Label the image A′B′C′.
   (d) Reflect △A′B′C′ in the y-axis. Label the image A″B″C″.
   (e) Reflect △A″B″C″ in the line $y = x$. Label the image A*B*C*.
   (f) Write down the coordinates of A′, A″ and A*.

6. (a) Copy the diagram below.

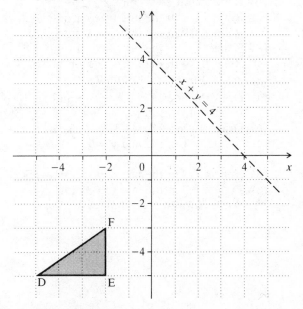

   (b) Reflect △DEF in the x-axis. Label the image D′E′F′.
   (c) Reflect △D′E′F′ in the y-axis. Label the image D″E″F″.
   (d) Reflect △D″E″F″ in the line $x + y = 4$. Label the image D*E*F*.
   (e) Write down the coordinates of D′, D″ and D*.

For questions **7** to **10** draw a pair of axes so that both x and y can take values from -7 to $+7$.

7. (a) Draw the line $x + y = 7$. [It passes through (0,7) and (7,0).]
   (b) Draw $\triangle 1$ at $(-3,-1)$, $(-1,-1)$, $(-1,-4)$.
   (c) Reflect $\triangle 1$ in the y-axis onto $\triangle 2$.
   (d) Reflect $\triangle 2$ in the x-axis onto $\triangle 3$.
   (e) Reflect $\triangle 3$ in the line $x + y = 7$ onto $\triangle 4$.
   (f) Reflect $\triangle 4$ in the y-axis onto $\triangle 5$.
   (g) Write down the coordinates of $\triangle 5$.

8. (a) Draw the lines $y = 2$, $x = -1$ and $y = x$.
   (b) Draw $\triangle 1$ at $(1,-3)$, $(-3,-3)$, $(-3,-5)$.
   (c) Reflect $\triangle 1$ in the line $y = x$ onto $\triangle 2$.
   (d) Reflect $\triangle 2$ in the line $y = 2$ onto $\triangle 3$.
   (e) Reflect $\triangle 3$ in the line $x = -1$ onto $\triangle 4$.
   (f) Reflect $\triangle 4$ in the line $y = x$ onto $\triangle 5$.
   (g) Write down the coordinates of $\triangle 5$.

9. (a) Draw the lines $y = x$, $y = -x$ and $y = -1$.
   (b) Draw $\triangle 1$ at $(-5,7)$, $(-2,7)$, $(-2,5)$.
   (c) Reflect $\triangle 1$ in the line $y = -x$ onto $\triangle 2$.
   (d) Reflect $\triangle 2$ in the line $y = x$ onto $\triangle 3$.
   (e) Reflect $\triangle 3$ in the line $y = -1$ onto $\triangle 4$.
   (f) Reflect $\triangle 4$ in the line $y = x$ onto $\triangle 5$.
   (g) Write down the coordinates of $\triangle 5$.

10. (a) Draw the lines $y = -1$, $x = 3$ and $y = x + 4$.
    (b) Draw $\triangle 1$ at $(1,7)$, $(-3,7)$, $(-3,5)$.
    (c) Reflect $\triangle 1$ in the line $y = x + 4$ onto $\triangle 2$.
    (d) Reflect $\triangle 2$ in the line $y = -1$ onto $\triangle 3$.
    (e) Reflect $\triangle 3$ in the line $x = 3$ onto $\triangle 4$.
    (f) Write down the coordinates of $\triangle 4$.

Describing a given reflection

Exercise 4

1. Copy the diagram below.

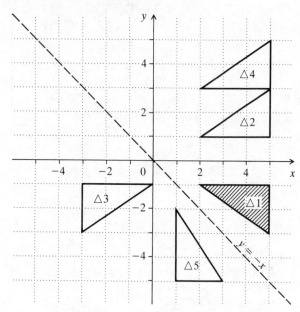

Find the equation of the mirror line for the reflection:
(a) $\triangle 1$ onto $\triangle 2$
(b) $\triangle 1$ onto $\triangle 3$
(c) $\triangle 1$ onto $\triangle 4$
(d) $\triangle 1$ onto $\triangle 5$.

For questions **2** to **5** draw a pair of axes so that both x and y can take values from -7 to $+7$.

2. (a) Draw and label the following triangles:
   $\triangle 1 : (3,7), (7,7), (7,5)$
   $\triangle 2 : (7,-5), (7,-7), (3,-7)$
   $\triangle 3 : (7,3), (7,1), (3,1)$
   $\triangle 4 : (-3,7), (-7,7), (-7,5)$
   $\triangle 5 : (3,7), (-1,7), (-1,5)$
   (b) Find the equation of the mirror-line for the reflection:
   (i) $\triangle 1$ onto $\triangle 2$ (ii) $\triangle 1$ onto $\triangle 3$
   (iii) $\triangle 1$ onto $\triangle 4$ (iv) $\triangle 1$ onto $\triangle 5$.

3. (a) Draw and label the following triangles
   $\triangle 1 : (2,7), (4,7), (2,4)$
   $\triangle 2 : (2,-4), (2,-7), (4,-7)$
   $\triangle 3 : (0,4), (0,7), (-2,7)$
   $\triangle 4 : (2,4), (2,1), (4,1)$
   $\triangle 5 : (7,4), (7,2), (4,2)$
   (b) Find the equation of the mirror-line for the reflection:
   (i) $\triangle 1$ onto $\triangle 2$ (ii) $\triangle 1$ onto $\triangle 3$
   (iii) $\triangle 1$ onto $\triangle 4$ (iv) $\triangle 1$ onto $\triangle 5$.

4. (a) Draw and label the following triangles:
   △1 : (3,5), (−1,5), (−1,3)
   △2 : (5,3), (5,−1), (3,−1)
   △3 : (3,−5), (−1,−3), (−1,−5)
   △4 : (−3, 1), (−5,1), (−5,−3)

(b) Find the equation of the mirror-line for the reflection:
   (i) △1 onto △2   (ii) △1 onto △3
   (iii) △1 onto △4.

5. (a) Draw and label the following triangles
   △1 : (3,−5), (7,−5), (7,−7)
   △2 : (7,1), (7,−1), (3,−1)
   △3 : (2,−5), (−2,−5), (−2,−7)
   △4 : (7,6), (7,4), (3,4)
   △5 : (−5,3), (−5,7), (−7,7)

(b) Find the equation of the mirror-line for the reflection:
   (i) △1 onto △2   (ii) △1 onto △3
   (iii) △1 onto △4   (iv) △1 onto △5.

8.2 ROTATIONS

△A′B′C′ is the image of △ABC after a 90° clockwise rotation about centre O.

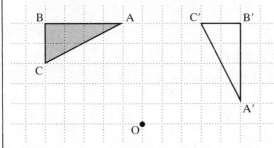

Exercise 5

Draw the object and its image under the rotation given. Take O as the centre of rotation in each case.

1.   **2.**

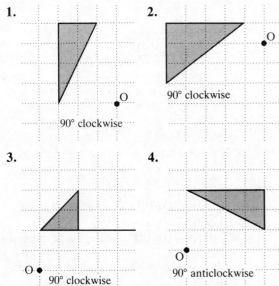

90° clockwise   90° clockwise

3.   **4.**

90° clockwise   90° anticlockwise

5.   **6.**

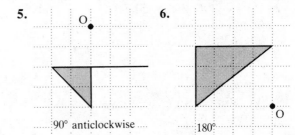

90° anticlockwise   180°

7.   **8.**

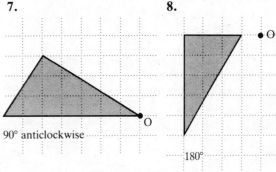

90° anticlockwise   180°

9.   **10.**

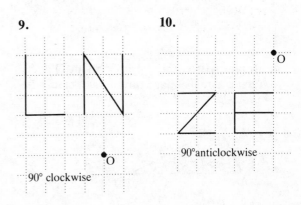

90° clockwise   90°anticlockwise

Exercise 6

1. Rotate △ABC 90° clockwise about O and then rotate its image through 90° clockwise about P.

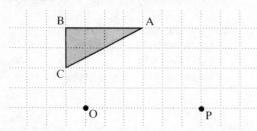

2. Rotate △XYZ through 90° clockwise about O and then rotate its image through 180° about P.

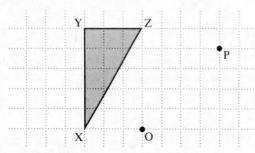

3. Rotate △DEF through 90° anticlockwise about O and then rotate its image through 90° clockwise about P.

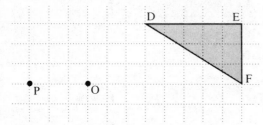

4. Rotate ABCD through 180° about O and then rotate its image through 90° clockwise about P.

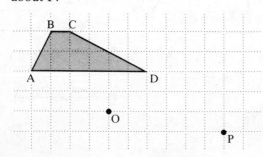

5. Rotate ABCD through 90° anticlockwise about O and then reflect its image in the broken line.

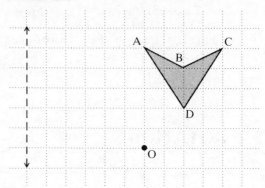

Exercise 7

1. Copy the diagram below.

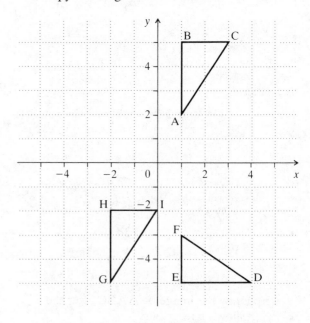

(a) Rotate △ABC 90° clockwise about (0,0) onto △A′B′C′.
(b) Rotate △DEF 180° about (0,0) onto △D′E′F′.
(c) Rotate △GHI 90° clockwise about (0,0) onto △G′H′I′.
(d) Write down the coordinates of A′, D′ and G′.

For questions **2** to **6** draw a pair of axes with values of x and y from -7 to $+7$.

2. (a) Plot and label A(3,3), B(7,3), C(7,1) and D(−1,−3), E(−1,−7), F(−3,−7).
   (b) Rotate △ABC 90° anticlockwise about (0,0) onto △A′B′C′.
   (c) Rotate △ABC 90° clockwise about (0,0) onto △A″B″C″.
   (d) Rotate △DEF 180° about (0,0) onto △D′E′F′.
   (e) Write down the coordinates of A′, A″ and D′.

3. (a) Plot and label P(1,6), Q(5,6), R(5,4).
   (b) Rotate △PQR 90° clockwise about (2,2) onto △P′Q′R′.
   (c) Rotate △PQR 180° about (1,4) onto △P″Q″R″.
   (d) Rotate △PQR 90° anticlockwise about (4,−3) onto △P*Q*R*.
   (e) Write down the coordinates of P′, P″ and P*.

4. (a) Plot and label K(−6,−6), L(−2,−6), M(−2,−3).
   (b) Draw the image of △KLM after the following rotations:
      (i) 90° clockwise about (0,0): label it K′L′M′.
      (ii) 90° anticlockwise about (−1,−1): label it K″L″M″.
      (iii) 180° about (0,−2): label it K*L*M*.
      (iv) 90° clockwise about (5,−4): label it K°L°M°.
   (c) Write down the coordinates of K′, K″, K* and K°.

5. (a) Plot and label A(1,3), B(3,6), C(1,7).
   (b) Draw the image of △ABC after the following rotations:
      (i) 90° clockwise about (1,1): label it A′B′C′.
      (ii) 180° about (2,1): label it A″B″C″.
      (iii) 90° anticlockwise about (1,0): label it A*B*C*.
      (iv) 180° about (−2,0): label it A°B°C°.
   (c) Write down the coordinates of A′, A″, A* and A°.

6. (a) Plot and label R(−1,6), S(−5,6), T(−5,4).
   (b) Draw the image of △RST after the following rotations:
      (i) 270° anticlockwise about (0,2): label it R′S′T′.
      (ii) 180° about (−2,0): label it R″S″T″.
      (iii) 90° anticlockwise about (2,6): label it R*S*T*.
      (iv) 270° clockwise about (6,4): label it R°S°T°.
   (c) Write down the coordinates of R′, R″, R* and R°.

Finding the centre of a rotation

Exercise 8

In questions **1** to **4** copy the diagram exactly and then use tracing paper to find the centre of the rotation which takes the shaded shape onto the unshaded shape. Mark the centre of rotation with a cross.

1.
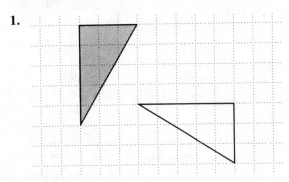

2.
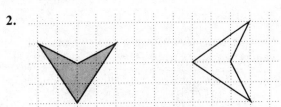

3.
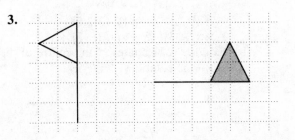

4.

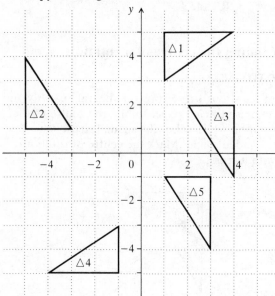

5. Copy the diagram below.

Find the coordinates of the centre of the following rotations:

(a) △1 → △2   (b) △1 → △3
(c) △1 → △4   (d) △1 → △5

For questions **6** to **9** draw a pair of axes with values of x and y from -7 to $+7$.

6. (a) Plot and label the following triangles:
   △1: (3,4), (7,4), (3,7)
   △2: (3,2), (6,2), (3,−2)
   △3: (−7,−4), (−3,−4), (−3,−7)
   △4: (−2,1), (−5,1), (−2,5)
   △5: (2,−3), (5,−3), (2,−7)
   (b) Find the coordinates of the centre of the following rotations:
      (i) △1 → △2
      (ii) △1 → △3
      (iii) △1 → △4
      (iv) △1 → △5.

7. (a) Plot and label the following triangles:
   △1: (−4,−3), (−4,−7), (−6,−7)
   △2: (−3,4), (−7,4), (−7,6)
   △3: (−2,1), (2,1), (2,−1)
   △4: (0,7), (4,7), (4,5)
   △5: (2,−3), (4,−3), (2,−7)
   (b) Find the coordinates of the centre of the following rotations:
      (i) △1 → △2   (ii) △1 → △3
      (iii) △1 → △4   (iv) △1 → △5.

8. (a) Plot and label the following triangles:
   △1: (1,3), (1,7), (3,7)
   △2: (3,3), (7,3), (7,1)
   △3: (−7,3), (−3,3), (−3,1)
   △4: (−2,−4), (−2,−6), (2,−6)
   △5: (3,−3), (7,−3), (7,−5)
   (b) Find the coordinates of the centre of the following rotations:
      (i) △1 → △2   (ii) △1 → △3
      (iii) △1 → △4   (iv) △1 → △5.

9. (a) Plot and label the following triangles:
   △1: (3,4), (3,7), (7,4)
   △2: (4,−2), (1,−2), (1,−6)
   △3: (1,2), (1,6), (−2,2)
   △4: (−4,1), (−4,−3), (−7,−3)
   △5: (−3,3), (−3,6), (−7,6)
   (b) Find the coordinates of the centre of the following rotations:
      (i) △1 → △2   (ii) △1 → △3
      (iii) △1 → △4   (iv) △1 → △5
      (v) △3 → △2   (vi) △2 → △5
      (vii) △5 → △3   (viii) △4 → △2

Exercise 9

1. Reflect the letter A in the line PQ and label the image A′. Reflect A′ in the line XY and label the image A″. What is the centre and angle of the rotation which takes A onto A″?

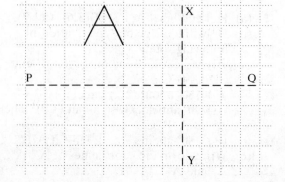

2. Reflect the letter N in the line PQ and label the image N′. Reflect N′ in the line XY and label the image N″. What is the centre and angle of the rotation which takes N onto N″?

3. Draw a capital L and reflect it successively in any two lines. What is the centre and angle of rotation of the resulting rotation?

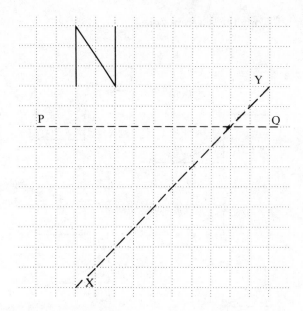

8.3   TRANSLATIONS

A translation is simply a 'shift'. There is no turning or reflection and the object stays the same size. In the diagram below:

(a) △1 is mapped onto △2 by the translation with vector $\begin{pmatrix} 4 \\ 2 \end{pmatrix}$

(b) △2 is mapped onto △3 by the translation with vector $\begin{pmatrix} 2 \\ -3 \end{pmatrix}$

(c) △3 is mapped onto △2 by the translation with vector $\begin{pmatrix} -2 \\ 3 \end{pmatrix}$

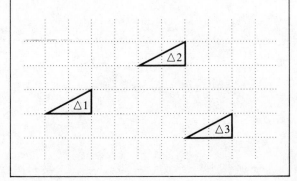

Exercise 10

1. Copy the diagram below.

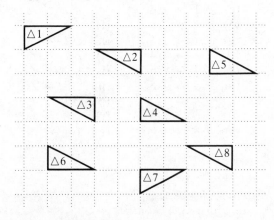

Decide which of these are translations; answer 'yes' or 'no' for each part.

(a) △1 → △2   (b) △1 → △3
(c) △1 → △4   (d) △1 → △5
(e) △1 → △6   (f) △1 → △7
(g) △1 → △8   (h) △2 → △3
(i) △2 → △4   (j) △2 → △5
(k) △2 → △6   (l) △2 → △7
(m) △2 → △8   (n) △3 → △6
(o) △3 → △8   (p) △4 → △6
(q) △4 → △5   (r) △4 → △1
(s) △5 → △3   (t) △6 → △4

2. Copy the diagram below.

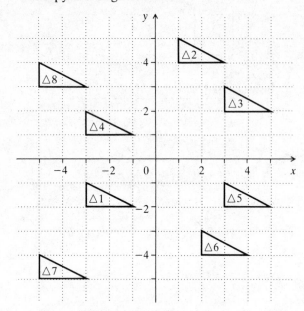

Write down the vector for each of the following translations:

(a) $\triangle 1 \rightarrow \triangle 2$ (b) $\triangle 1 \rightarrow \triangle 3$
(c) $\triangle 1 \rightarrow \triangle 4$ (d) $\triangle 1 \rightarrow \triangle 5$
(e) $\triangle 1 \rightarrow \triangle 6$ (f) $\triangle 1 \rightarrow \triangle 7$
(g) $\triangle 1 \rightarrow \triangle 8$ (h) $\triangle 2 \rightarrow \triangle 3$
(i) $\triangle 2 \rightarrow \triangle 4$ (j) $\triangle 2 \rightarrow \triangle 5$
(k) $\triangle 2 \rightarrow \triangle 6$ (l) $\triangle 2 \rightarrow \triangle 8$
(m) $\triangle 3 \rightarrow \triangle 5$ (n) $\triangle 8 \rightarrow \triangle 2$
(o) $\triangle 4 \rightarrow \triangle 2$ (p) $\triangle 7 \rightarrow \triangle 5$
(q) $\triangle 6 \rightarrow \triangle 3$ (r) $\triangle 8 \rightarrow \triangle 3$
(s) $\triangle 8 \rightarrow \triangle 7$ (t) $\triangle 4 \rightarrow \triangle 5$

3. (a) Draw a pair of axes with values of x and y from -7 to $+7$.
   (b) Plot and label $\triangle 1$ at $(-4, 3)$, $(-4, -5)$, $(-3, -3)$.
   (c) Draw and label $\triangle 2$, $\triangle 3$, $\triangle 4$, $\triangle 5$, $\triangle 6$, $\triangle 7$ and $\triangle 8$ as follows:

   (i) $\triangle 1 \rightarrow \triangle 2$ by translation $\begin{pmatrix} 5 \\ 6 \end{pmatrix}$.

   (ii) $\triangle 1 \rightarrow \triangle 3$ by translation $\begin{pmatrix} 6 \\ 1 \end{pmatrix}$.

   (iii) $\triangle 1 \rightarrow \triangle 4$ by translation $\begin{pmatrix} 1 \\ 8 \end{pmatrix}$.

   (iv) $\triangle 1 \rightarrow \triangle 5$ by translation $\begin{pmatrix} 9 \\ -2 \end{pmatrix}$.

   (v) $\triangle 1 \rightarrow \triangle 6$ by translation $\begin{pmatrix} -2 \\ 6 \end{pmatrix}$.

   (vi) $\triangle 1 \rightarrow \triangle 7$ by translation $\begin{pmatrix} 1 \\ -2 \end{pmatrix}$.

   (vii) $\triangle 1 \rightarrow \triangle 8$ by translation $\begin{pmatrix} 9 \\ 9 \end{pmatrix}$.

   (d) Write down the coordinates of the 'pointed end' of the triangles $\triangle 2$, $\triangle 3$, $\triangle 4$, $\triangle 5$, $\triangle 6$, $\triangle 7$ and $\triangle 8$.

8.4 ENLARGEMENTS

The picture in fig. 2 below is a three times enlargement of the picture in fig. 1.

Fig. 1

Fig. 2

Notice that the *shape* of the face is exactly the same in both pictures. An enlargement does not change the shape of an object. The enlargement shown above has a *scale factor* of 3.

Exercise 11

1. A photographer makes a four times enlargement of the picture below.

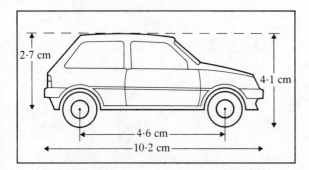

2·7 cm

4·1 cm

4·6 cm

10·2 cm

Calculate the corresponding dimensions on the enlarged picture.

2. In a photograph the wing-span of an aircraft is 8.5 cm. Calculate the wing-span of the aircraft as it appears on a ten times enlargement of the photograph.

3. In a photograph the height of a woman is 11.2 cm. Calculate the height of the woman as it appears on a five times enlargement of the photograph.

4. A girl has a model of a house which is an exact copy of the real house but made to a scale of $\frac{1}{10}$. Copy and complete the table.

	On real house	On model
(a) Height of front door	200 cm	
(b) Height of roof	600 cm	
(c) Width of building	850 cm	
(d) Height of windows		18 cm
(e) Length of gutter		70 cm
(f) Number of windows	20	

5. A boy has a model of a train made to a scale of $\frac{1}{5}$. Copy and complete the table.

	On real train	On model
(a) Length of train	20 m	
(b) Height of train		60 cm
(c) Diameter of wheels	1.2 m	
(d) Length of engine		80 cm
(e) Number of wheels	20	
(f) Distance between wheels		30 cm
(g) Number of passengers	100	

6. An architect makes a model of a new town centre to a scale of $\frac{1}{100}$. Copy and complete the table.

	In actual town	In model
(a) Length of main road	120 m	cm
(b) Width of high street	m	5 cm
(c) Height of office block	20 m	
(d) Number of street lights		30
(e) Height of street lights	4.2 m	cm
(f) Length of subway		25 cm
(g) Number of parking meters	300	

142   **Part 8**

Drawing enlargements

For a mathematical description of an enlargement we need two things:
  (a) the scale factor
  (b) the centre of enlargement.
The triangle ABC is enlarged onto triangle A′B′C′ with a scale factor of 3 and centre O.

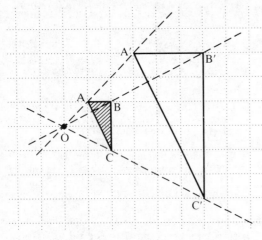

Note: OA′ = 3 × OA; OB′ = 3 × OB; OC′ = 3 × OC. All lengths are measured from the *centre of enlargement*.

Exercise 12

Copy each diagram and draw an enlargement using the centre O and the scale factor given.

1.
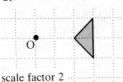
scale factor 2

2.
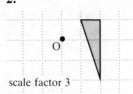
scale factor 3

3.
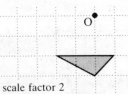
scale factor 2

4.
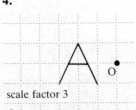
scale factor 3

5.
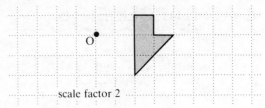
scale factor 2

6.
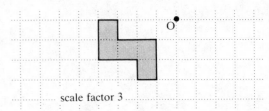
scale factor 3

7.
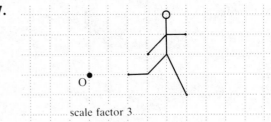
scale factor 3

8.
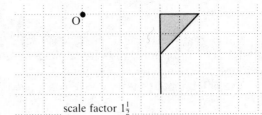
scale factor $1\frac{1}{2}$

9.
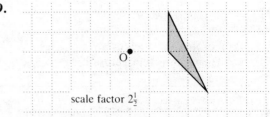
scale factor $2\frac{1}{2}$

10.
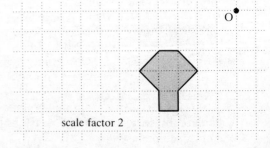
scale factor 2

Exercise 13

1. (a) Copy the diagram below.

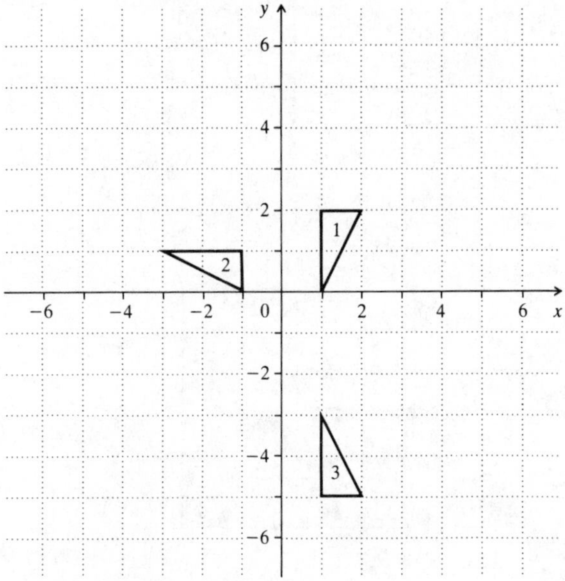

(b) Draw the image of △1 after enlargement with scale factor 3, centre (0,0). Label the image △4.
(c) Draw the image of △2 after enlargement with scale factor 2, centre (−1,3). Label the image △5.
(d) Draw the image of △3 after enlargement with scale factor 2, centre (−1,−5). Label the image △6.
(e) Write down the coordinates of the 'pointed ends' of △4, △5 and △6.
[The 'pointed end' is the vertex of the triangle with the smallest angle.]

For questions **2** to **6** draw a pair of axes with values from −7 to +7.

2. (a) Plot and label the triangles
△1: (5,5), (5,7), (4,7)
△2: (−6,−5), (−3,−5), (−3,−4)
△3: (1,−4), (1,−6), (2,−6).
(b) Draw the image of △1 after enlargement with scale factor 2, centre (7,7). Label the image △4.
(c) Draw the image of △2 after enlargement with scale factor 3, centre (−6,−7). Label the image △5.
(d) Draw the image of △3 after enlargement with scale factor 2, centre (−1,−5). Label the image △6.
(e) Write down the coordinates of the 'pointed ends' of △4, △5 and △6.

3. (a) Plot and label the triangles
△1: (−5,7), (−5,4), (−6,4)
△2: (−6,−2), (−6,−4), (−5,−4)
△3: (2,6), (5,6), (5,5)
(b) Draw the image of △1 after enlargement with scale factor 3, centre (−7,7). Label the image △4.
(c) Draw the image of △2 after enlargement with scale factor 2, centre (−7,−2). Label the image △5.
(d) Draw the image of △3 after enlargement with scale factor 2, centre (4,7). Label the image △6.
(e) Write down the coordinates of the 'pointed ends' of △4, △5 and △6.

4. (a) Plot and label the triangles
△1: (4,3), (7,3), (7,2)
△2: (2,−2), (2,−5), (3,−5)
△3: (−4,−2), (−7,−2), (−7,−3).
(b) Draw the image of △1 after enlargement with scale factor 3, centre (7,4). Label the image △4.
(c) Draw the image of △2 after enlargement with scale factor 2, centre (4,−3). Label the image △5.
(d) Draw the image of △3 after enlargement with scale factor 3, centre (−7,−5). Label the image △6.
(e) Write down the coordinates of the 'pointed ends' of △4, △5 and △6.

5. (a) Plot and label the triangles
△1: (4,−2), (7,−2), (7,−1)
△2: (−6,−1), (−3,−1), (−3,−2)
△3: (−1,−5), (−1,−7), (0,−7).
(b) Draw the image of △1 after enlargement with scale factor 4, centre (7,−3). Label the image △4.
(c) Draw the image of △2 after enlargement with scale factor 2, centre (−5,0). Label the image △5.
(d) Draw the image of △3 after enlargement with scale factor 3, centre (−2,−7). Label the image △6.
(e) Write down the coordinates of the 'pointed ends' of △4, △5 and △6.

144   **Part 8**

6. (a) Plot and label the triangles
  △1: (5,3), (5,6), (4,6)
  △2: (4,−3), (1,−3), (1,−2)
  △3: (−4,−7), (−7,−7), (−7,−6).
  (b) Draw the image of △1 after enlargement
  with scale factor 2, centre (7,7). Label the
  image △4.
  (c) Draw the image of △2 after enlargement
  with scale factor 3, centre (5,−4). Label
  the image △5.
  (d) Draw the image of △3 after enlargement
  with scale factor 4, centre (−7,−7). Label
  the image △6.
  (e) Write down the coordinates of the pointed
  ends of △4, △5 and △6.

Enlargements with fractional scale factors

Exercise 14

Copy each diagram and draw an enlargement
using the centre O and the scale factor given.

1.

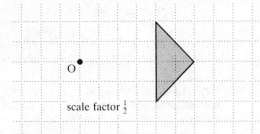

scale factor ½

2.

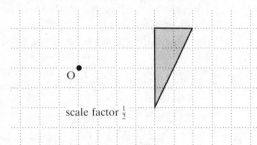

scale factor ½

3.

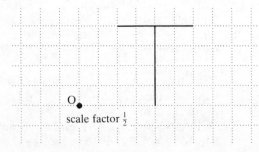

scale factor ½

4.

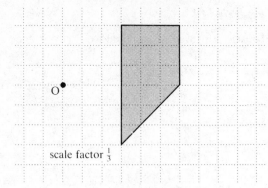

scale factor ⅓

5.

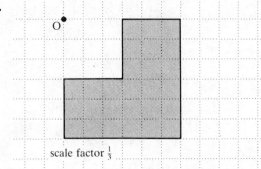

scale factor ⅓

6.

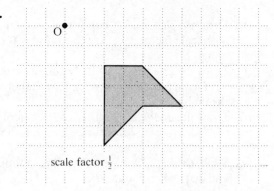

scale factor ½

Exercise 15

1. (a) Copy the diagram below.

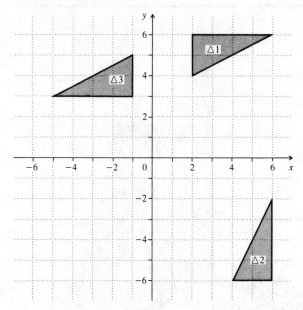

(b) Draw △4, the image of △1 after an enlargement with scale factor $\frac{1}{2}$, centre (0,0).

(c) Draw △5, the image of △2 after an enlargement with scale factor $\frac{1}{2}$, centre (0,0).

(d) Draw △6, the image of △3 after an enlargement with scale factor $\frac{1}{2}$, centre (−3,−1).

(e) Write down the coordinates of the 'pointed ends' of △4, △5 and △6.

For questions **2** to **5** draw axes with x and y from −7 to +7.

2. (a) Plot and label the triangles
△1: (7,6), (1,6), (1,3)
△2: (7,−1), (7,−7), (3,−7)
△3: (−5,7), (−5,1), (−7,1).

(b) Draw △4, the image of △1 after an enlargement with scale factor $\frac{1}{3}$, centre (−2,0).

(c) Draw △5, the image of △2 after an enlargement with scale factor $\frac{1}{2}$, centre (−5,−7).

(d) Draw △6, the image of △3 after an enlargement with scale factor $\frac{1}{2}$, centre (−7,−5).

(e) Write down the coordinates of the 'pointed ends' of △4, △5 and △6.

3. (a) Plot and label the triangle △1 at (1,3), (−7,3), (−7,7).

(b) Draw △2, the image of △1 after an enlargement with scale factor $\frac{1}{4}$, centre (5,3).

(c) Draw △3, the image of △1 after an enlargement with scale factor $\frac{1}{4}$, centre (−3,−5).

(d) Draw △4, the image of △1 after an enlargement with scale factor $\frac{1}{2}$, centre (5,−5).

(e) Write down the coordinates of the 'pointed ends' of △2, △3 and △4.

4. (a) Plot and label the triangle △1 at (1,7), (7,7), (7,4).

(b) Draw △2, the image of △1 after an enlargement scale factor $\frac{1}{3}$, centre (−5,7).

(c) Draw △3, the image of △1 after an enlargement scale factor $\frac{1}{3}$, centre (7,−5).

(d) Draw △4, the image of △1 after an enlargement scale factor $\frac{1}{3}$, centre (−5,−5).

(e) Write down the coordinates of the 'pointed ends' of △2, △3 and △4.

5. (a) Plot and label the triangle △1 at (5,−7), (−7,−7), (−7,−1).

(b) Draw △2, the image of △1 after an enlargement with scale factor $\frac{1}{3}$, centre (−7,5).

(c) Draw △3, the image of △1 after an enlargement with scale factor $\frac{1}{2}$, centre (5,7).

(d) Draw △4, the image of △2 (not △1) after an enlargement with scale factor $\frac{1}{2}$, centre (−1,7).

(e) Write down the coordinates of the 'pointed ends' of △2, △3 and △4.

Part 9

9.1   SCALE DRAWINGS

Measuring angles

Exercise 1

This exercise provides practice in the accurate use of a protractor. Give your answers correct to the nearest half degree.

In questions **1** to **6** measure the angles shown.

1.   **2.**   **3.**

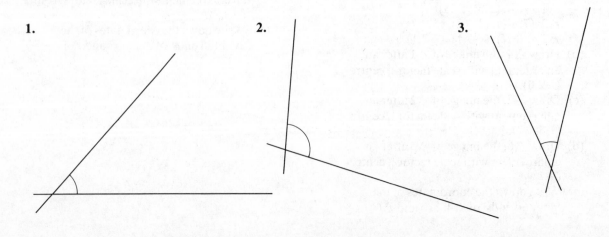

4.

5.

6.

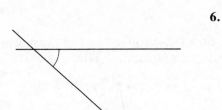

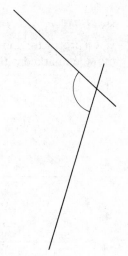

7. Measure the angles given on the diagram below.

(a) EĜH   (b) AB̂M   (c) CD̂N   (d) LK̂N   (e) IĴL
(f) LM̂F   (g) KÊE   (h) BÂM   (i) HL̂J   (j) JĈE
(k) LĤI   (l) KN̂D   (m) DĤG   (n) NK̂J   (o) LĤD
(p) AB̂E   (q) HD̂E   (r) BÂI   (s) CÊG   (t) CK̂A

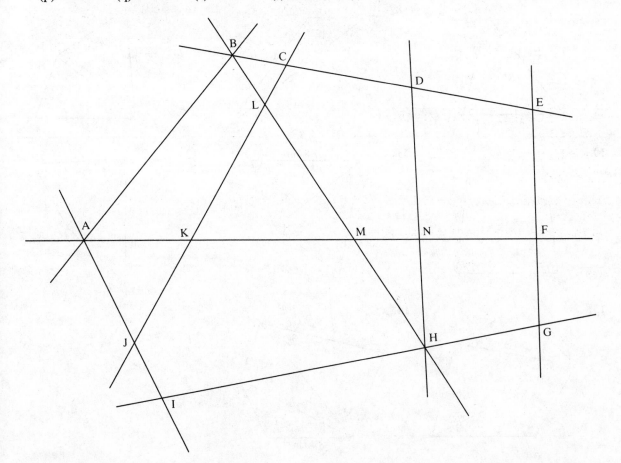

Exercise 2

Use a protractor and ruler to draw full size diagrams and measure
the sides marked with letters.

1.

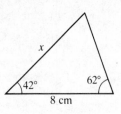

2.

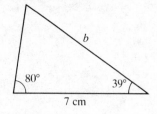

3.

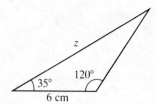

4.

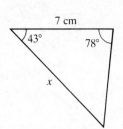

5.

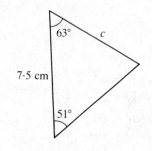

6.

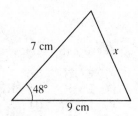

7.

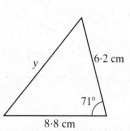

8.

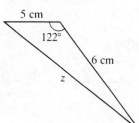

9.

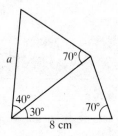

10.

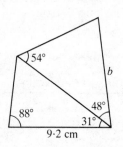

11.

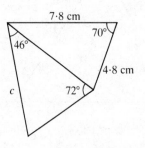

12.

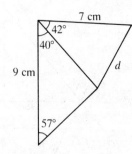

13.

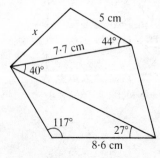

14.

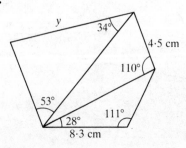

In questions **15** to **20** construct the triangles using a pair of compasses.
Measure the angles marked with letters.

15.

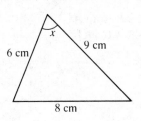

16.

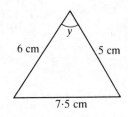

17.

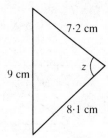

18.

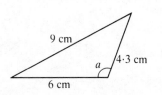

19.

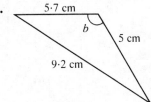

20.

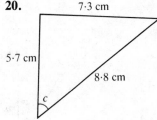

9.2 BEARINGS

Bearings are measured *clockwise from North*.

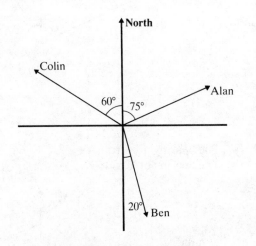

Alan is walking on a bearing of 075°.
Ben is walking on a bearing of 160°.
Colin is walking on a bearing of 300°.

Exercise 3

The diagrams show the directions in which several people are travelling. Copy each diagram and work out the bearing for each person.

1.

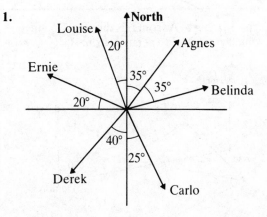

2.

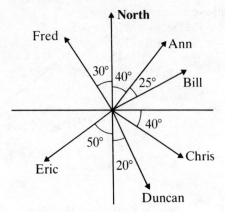

3.

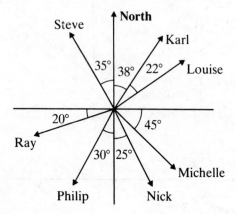

Relative bearings

The bearing of A from B is the direction in which you travel to get to A from B.

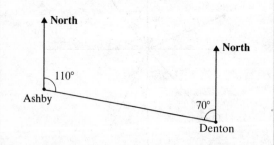

The bearing of Denton from Ashby is 110°.
The bearing of Ashby from Denton is 290°.

Exercise 4

Write down the bearings using the angles given.
Remember: bearings are 'clockwise from North'.

1. (a) The bearing of B from A.
   (b) The bearing of A from B.

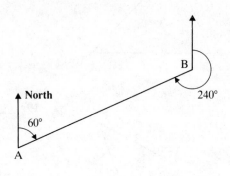

2. (a) The bearing of Q from P.
   (b) The bearing of P from Q.

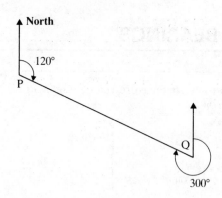

3. (a) The bearing of X from Y.
   (b) The bearing of Y from X.

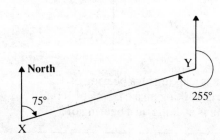

4. (a) The bearing of C from D.
   (b) The bearing of D from C.

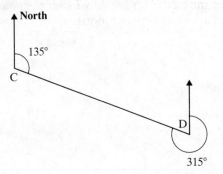

7. (a) The bearing of B from A.
   (b) The bearing of B from C.
   (c) The bearing of A from B.
   (d) The bearing of C from B.

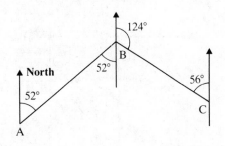

5. (a) The bearing of F from E.
   (b) The bearing of E from F.

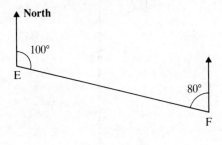

8. (a) The bearing of Q from P.
   (b) The bearing of R from Q.
   (c) The bearing of P from Q.
   (d) The bearing of Q from R.

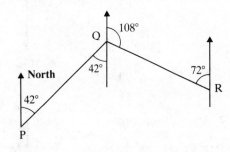

6. (a) The bearing of H from G.
   (b) The bearing of G from H.

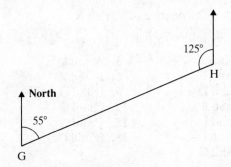

Exercise 5

The map below shows the positions of seven towns: A; B; C; D; E; F; G. Copy the map onto 1 cm graph paper which is at least 20 cm by 15 cm. The axes at the bottom and on the left are shown only to make it easier to draw an accurate copy. You do not use the axes when answering the questions.

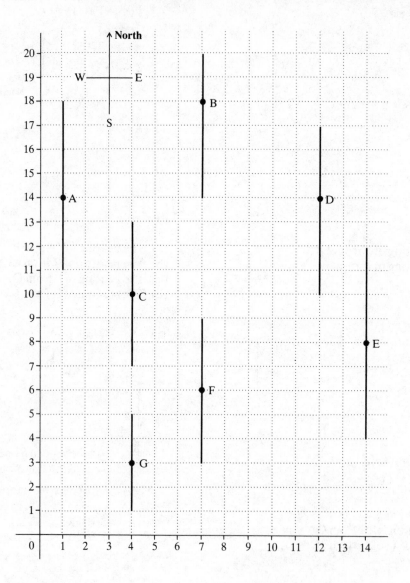

Given that 1 cm represents 1 km, find the distances between the following pairs of places.

1. A and B	**2.** A and C	**3.** A and D
4. A and G	**5.** A and E	**6.** A and F
7. B and C	**8.** B and D	**9.** B and G
10. B and E	**11.** B and F	**12.** C and D
13. C and E	**14.** C and F	**15.** C and G
16. D and E	**17.** D and F	**18.** D and G
19. E and F	**20.** E and G	

Exercise 6

Use the map you made in Exercise 5 to make the following measurements.

1. From A, measure the bearing of
    (a) B, (b) D, (c) E, (d) C, (e) G.

2. From C, measure the bearing of
    (a) B, (b) D, (c) E, (d) F, (e) G.

3. From G, measure the bearing of
    (a) B, (b) D, (c) F, (d) A, (e) E.

4. From B, measure the bearing of
    (a) D, (b) E, (c) F, (d) C, (e) A.

5. From F, measure the bearing of
    (a) D, (b) E, (c) G, (d) C, (e) B.

6. From D, measure the bearing of
    (a) E, (b) F, (c) C, (d) A, (e) B.

Exercise 7

Draw the points P and Q below in the middle of a clean page of squared paper. Mark the points A, B, C, D and E accurately, using the information given.

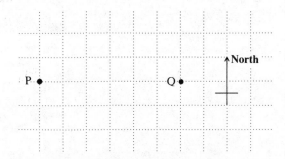

1. A is on a bearing of 040° from P and 015° from Q.
2. B is on a bearing of 076° from P and 067° from Q.
3. C is on a bearing of 114° from P and 127° from Q.
4. D is on a bearing of 325° from P and 308° from Q.
5. E is on a bearing of 180° from P and 208° from Q.

Exercise 8

Draw the points X and Y below in the middle of a clean page of squared paper. Mark the points K, L, M, N and O accurately, using the information given.

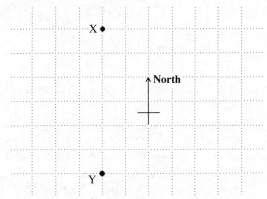

1. K is on a bearing of 041° from X and 025° from Y.
2. L is on a bearing of 090° from X and 058° from Y.
3. M is on a bearing of 123° from X and 090° from Y.
4. N is on a bearing of 203° from X and 215° from Y.
5. O is on a bearing of 288° from X and 319° from Y.

Exercise 9

Make accurate scale drawings with a scale of 1 cm to 1 km. Use squared paper and begin each question by drawing a small sketch of the journey.

1. A ship sails 8 km due North and then a further 7 km on a bearing 080°, as in the diagram (which is not drawn to scale).

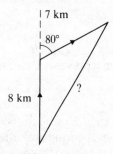

    How far is the ship now from its starting point?

2. A ship sails 9 km on a bearing 090° and then a further 6 km on a bearing 050°, as shown in the diagram.

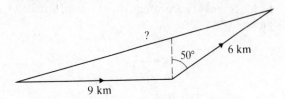

How far is the ship now from its starting point?

3. A submarine sails 7 km on a bearing 180° and then a further 5 km on a bearing 130°. How far is the submarine from its starting point?

4. A ship sails 6 km on a bearing 040° and then a further 6 km on a bearing 100°. How far is the ship from its starting point?

5. A shark swims 7 km on a bearing 055° and then a further 10 km on a bearing 180°. How far is the shark from its starting point?

6. A ship sails 6 km due South and then a further 8 km on a bearing 270°. How far is the ship from its starting point?

7. A ship sails 8 km on a bearing 200° and then a further 9 km on a bearing 100°. How far is the ship from its starting point?

8. A ship sails 6 km on a bearing 160° and then a further 10 km on a bearing 240°, as shown.

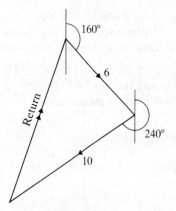

(a) How far is the ship from its starting point?
(b) On what bearing must the ship sail so that it returns to its starting point?

9. A ship sails 5 km on a bearing 030°, then 3 km on a bearing 090° and finally 4 km on a bearing 160°. How far is the ship now from its starting point?

10. A ship sails 6 km on a bearing 070°, then 7 km on a bearing 180° and finally 8 km on a bearing 270°. How far is the ship now from its starting point?

11. Point B is 8 km from A on a bearing 140° from A. Point C is 9 km from A on a bearing 200° from A.
(a) How far is B from C?
(b) What is the bearing of B from C?

12. Point Q is 10 km from P on a bearing 052° from P. Point R is 4 km from P on a bearing 107° from P.
(a) How far is Q from R?
(b) What is the bearing of Q from R?

9.3 TRIGONOMETRY

Labelling the sides of a triangle

The opposite, the hypotenuse and the adjacent are marked with respect to the angle x.

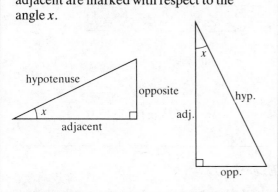

Exercise 10

In each question, use the letters to indicate the opposite, the hypotenuse and the adjacent (in that order) with respect to the angle marked x. The answer to each question will consist of just 3 letters.

9.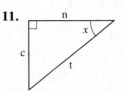

10.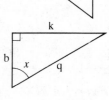

11.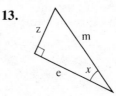

12.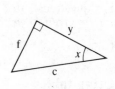

13.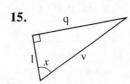

14.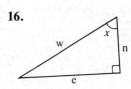

15.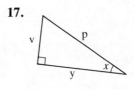

16.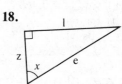

17.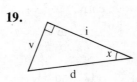

18.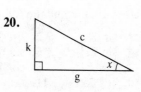

1.

2.

3.

4.

5.

6.

7.

8.

19.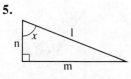

20.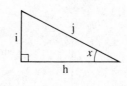

21.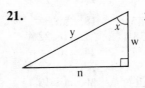

22.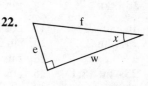

23.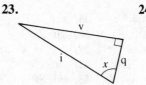

24.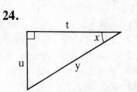

Sine, cosine and tangent

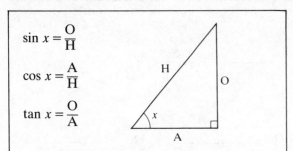

$$\sin x = \frac{O}{H}$$

$$\cos x = \frac{A}{H}$$

$$\tan x = \frac{O}{A}$$

Remember: 'SOH CAH TOA'

Exercise 11

For questions **1** to **8** in Exercise 10, use the letters given to write down an expression for:

(a) $\sin x$ (b) $\cos x$ (c) $\tan x$

Using tables

Trigonometric tables are given at the end of this book.

Find the following, using 3 figure tables:
(a) $\sin 28°$ (b) $\tan 64°$ (c) $\cos 64.3°$

(a) $\sin 28° = 0.469$
(b) $\tan 64° = 2.05$
(c) $\cos 64.3° = 0.434$

Exercise 12

Use tables to find the following, correct to 3 s.f.

1. $\sin 38°$	**2.** $\sin 65°$	**3.** $\sin 82°$
4. $\sin 21°$	**5.** $\sin 8°$	**6.** $\cos 53°$
7. $\cos 82°$	**8.** $\cos 26°$	**9.** $\cos 18°$
10. $\cos 7°$	**11.** $\tan 11°$	**12.** $\tan 53°$
13. $\tan 37°$	**14.** $\tan 66°$	**15.** $\tan 79°$
16. $\sin 31°$	**17.** $\cos 45°$	**18.** $\tan 76°$
19. $\tan 25.4°$	**20.** $\sin 33.1°$	**21.** $\cos 22.4°$
22. $\cos 60.8°$	**23.** $\tan 31.3°$	**24.** $\sin 74.6°$
25. $\sin 18.1°$	**26.** $\cos 9.5°$	**27.** $\tan 69.5°$
28. $\tan 11.4°$	**29.** $\sin 56°$	**30.** $\cos 19°$
31. $\cos 84.7°$	**32.** $\tan 80°$	**33.** $\sin 21.7°$
34. $\sin 6.4°$	**35.** $\cos 0.9°$	**36.** $\tan 28°$
37. $\tan 12.8°$	**38.** $\sin 88°$	**39.** $\cos 17.4°$
40. $\cos 16°$	**41.** $\tan 72.6°$	**42.** $\sin 6.6°$
43. $\sin 29.9°$	**44.** $\cos 57.1°$	**45.** $\tan 88°$

Finding the length of a side

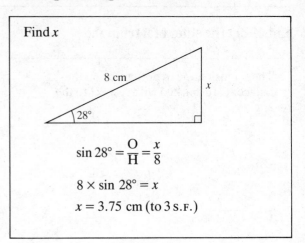

Find x

$$\sin 28° = \frac{O}{H} = \frac{x}{8}$$

$$8 \times \sin 28° = x$$

$$x = 3.75 \text{ cm (to 3 s.f.)}$$

Exercise 13

Find the length of the side marked with a letter.

1.

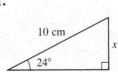

2.

3.

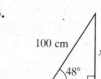

4.

5.

6.

7.

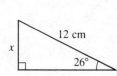

8.

9.

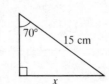

10.

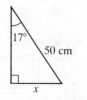

11.

12.

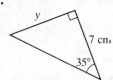

13.

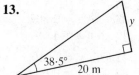

14.

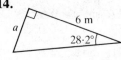

15.

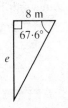

16.

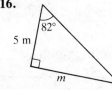

17.

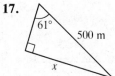

18.

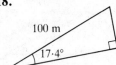

19.

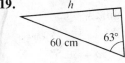

20.

Find *y*.

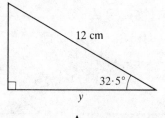

$$\cos 32.5° = \frac{A}{H} = \frac{y}{12}$$

$$12 \times \cos 32.5° = y$$

$$y = 10.1 \text{ cm (to 3 s.f.)}$$

Exercise 14

Find the length of the side marked with a letter.

1.

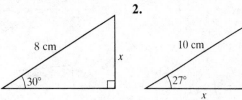

2.

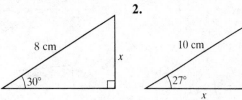

3.

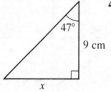

4.

5.

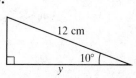

6.

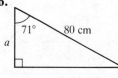

7.

8.

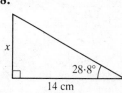

9.

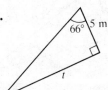

10.

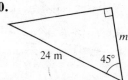

11.

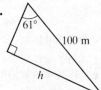

12.

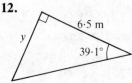

13.

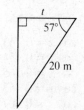

14.

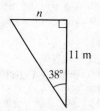

15.
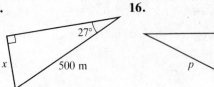

16.

17.
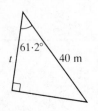

18.
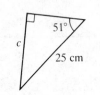

19.
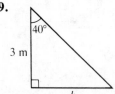

20.
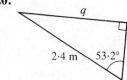

21.
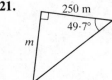

22.
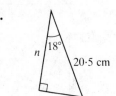

23.
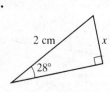

24.
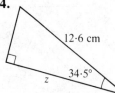

21. tan $x = 2.61$ **22.** tan $x = 2.39$
23. tan $x = 0.366$ **24.** tan $x = 3.49$
25. sin $x = 0.54$ **26.** cos $x = 0.284$
27. cos $x = 0.825$ **28.** tan $x = 0.735$
29. tan $x = 0.561$ **30.** sin $x = 0.007$

31. sin $x = 0.8$ **32.** cos $x = 0.204$
33. cos $x = 0.771$ **34.** tan $x = 0.264$
35. tan $x = 3.08$ **36.** sin $x = 0.6$
37. sin $x = 0.605$ **38.** cos $x = 0.807$
39. cos $x = 0.052$ **40.** tan $x = 35.8$

41. tan $x = 1.6$ **42.** sin $x = 0.010$
43. tan $x = 0.620$ **44.** cos $x = 0.639$
45. sin $x = 0.019$ **46.** cos $x = 0.815$
47. sin $x = 0.491$ **48.** tan $x = 9.84$
49. cos $x = 0.187$ **50.** sin $x = 0.936$

Finding angles

Find the angle marked with a letter.

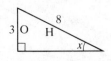
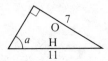

$$\sin x = \frac{O}{H} = \frac{3}{8}$$

$$\sin a = \frac{O}{H} = \frac{7}{11}$$

$$\sin x = 0.375$$

$$\sin a = 0.6364$$
(4 D.P.)

$$x = 22.0°$$

$$a = 39.5°$$

Using tables 'in reverse'

Exercise 15

Find the angle x, correct to one decimal place.

1. sin $x = 0.857$ **2.** sin $x = 0.574$
3. sin $x = 0.191$ **4.** sin $x = 0.620$
5. sin $x = 0.966$ **6.** sin $x = 0.181$
7. sin $x = 0.915$ **8.** sin $x = 0.833$
9. sin $x = 0.713$ **10.** sin $x = 0.774$

11. cos $x = 0.292$ **12.** cos $x = 0.743$
13. cos $x = 0.866$ **14.** cos $x = 0.454$
15. cos $x = 0.105$ **16.** cos $x = 0.765$
17. cos $x = 0.915$ **18.** cos $x = 0.153$
19. cos $x = 0.049$ **20.** cos $x = 0.007$

Exercise 16

Find the angle marked with a letter.

1.
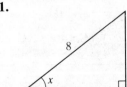

2.
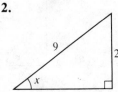

3.
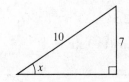

4.
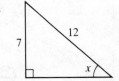

5.
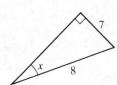

6.
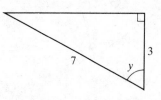

7.
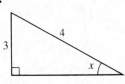

8.
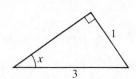

Find the angle y.

$$\cos y = \frac{A}{H} = \frac{3}{7}$$

$$\cos y = 0.4286 \, (4 \, \text{D.P.})$$

$$y = 64.6°$$

9.
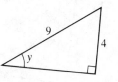

10.
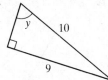

Exercise 17

In each question find the angle marked with a letter.

11.
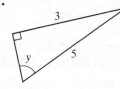

12.
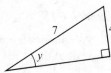

1.
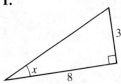

2.
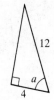

13.
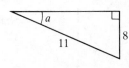

14.
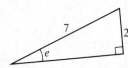

3.
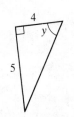

4.

15.
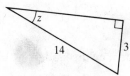

16.
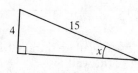

5.
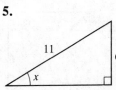

6.
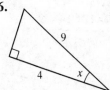

17.
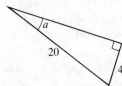

18.
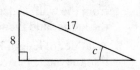

7.
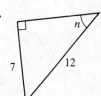

8.
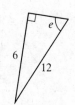

19.
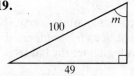

20.
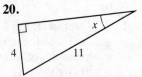

9.

10
a
11

10.
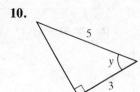
5
y
3

11.
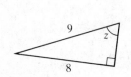
9
z
8

12.
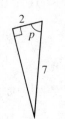
2
p
7

13.
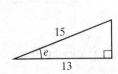
15
e
13

14.
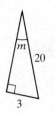
m
20
3

15.
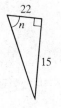
22
n
15

16.
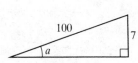
100
a
7

17.
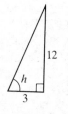
12
h
3

18.
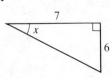
7
x
6

19.
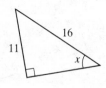
16
11
x

20.
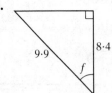
9.9
8·4
f

21.
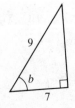
9
b
7

22.

f
3
8

23.
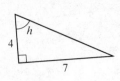
h
4
7

24.

3
w
2·4

25.
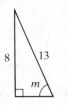
8
13
m

26.
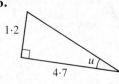
1·2
4·7
u

27.
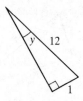
y
12
1

28.
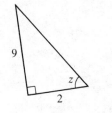
9
z
2

Exercise 18

1. A ladder of length 5 m leans against a vertical wall so that the base of the ladder is 2 m from the wall.

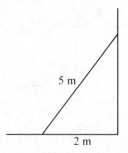

5 m

2 m

Calculate the angle between the ladder and the wall.

2. A ladder of length 6 m rests against a vertical wall so that the base of the ladder is 2.5 m from the wall. Calculate the angle between the ladder and the wall.

3. A ladder of length 7 m rests against a wall so that the angle between the ladder and the wall is 28°. How far is the base of the ladder from the wall?

4. A ladder of length 5 m rests against a vertical wall so that the angle between the ladder and the ground is 68°. How high does the ladder reach up the wall?

5. An isosceles triangle has sides of length 7 cm, 7 cm and 4 cm.

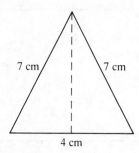

Calculate the angle between the two equal sides.

6. An isosceles triangle has sides of length 8 cm, 8 cm and 4 cm. Calculate the angle between the two equal sides.

7. An isosceles triangle has sides of length 9 cm, 9 cm and 6 cm. Calculate the size of each of the angles in the triangle.

8. A rectangle has sides of length 20 cm and 8 cm.

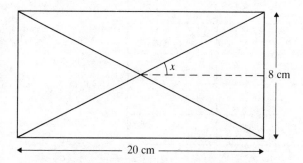

Calculate the size of angle x above and hence find the size of the smaller angle between the diagonals of the rectangle.

9. A rectangle has sides of length 12 cm and 7 cm. Calculate the smaller angle between the diagonals of the rectangle.

10. A rectangle has sides of length 16 cm and 10 cm. Calculate the smaller angle between the diagonals of the rectangle.

11. The points C(2,0) and D(7,4) are plotted on the graph below.

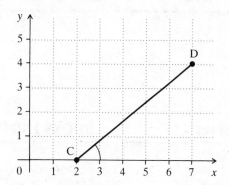

Calculate the angle between the line CD and the x-axis.

For questions **12** to **16** plot the points for each question on a small graph with x- and y-axes drawn to the same scale.
Take x and y from 0 to 8.

12. For the points A(4,0) and B(8,3), calculate the angle between the line AB and the x-axis.

13. For the points M(0,0) and N(7,5), calculate the angle between the line MN and the x-axis.

14. For the points P(7,0) and Q(1,4), calculate the angle between the line PQ and the x-axis.

15. For the points A(3,0), B(6,1) and C(6,5), calculate the angle BAC. (i.e. the angle between BA and CA.)

16. For the points P(6,8), Q(1,3) and R(4,1), calculate the angle PQR. (i.e. the angle between PQ and QR.)

Think about it 3

CROSS NUMBERS

Draw a copy of the crossnumber pattern below and work out the answers using the clues. You can check your working by doing *all* the across and *all* the down clues.

Part A

Across

1. $327 + 198$
3. $245 \div 7$
5. $3146 - 729$
6. $248 - 76$
7. 2^6
8. $850 \div 5$
10. $10^2 + 1^2$
11. $3843 \div 7$
12. $1000 - 913$
13. $37 \times 5 \times 3$
16. $152\,300 \div 50$
19. 3^6
20. $100 - \left(\dfrac{17 \times 10}{5} \right)$

Down

1. $3280 + 1938$
2. $65\,720 - 13\,510$
3. 3.1×1000
4. $1284 \div 6$
7. $811 - 127$
9. 65×11
10. $(12^2 - 8) \div 8$
11. $(7^2 + 1^2) \times 11$
12. $7 + 29 + 234 + 607$
14. $800 - 265$
15. $1 + 2 + 3 + 4 + 5 + 6 + 7 + 8 + 13$
17. $(69 \times 6) \div 9$
18. $3^2 + 4^2 + 5^2 + 2^4$

Part B   Draw decimal points on the lines between squares where necessary.

Across

1. $4.2 + 1.64$
3. 7×0.5
5. $20.562 \div 6$
6. $(2^3 \times 5) \times 10 - 1$
7. 0.034×1000
8. 61×0.3
10. $8 - 0.36$
11. 19×50
12. $95.7 \div 11$
13. 8.1×0.7
16. $(11 \times 5) \div 8$
19. $(44 - 2.8) \div 5$
20. Number of inches in a yard

Down

1. $62.6 - 4.24$
2. $48.73 - 4.814$
3. $25 + 7.2 + 0.63$
4. $2548 \div 7$
7. 0.315×100
9. 169×0.05
10. $770 \div 100$
11. $14.2 + 0.7 - 5.12$
12. $11.4 - 2.64 - 0.18$
14. 0.0667×10^3
15. $0.6 + 0.7 + 0.8 + 7.3$
17. 0.73 m written in cm
18. 0.028×200

Part C   *Across*

1. Eleven squared take away six
3. Next in the sequence 21, 24, 28, 33,
5. Number of minutes in a day
6. $2 \times 13 \times 5 \times 5$
7. Next in the sequence 92, 83, 74,
8. 5% of 11 400
10. $98 + 11^2$
11. $(120 - 9) \times 6$
12. $1\frac{2}{5}$ as a decimal
13. $2387 \div 7$
16. 9.05×1000
19. 8 m − 95 cm (in cm)
20. 3^4

Down

1. Write 18.6 m in cm
2. Fifty-one thousand and fifty-one
3. Write 3.47 km in m
4. $1\frac{1}{4}$ as a decimal
7. 7 m − 54 cm (in cm)
9. 0.0793×1000
10. 2% of 1200
11. $\frac{1}{5}$ of 3050
12. $127 \div 100$
14. Number of minutes between 12 00 and 20 10
15. 4% of 1125
17. $7^2 + 3^2$
18. Last two digits of (67×3)

Part D   *Across*

1. $1\frac{3}{4}$ as a decimal
3. Two dozen
5. Forty less than ten thousand
6. Emergency
7. 5% of 740
8. Nine pounds and five pence
10. 1.6 m written in cm.
11. $5649 \div 7$
12. One-third of 108
13. $6 - 0.28$
16. A quarter to midnight on the 24 h clock
19. 10% of 57.1
20. 'Catch . . .' or 'Yards in a chain' or $3300 \div 150$

Down

1. Twelve pounds 95 pence
2. Four less than sixty thousand
3. 245×11
4. James Bond
7. Number of minutes between 09 10 and 15 30
9. $\frac{1}{20}$ as a decimal
10. Ounces in a pound
11. 8.227 to two decimal places
12. 4 m − 95 cm (in cm)
14. Three to the power six
15. 20.64 to the nearest whole number
17. $(6\frac{1}{2})^2$ to the nearest whole number
18. Number of minutes between 14 22 and 15 14

Exercise A

1. An athlete started a training run at 11 15 and finished at 13 05. How long had he been running in hours and minutes?

2. Calculate the perimeter of a square which has an area of 36 cm².

3. The bill for 5 people in a restaurant is £31.80. Find the cost per person correct to the nearest pound.

4. Calculate the area of the shape below.

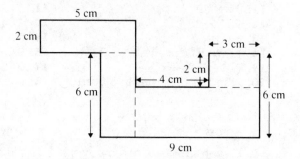

5. A map uses a scale of 1 to 1000.
   (a) Calculate the actual length in metres of a road which is 5 cm long on the map.
   (b) A lake is 800 m long. Calculate in centimetres the length this would be on the map.

6. A shop buys cans of drink at £7.20 for 48 cans and sells them at 17p per can. Calculate the profit on one can.

7. How many seconds are there in 3 days?

8. How many stamps each costing 14p can be bought for £2?

9. Find the angles marked with letters.

(a)   (b)

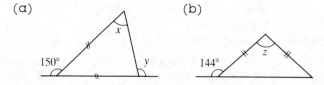

10. There is one road from Ansell to Royton and it passes through Banton, Fixton and Garston. At Ansell a traveller sees the road sign below.

Banton	4 miles
Fixton	6½ miles
Garston	9 miles
Royton	14 miles

   (a) How far is it from Ansell to Garston?
   (b) How far is it from Banton to Royton?
   (c) How far is it from Fixton to Garston?
   (d) How far is it from Royton to Fixton?

Project 2   TWO UNUSUAL NUMBERS

Here is an interesting exercise with a surprising result. It is easier when a calculator is used but this is not essential.

1. (a) Take a three-digit number
   (Not a number like 444 or 777 with the same three digits)

   374

   (i) Write down the largest number which can be formed using the digits of the number.

   743

   (ii) Write down the smallest number which can be formed using the digits of the number.

   347

   (iii) Subtract the smaller number from the larger number.

$$\begin{array}{r} 743 \\ -347 \\ \hline 396 \end{array}$$

   (b) Take the answer and repeat (i), (ii) and (iii) above.

$$\begin{array}{r} 963 \\ -369 \\ \hline 594 \end{array}$$

   (c) Repeat (b) until you get stuck with one number.

$$\begin{array}{r} 954 \\ -459 \\ \hline 459 \end{array}$$

$$\begin{array}{r} 954 \\ -459 \\ \hline 495 \end{array}$$ Stuck!

   Note: If you obtain a two-digit answer, write a nought at the front.

   e.g.
$$\begin{array}{r} 433 \\ -334 \\ \hline 099 \end{array} \qquad \begin{array}{r} 990 \\ -099 \\ \hline 891 \end{array} \text{ etc.}$$

2. Try this sequence of operations with the following starting numbers: 623, 464, 491, 672, 343.
   What do you notice each time?

3. Try any starting numbers of your own choice.

4. Now let's try four-digit numbers. The only restriction is that we do not choose numbers like 6666 or 2222 with the same four digits.
   Try the following starting numbers: 3591, 5746, 4824, 7345, 9501, 6966.
   What do you notice this time?

5. If you are really ambitious, you may like to investigate what happens when you choose five-digit numbers. There are in fact three ways in which you can finish. But now you are on your own!

Exercise B

1. A pile of 56 tiles is 40.32 cm thick. How thick is each tile?

2. Six metres of rope costs £3.30. Find the cost of 11 metres of the same rope.

3. The moving pavement at an airway terminal moves at a speed of 0.8 m/s. If you are standing on the pavement, how far do you travel in (a) 10 s? (b) 1 minute? (c) 45 s?

4. Write correct to the nearest penny:
   (a) £5.638   (b) £0.721   (c) £11.655
   (d) £2.0725   (e) £8.111   (f) £7.077

5. A businessman is paid travelling expenses at 22.4p per mile. How much does he receive (to the nearest 1p) for (a) a 15 mile journey? (b) an 18 mile journey? (c) a 7.2 mile journey?

6. During a sale the marked price of each article was reduced. Copy and complete.

	Marked price	Percentage reduction	Cash reduction	Sale price
(a)	£20	10%		
(b)	£50	20%		
(c)	£60	75%		

7. Amongst other ingredients 240 g of butter and 2 teaspoons of sugar are needed to make 6 scones.
   (a) What weight of butter is needed to make 30 scones?
   (b) How many teaspoons of sugar are needed to make 9 scones?

8. A number of tins of soup are packed in a box which weighs 2 kg. The total weight of the box and its contents is 19.5 kg. How many tins are in the box if each tin weighs 350 g?

9. The owner of a garage offers all of his workers a choice of two pay rises. Workers can choose either a 6.2% increase on their salaries or they can accept a rise of £400.
   (a) A petrol pump attendant earns £4650 a year. Which pay rise should he choose?
   (b) A forecourt manager earns £8600 a year. Which pay rise should he choose?

10. A strand of cotton is 4 m long and is cut into several pieces each of length 30 cm.
    (a) How many 30 cm lengths can be cut?
    (b) How much cotton is left over?

Project 3   AN EXPANDING DIAGRAM

The first diagram is a single square.

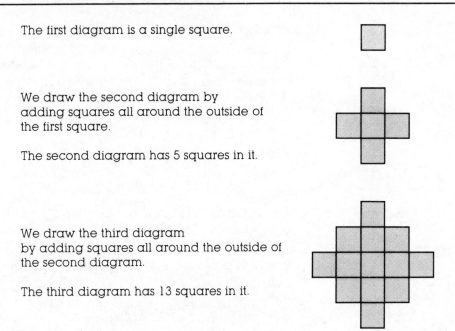

We draw the second diagram by adding squares all around the outside of the first square.

The second diagram has 5 squares in it.

We draw the third diagram by adding squares all around the outside of the second diagram.

The third diagram has 13 squares in it.

Continue the series by drawing the fourth, fifth and sixth diagrams in the sequence. Each new diagram is obtained by drawing squares all around the outside of the previous diagram. For each diagram count the number of squares it contains.

Using the results of the first six diagrams, can you predict the number of squares in the seventh diagram? See if you were right by drawing the diagram.

Can you predict the number of squares in the eighth diagram? Again draw the diagram to see if you were right.

Can you predict the number of squares in
(a) the 12th diagram,
(b) the 20th diagram?

Try to find a rule which will enable you to predict the number of squares for any member of the sequence of diagrams.

Exercise C

1. How many minutes are there in 2 days?

2. If 208 oranges are divided equally between 9 children, how many will each child get and how many will be left over?

3. During a storm 3 cm of rain falls onto a rectangular field which is 200 m by 100 m. What volume of water in m³ falls onto the field?

4. Find the angles marked with letters.

(a)   (b)

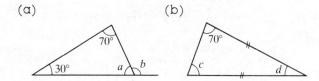

5. A model aeroplane is built to a scale of 1:40. The wing span of the actual aeroplane is 20 m. Find the wing span of the model.

6. Work out $\frac{5}{7} \times \frac{1}{2}$.

7. During the night the temperature falls by 3 °C every hour. Given that the temperature at 8.00 p.m. was 8 °C, find the temperature at:
(a) 9.00 p.m.   (b) 11.00 p.m.   (c) midnight.

8. A film lasting 1 hour 45 minutes starts at 19 35. At what time does the film finish?

9. We can estimate the value of 19.7 × 11.2 correct to 1 significant figure by working out 20 × 10 = 200. Use this method to estimate, correct to 1 significant figure the value of:

(a) 198 × 98.5;   (b) 0.102 × 49.2;   (c) $\dfrac{211 \times 9.85}{10.04}$;   (d) $\dfrac{59.7 \times 98.4}{6.05}$.

10. I am thinking of a number which is less than 100. The number is exactly divisible by 5 but not by 2. The two digits of the number add up to 11. Find the number I am thinking of.

Exercise D

1. The chart shows a patient's temperature in °C.

Time	06 00	08 00	10 00	12 00	14 00
Temperature (°C)	37.5	38.2	39.1	39.6	38.8

The normal temperature is 36.9 °C.
How many degrees above normal was his temperature at (a) 06 00 (b) 10 00 (c) 12 00 (d) 08 00?

2. In 1990 it is forecast that the price of one litre of petrol will be 100p and that the price will rise by 10% each year over the next few years. Calculate the price forecast for (a) 1991 (b) 1992.

3. Paint can be bought in two sizes:
  2 litre tin for £5.60
  3 litre tin for £7.80.
How much would you save if you bought two 3 litre tins instead of three 2 litre tins?

4. A salesman is paid a basic salary of £5400 per year, plus commission of 5% on all his sales. Calculate his total salary if his sales totalled
(a) £40 000 (b) £50 000 (c) £100 000.

5. A glass has a volume of 0.02 litres. How many times can the glass be filled from a can containing 4 litres of water?

6. One hundred small cakes cost £7.50 and weigh 5.5 kg. Find (a) the cost and (b) the weight of 16 of these cakes.

7. In 1984 the population of the Soviet Union was 272 million. Forecasters estimated that the population would increase by 15% by the end of the century. Work out the estimated population at the end of the century, correct to the nearest million.

8. The diagram shows the plan of a room with a carpet shaded.

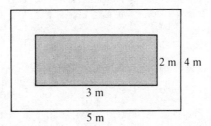

Calculate (a) the length of the carpet as a percentage of the length of the room.
  (b) the area of the carpet as a percentage of the area of the room.
  (c) the area of the room uncarpeted as a percentage of the area of the room.

9. A car travels for 2 hours at a speed of 65 km/h and for 3 hours at a speed of 70 km/h.
(a) How far does it travel in the 5 hours?
(b) What is the average speed for the whole journey?

10. Train fares are increased by 25%.
Find (a) the new price of a ticket which cost 60p before the increase
  (b) the old price of a ticket which costs 50p after the increase.

Project 4   CAR FERRIES

Life can be very complicated! Below there are extracts from the car ferry timetables for three different journeys. In a separate table there is information about the fares for the journeys.

Dover → Calais

August Time	W 1	T 2	F 3	S 4	S 5	M 6	T 7	W 8	T 9	F 10	S 11	S 12	M 13	T 14	W 15	T 16	F 17	S 18	S 19	M 20	T 21	W 22	T 23	F 24	S 25	S 26	M 27	T 28	W 29	T 30	F 31
0100	D	D	C	C	D	D	D	D	D	C	C	D	D	D	D	D	D	D	D	D	D	D	D	D	D	D	D	D	D	D	D
0500	D	D	D	D	D	D	D	D	D	D	D	D	D	D	D	D	D	D	D	D	D	D	D	D	D	D	D	D	D	D	D
0630	C	C	C	C	C	C	C	C	C	C	C	C	C	C	C	C	C	C	C	C	C	C	C	C	C	C	C	C	C	C	C
0800	C	C	C	C	C	C	C	C	C	C	C	C	C	C	C	C	C	C	C	C	C	C	C	C	C	C	C	C	C	C	C
1000	B	B	B	B	B	B	B	B	B	B	B	B	B	B	B	B	B	B	B	B	B	B	B	B	B	B	B	B	B	B	B
1240	B	B	B	B	B	B	B	B	B	B	B	B	B	B	B	B	B	B	B	B	B	B	B	B	B	B	B	B	B	B	B
1515	B	B	B	B	B	B	B	B	B	B	B	B	B	B	B	B	B	B	B	B	B	B	B	B	B	B	B	B	B	B	B
1730	B	B	B	B	B	B	B	B	B	B	B	B	B	B	B	B	B	B	B	B	B	B	B	B	B	B	B	B	B	B	B
1900	B	B	B	B	B	B	B	B	B	B	B	B	B	B	B	B	B	B	B	B	B	B	B	B	B	B	B	B	B	B	B
2200	C	C	C	C	C	C	C	C	C	C	C	C	C	C	C	C	C	C	C	C	C	C	C	C	C	C	C	C	C	C	C
2330	C	C	C	C	C	C	C	C	C	C	C	C	C	C	C	C	C	C	C	C	C	C	C	C	C	C	C	C	C	C	C

September Time	S 1	M 2	T 3	W 4	T 5	F 6	S 7	S 8	M 9	T 10	W 11	T 12	F 13	S 14	S 15	M 16	T 17	W 18	T 19	F 20	S 21	S 22	M 23	T 24	W 25	T 26	F 27	S 28	S 29	S 30
0100	D	D	D	D	D	D	D	D	D	D	D	D	D	D	D	D	D	D	D	D	D	D	D	D	D	D	D	D	D	D
0500	D	D	D	D	D	D	D	D	D	D	D	D	D	D	D	D	D	D	D	D	D	D	D	D	D	D	D	D	D	•
0630	C	C	D	D	D	D	D	D	D	D	D	D	D	D	D	D	D	D	D	D	D	D	D	D	D	D	D	D	D	D
0800	C	C	D	D	D	D	D	D	D	D	D	D	D	D	D	D	D	D	D	D	D	D	D	D	D	D	D	D	D	D
1000	B	B	C	C	C	C	C	C	C	C	C	C	C	C	C	C	C	C	C	C	C	C	C	C	C	C	C	C	C	C
1240	B	B	C	C	C	C	C	C	C	C	C	C	C	C	C	C	C	C	C	C	C	C	C	C	C	C	C	C	C	C
1515	B	B	C	C	C	C	C	C	C	C	C	C	C	C	C	C	C	C	C	C	C	C	C	C	C	C	C	C	C	C
1730	B	B	C	C	C	C	C	C	C	C	C	C	C	C	C	C	C	C	C	C	C	C	C	C	C	C	C	C	C	•
1900	B	B	C	C	C	C	C	C	C	C	C	C	C	C	C	C	C	C	C	C	C	C	C	C	C	C	C	C	C	C
2200	C	C	D	D	D	D	D	D	D	D	D	D	D	D	D	D	D	D	D	D	D	D	D	D	D	D	D	D	D	D
2330	C	C	D	D	D	D	D	D	D	D	D	D	D	D	D	D	D	D	D	D	D	D	D	D	D	D	D	D	D	D

Folkestone → Boulogne

June Time	F 1	S 2	S 3	M 4	T 5	W 6	T 7	F 8	S 9	S 10	M 11	T 12	W 13	T 14	F 15	S 16	S 17	M 18	T 19	W 20	T 21	F 22	S 23	S 24	M 25	T 26	W 27	T 28	F 29	S 30
0745	D	D	D	D	D	D	D	D	D	D	D	D	D	D	D	D	D	D	D	D	D	D	D	D	D	D	D	D	D	D
0945	C	C	C	C	C	C	C	C	C	C	C	C	C	C	C	C	C	C	C	C	C	C	C	C	C	C	C	C	C	C
1145	•	•	C	C	C	C	C	C	C	C	C	C	C	C	C	C	C	C	C	C	C	C	C	C	C	C	C	C	C	C
1345	C	C	C	C	C	C	C	C	C	C	C	C	C	C	C	C	C	C	C	C	C	C	C	C	C	C	C	C	C	C
1545	•	•	C	C	C	C	C	C	C	C	C	C	C	C	C	C	C	C	C	C	C	C	C	C	C	C	C	C	C	C
1745	C	C	C	C	C	C	C	C	C	C	C	C	C	C	C	C	C	C	C	C	C	C	C	C	C	C	C	C	C	C
2200	•	•	D	D	D	D	D	D	D	D	D	D	D	D	D	D	D	D	D	D	D	D	D	D	D	D	D	D	D	D
2345	D	D	•	•	•	•	•	•	•	•	•	•	•	•	•	•	•	•	•	•	•	•	•	•	•	•	•	•	•	•

July	S	M	T	W	T	F	S	S	M	T	W	T	F	S	S	M	T	W	T	F	S	S	M	T	W	T	F	S	S	M	T
Time	1	2	3	4	5	6	7	8	9	10	11	12	13	14	15	16	17	18	19	20	21	22	23	24	25	26	27	28	29	30	31
0345	•	•	•	•	•	•	•	•	•	•	•	•	•	D	D	D	D	D	D	D	D	D	D	D	D	D	D	D	D	D	D
0745	C	C	C	C	C	C	C	C	C	C	C	C	C	C	C	C	C	C	C	C	C	C	C	C	C	C	C	C	C	C	C
0945	B	B	B	B	B	B	B	B	B	B	B	B	B	B	B	B	B	B	B	A	B	B	B	B	B	B	B	A	B	B	B
1145	B	B	B	B	B	B	B	B	B	B	B	B	B	B	B	B	B	B	B	A	B	B	B	B	B	B	B	A	B	B	B
1345	B	B	B	B	B	B	B	B	B	B	B	B	B	B	B	B	B	B	B	A	B	B	B	B	B	B	B	A	B	B	B
1545	B	B	B	B	B	B	B	B	B	B	B	B	B	B	B	B	B	B	B	A	B	B	B	B	B	B	B	A	B	B	B
1745	B	B	B	B	B	B	B	B	B	B	B	B	B	B	B	B	B	B	B	A	B	B	B	B	B	B	B	A	B	B	B
2200	C	C	C	C	C	C	C	C	C	C	C	C	C	C	C	C	C	C	C	C	C	C	C	C	C	C	C	C	C	C	C

Newhaven → Dieppe

July	S	M	T	W	T	F	S	S	M	T	W	T	F	S	S	M	T	W	T	F	S	S	M	T	W	T	F	S	S	M	T
Time	1	2	3	4	5	6	7	8	9	10	11	12	13	14	15	16	17	18	19	20	21	22	23	24	25	26	27	28	29	30	31
0100	•	•	•	•	•	•	•	•	•	•	•	•	•	•	C	C	C	C	C	C	B	A	B	B	B	B	C	B	A	B	C	C
0700	C	C	C	C	C	B	B	C	C	C	C	C	B	B	B	C	C	C	C	B	A	B	C	B	B	B	B	A	B	B	B
1000	C	C	C	C	C	B	B	B	C	C	C	B	A	A	B	B	B	B	B	A	A	B	B	B	B	B	A	A	B	B	B
1300	C	C	C	C	C	C	C	C	C	C	C	C	B	C	C	C	C	A	A	B	B	B	B	B	A	A	B	B	B		
1830	D	D	D	D	D	C	C	D	D	D	D	D	C	C	C	D	D	D	D	B	B	B	C	C	C	C	B	B	C	C	C
2245	C	C	C	C	C	C	C	C	C	C	C	B	B	B	C	C	C	B	A	B	B	B	C	C	C	B	A	B	C	C	C

August	W	T	F	S	S	M	T	W	T	F	S	S	M	T	W	T	F	S	S	M	T	W	T	F	S	S	M	T	W	T	F
Time	1	2	3	4	5	6	7	8	9	10	11	12	13	14	15	16	17	18	19	20	21	22	23	24	25	26	27	28	29	30	31
0100	C	C	C	B	B	C	C	C	C	C	B	B	C	C	C	C	C	B	B	C	C	C	C	B	B	C	C	C	C	C	C
0700	B	B	B	C	B	B	B	B	B	B	C	B	B	B	B	B	B	C	C	B	B	B	B	C	C	B	B	B			
1000	B	B	A	A	B	B	B	B	B	A	A	B	B	B	B	B	A	A	B	B	B	B	B	A	A	B	B	B	B	B	B
1300	C	C	B	B	C	C	C	C	B	B	C	B	C	C	C	C	C	B	B	C	C	C	C	B	B	C	C	C	C	C	C
1830	C	C	C	C	C	C	C	C	C	C	C	D	D	D	D	C	C	D	D	D	D	D	C	C	D	D	D	D	D	D	D
2245	C	B	A	B	B	C	C	C	B	A	B	C	C	C	C	C	B	B	C	C	C	C	C	B	C	C	C	C	C	C	C

Car Ferry Tariffs
Motorist Fares/Vehicle Rates for Single Journeys

	DOVER –CALAIS				FOLKESTONE –BOULOGNE					NEWHAVEN –DIEPPE				
	Tariff	Tariff	Tariff	Tariff	Tariff	Tariff	Tariff	Tariff	Tariff	Tariff	Tariff	Tariff	Tariff	Tariff
MOTORIST FARES (driver and accompanying passengers)	**E** £	**D** £	**C** £	**B** £	**E** £	**D** £	**C** £	**B** £	**A** £	**E** £	**D** £	**C** £	**B** £	**A** £
Adult	10.00	10.00	10.00	10.00	10.00	10.00	10.00	10.00	10.00	15.00	15.00	15.00	15.00	15.00
Child (4 but under 14 years)	5.00	5.00	5.00	5.00	5.00	5.00	5.00	5.00	5.00	7.50	7.50	7.50	7.50	7.50
VEHICLE RATES **Cars, Motorised Caravans, Minibuses and Three-wheeled Vehicles**														
Up to 4.00m in length	16.00	24.00	33.00	43.00	16.00	21.00	33.00	43.00	50.00	19.00	27.00	37.00	47.00	54.00
Up to 4.50m in length	16.00	30.00	42.00	52.00	16.00	27.00	42.00	52.00	60.00	19.00	34.00	47.00	57.00	65.00
Up to 5.50m in length	16.00	34.00	50.00	60.00	16.00	31.00	50.00	60.00	70.00	19.00	39.00	56.00	66.00	75.00
Over 5.50m: each additional metre (or part thereof)	9.00	9.00	9.00	9.00	9.00	9.00	9.00	9.00	9.00	9.00	9.00	9.00	9.00	9.00
CARAVANS/TRAILERS **To Calais, Boulogne, Dieppe**														
Up to 3.00m in length	12.00	16.00	14.00	12.00	12.00	16.00	14.00	12.00	12.00	16.00	16.00	16.00	16.00	16.00
Up to 5.50m in length	12.00	20.00	18.00	16.00	12.00	20.00	18.00	16.00	14.00	38.00	38.00	38.00	38.00	38.00
Over 5.50m: each additional metre (or part thereof)	9.00	9.00	9.00	9.00	9.00	9.00	9.00	9.00	9.00	9.00	9.00	9.00	9.00	9.00

Part A   Find the tariff letter for the following journeys.

1. Newhaven → Dieppe; July 28; 10 00.
2. Dover → Calais; August 18; 12 40.
3. Dover → Calais; September 2; 08 00.
4. Newhaven → Dieppe; August 11; 10 00.
5. Folkestone → Boulogne; June 7; 13 45.
6. Dover → Calais; September 25; 08 00.
7. Newhaven → Dieppe; August 28; 10 00.
8. Folkestone → Boulogne; July 18; 09 45.
9. Newhaven → Dieppe; August 5; 07 00.
10. Dover → Calais; September 21; 08 00.
11. Folkestone → Boulogne; June 25; 11 45.
12. Newhaven → Dieppe; August 24; 10 00.
13. Dover → Calais; August 19; 10 00.
14. Newhaven → Dieppe; August 10; 22 45.
15. Folkestone → Boulogne; July 27; 07 45.
16. Dover → Calais; September 2; 19 00.
17. Newhaven → Dieppe; July 25; 13 00.
18. Folkestone → Boulogne; June 29; 22 00.
19. Dover → Calais; August 10; 05 00.
20. Newhaven → Dieppe; July 7; 07 00.

Part B   Find the cost for each of the following.

1. Dover–Calais; 1 adult, Tariff B.
2. Dover–Calais; 1 child; Tariff D.
3. Newhaven–Dieppe; 1 adult; Tariff C.
4. Folkestone–Boulogne; car 4.30 m; Tariff E.
5. Dover–Calais; car 5.10 m; Tariff B.
6. Newhaven–Dieppe; car 3.95 m; Tariff A.
7. Newhaven–Dieppe; 2 adults; Tariff C.
8. Folkestone–Boulogne; 4 children; Tariff E.
9. Dover–Calais; car 4.80 m; Tariff B.
10. Newhaven–Dieppe; caravan 4.00 m; Tariff C.
11. Folkestone–Boulogne; caravan 3.60 m; Tariff D.
12. Dover–Calais; 3 adults; Tariff C.
13. Newhaven–Dieppe; car 4.75 m; Tariff E.
14. Folkestone–Boulogne; caravan 5.00 m; Tariff A.
15. Dover–Calais; 3 children; Tariff E.
16. Folkestone–Boulogne; car 4.85 m; Tariff B.
17. Newhaven–Dieppe; 3 children; Tariff D.
18. Dover–Calais; caravan 4.80 m; Tariff B.
19. Folkestone–Boulogne; car 5.25 m; Tariff C.
20. Newhaven–Dieppe; car 5.45 m; Tariff A.

Part C Copy the table below and find the total cost for each of the
following journeys.

	Journey	Depart	Adults	Children	Car	Caravan
1.	Newhaven–Dieppe	July 18 07 00	2	2	4.20 m	
2.	Folkestone–Boulogne	June 2 23 45	2	1	4.00 m	
3.	Folkestone–Boulogne	July 3 11 45	2	3	4.80 m	
4.	Dover–Calais	August 13 06 30	2	4	3.80 m	4 m
5.	Newhaven–Dieppe	August 3 10 00	2	1	4.60 m	
6.	Folkstone–Boulogne	June 10 07 45	4	0	5.00 m	5.00 m
7.	Dover–Calais	Sept 12 10 00	3	2	4.80 m	
8.	Newhaven–Dieppe	July 25 13 00	2	4	5.20 m	4.50 m
9.	Folkestone–Boulogne	July 6 11 45	1	6	4.85 m	4.20 m
10.	Dover–Calais	August 27 06 30	2	3	3.75 m	
11.	Newhaven–Dieppe	July 20 13 00	1	4	4.40 m	3.90 m
12.	Folkestone–Boulogne	July 21 09 45	2	2	5.10 m	5.00 m
13.	Dover–Calais	August 20 22 00	4	0	5.20 m	
14.	Newhaven–Dieppe	August 2 10 00	2	5	5.40 m	
15.	Folkestone–Boulogne	July 13 03 45	3	1	4.95 m	
16.	Dover–Calais	August 13 05 00	2	2	4.60 m	
17.	Newhaven–Dieppe	July 14 10 00	3	2	3.95 m	
18.	Folkestone–Boulogne	June 8 09 45	2	4	5.20 m	

Project 5   THE TOWERS OF HANOI

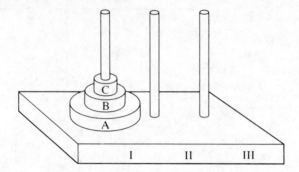

We have a board with three pegs I, II and III.

On one of the pegs we place several discs with the largest at the bottom, the next largest on top of that and so on.

The problem is to transfer all the discs from the first peg to one of the others in such a way that the final arrangement is the same as the original one.

The rules are that only one disc is moved at a time and no disc shall ever be placed on top of a disc smaller than itself.

Start with just two discs and count the minimum number of moves required to transfer the discs to one of the other pegs.

Then try it with 3 discs, 4 discs and so on.

Make a table like the one below.

Number of discs	Minimum number of moves needed
2	3
3	
4	
5	
6	

It is not necessary to use a proper board with pegs. You can perform the investigation with any objects which are different in size (e.g. coins, pieces of cardboard, books).

The final object is to find a rule which connects the number of *moves* with the number of *discs*.

Hint: If the number of discs is even, move the first disc to peg II; if it is odd, move the first disc to peg III.

175

Exercise E

1. After donations of £825.50, £270 and £585.40 how much is needed to reach a target of £2000?

2. An oil drum contains 39 litres when it is three-quarters full. How many litres will it contain when it is full?

3. The results of a test given to 50 children are shown below.

Mark	0	1	2	3	4	5
Number of pupils	1	4	10	12	15	8

   (a) How many pupils scored less than 3 marks?
   (b) Find the percentage of the pupils who scored
       (i) 2 marks   (ii) 5 marks
     (iii) 3 marks or more   (iv) No marks.

4. A crate contains 15 dozen tomatoes, of which 11 are squashed. How many good tomatoes are there?

5. A cyclist starts a journey at 3.10 p.m. and travels 70 km at an average speed of 20 km/h. At what time will he finish?

6. Change to top-heavy fractions
   (a) $2\frac{1}{4}$ (b) $1\frac{3}{4}$ (c) $3\frac{1}{2}$ (d) $4\frac{2}{5}$.

7. The thirteenth number in the sequence 1, 3, 9, 27, . . . is 531 441. What is
   (a) the twelfth number
   (b) the fourteenth number?

8. Find the missing digits:

```
(a)    8 2 *    (b)    * 4 1    (c)    3 * 4
       * 1 3          4 5 *           2 1 *
     + 2 * 0        + 2 * 9         + * 0 4
     -------        -------         -------
     1 4 6 4          9 7 3         1 3 7 9
```

9. An antiques dealer sells a painting at a profit of 70% on the cost price of £250. For how much does he sell the painting?

10. How many triangles can you see in this diagram?

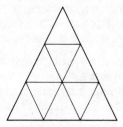

Project 6   **FINDING A STRATEGY**

Here is an interesting mathematical game where you have two objectives:

(a) to enjoy the game;

(b) to find a strategy so that you always win!

Two players take turns to select one number from the numbers 1, 2, 3, 4, 5, 6. Each number is added to the sum of the others until one player reaches 33. The winner is the player who makes the total up to 33.

Here is a game between David and John

	David	John	David	John	David	John	David	John
	4	5	1	6	6	3	6	2
Total	4	9	10	16	22	25	31	**33**

John is the winner.

(a) Play the game many times and keep the score. After a while you may begin to see how you can win more often. When you think you have discovered a winning strategy try to describe it in words.

(b) Now change the rules so that any number from 1, 2, 3, 4, 5, 6, 7, 8 can be chosen and the target number is **47**. Again try to find the winning strategy and write it down in words.

(c) Change the rules again so that any number from 1, 2, 3, 4, 5, 6, 7, 8, 9 can be chosen and the target number is **63**. What is the winning strategy this time?

Exercise F

1. A girl puts 1p in her piggy-bank on the first day, 2p on the second day, 4p on the third day and carries on like this, doubling the amount each day.
   (a) How much does she put in on the 8th day?
   (b) How much does she put in on the 12th day?
   (c) How much is in the piggy-bank after 5 days?

2. Four boys have weights of 44 kg, 45 kg, 49 kg and 51 kg.
   (a) What is their average weight?
   When another boy joins them, the average weight becomes 48 kg.
   (b) What is the weight of the fifth boy?

3. If 150 bananas are divided equally between 11 girls, how many will each girl receive and how many will be left over?

4. A man drives a car which does 8 km to one litre of petrol and petrol costs 42p per litre. The man drives 144 km every day for a week of 7 days. What is his petrol bill for the week?

5. 6 sacks of corn will feed 80 hens for 12 days.
Copy and complete the following:
(a) 18 sacks of corn will feed 80 hens for . . . days.
(b) 6 sacks of corn will feed 40 hens for . . . days.
(c) 60 sacks of corn will feed 40 hens for . . . days.
(d) 30 sacks of corn will feed 80 hens for . . . days.

6. Calculate the area of the shape below. Take $\pi = 3$.

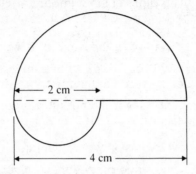

7. Arrange the numbers in order of size, smallest first.
(a) 0.571, 0.5, 0.617, 0.517, 0.5171
(b) 0.03, 0.029, 0.31, 0.1
(c) 0.55, 0.555, 0.505, 0.0555
(d) 0.09, 0.11, 0.011, 0.089

8. Divide £90 in the ratio 2:3:5.

9. An overnight train journey started at 19 40 on Thursday and ended at 06 10 on the Friday. How long was the journey in hours and minutes?

10. Find the missing numbers

(a) $6 * 2$ (b) $2 5 *$ (c) $9 * 2$
      $+ * 5 6$ $+ * 2 3$ $- * 2 2$
      ─────────   ─────────   ─────────
       $7 9 *$ $1 1 * 7$ $2 4 *$

Project 7   SQUARE NUMBERS

(a) Write down all the square numbers from 1 to 144.
     1, 4, 9, . . . 144.
(b) A famous mathematician named Lagrange stated a theorem that all whole numbers could always be split into square numbers.

   e.g. $24 = 16 + 4 + 4$
        $35 = 25 + 9 + 1$

   Split the following numbers into square numbers.

   (i)   29   (ii)   37   (iii) 52   (iv)   72   (v)   47
   (vi) 59   (vii) 68   (viii) 91   (ix) 107   (x) 131
   (xi) 157   (xii) 137   (xiii) 140   (xiv) 150   (xv) 167

(c) Lagrange also stated that there are no numbers which need more than four square numbers. Try to find a number which *does* need more than four square numbers. If you can think of such a number, a new theorem will be named after you.

178

Project 8   FIND THE CONNECTION

1. Try this on your calculator.
   (a) Enter any number, e.g. 7.
   (b) Take the square root of the number.
   (c) Take the square root again and this time write down the first 5 digits of the number showing.
   (c) Multiply by the original number.
   (e) Repeat steps (b), (c) and (d) until the number you write down in step (c) is the same as it was last time.

What have you done? What is the connection between the original number and the final number?

Try it out on several other numbers until you can find the connection. (Suggestions: 10; 16; 100; 8; 27).

2. Now try this on your calculator.

Follow the same procedure as given above but this time take the square root *three* times.

Again try to work out the connection between the original number and the final number.
(Suggestions: 7; 128; 2187)

Exercise G

1. How many 18p stamps can be bought for £5 and how much change will there be?

2. A cook uses 250 ml of oil in 4 days. How many days will a 10 litre drum last?

3. Work out the cost per gram of the metal used in various items of jewellery:
   A: gold chain, £33.00, 15 g
   B: silver ring, £6.30, 4.5 g
   C: chrome earrings, £5.85, 7.8 g
   D: steel bracelet, £13.75, 25 g

4. A car left London at 10 00 and arrived in Cardiff at 12 15. Cardiff is 225 km from London. What was the average speed of the car in km/h?

5. The numbers '−2' and '5' multiply to give −10 and add up to 3. Find two numbers which:
   (a) multiply to give −12 and add up to 1.
   (b) multiply to give −12 and add up to 4.
   (c) multiply to give −3 and add up to 2.

6. In a class of 25 children, 11 were girls. What percentage of the class were boys?

7. When a man works 40 hours, he is paid £180. How much is he paid when he works 25 hours?

8. A lady sells a car at a loss of 60% on the original cost price of £5450. How much does she receive for the car?

9. The maps below consist of several roads joining towns. For each map can you plan a route which uses each road only once? Answer 'yes' or 'no'.

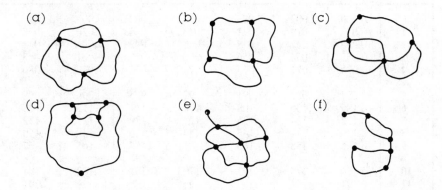

(a)   (b)   (c)

(d)   (e)   (f)

10. The fifteenth number in the sequence 1, 2, 4, 8, 16, . . . is 16 384. What is
(a) the fourteenth number
(b) the sixteenth number?

Project 9   **FRACTIONS AND DECIMALS GAME**

(a) Draw a large copy of table A.

Table A

0·375	0·$\dot{2}$	2·$\dot{6}$	0·4	0·$\dot{8}$	1·$\dot{3}$
1·2	0·$\dot{3}$	0·$\dot{5}$	0·5	0·$\dot{7}$	0·$\dot{6}$
0·6	0·625	0·25	0·8	0·875	1·1$\dot{6}$
4·5	2·5	0·8$\dot{3}$	0·125	1·25	1·6
0·1$\dot{6}$	2·$\dot{3}$	2·25	3·5	0·$\dot{1}$	1·4
0·$\dot{4}$	1·8	0·2	1·75	1·125	0·75

Table B

1	2	3
4	5	6
7	8	9

(b) Two players take it in turn to select a pair of numbers from table B and divide them on a calculator. If the answer is in table A and if the number is not yet crossed out the player crosses out that square with a coloured pencil.

(c) The winner is the first player to cross out four squares in a line, either in a column or a row or a diagonal.

TABLE OF SINES

Angle in degrees	.0	.1	.2	.3	.4	.5	.6	.7	.8	.9
0	0.000	.002	.003	.005	.007	.009	.010	.012	.014	.016
1	0.017	.019	.021	.023	.024	.026	.028	.030	.031	.033
2	0.035	.037	.038	.040	.042	.044	.045	.047	.049	.051
3	0.052	.054	.056	.058	.059	.061	.063	.065	.066	.068
4	0.070	.071	.073	.075	.077	.078	.080	.082	.084	.085
5	0.087	.089	.091	.092	.094	.096	.098	.099	.101	.103
6	0.105	.106	.108	.110	.111	.113	.115	.117	.118	.120
7	0.122	.124	.125	.127	.129	.131	.132	.134	.136	.137
8	0.139	.141	.143	.144	.146	.148	.150	.151	.153	.155
9	0.156	.158	.160	.162	.163	.165	.167	.168	.170	.172
10	0.174	.175	.177	.179	.181	.182	.184	.186	.187	.189
11	0.191	.193	.194	.196	.198	.199	.201	.203	.204	.206
12	0.208	.210	.211	.213	.215	.216	.218	.220	.222	.223
13	0.225	.227	.228	.230	.232	.233	.235	.237	.239	.240
14	0.242	.244	.245	.247	.249	.250	.252	.254	.255	.257
15	0.259	.261	.262	.264	.266	.267	.269	.271	.272	.274
16	0.276	.277	.279	.281	.282	.284	.286	.287	.289	.291
17	0.292	.294	.296	.297	.299	.301	.302	.304	.306	.307
18	0.309	.311	.312	.314	.316	.317	.319	.321	.322	.324
19	0.326	.327	.329	.331	.332	.334	.335	.337	.339	.340
20	0.342	.344	.345	.347	.349	.350	.352	.353	.355	.357
21	0.358	.360	.362	.363	.365	.367	.368	.370	.371	.373
22	0.375	.376	.378	.379	.381	.383	.384	.386	.388	.389
23	0.391	.392	.394	.396	.397	.399	.400	.402	.404	.405
24	0.407	.408	.410	.412	.413	.415	.416	.418	.419	.421
25	0.423	.424	.426	.427	.429	.431	.432	.434	.435	.437
26	0.438	.440	.442	.443	.445	.446	.448	.449	.451	.452
27	0.454	.456	.457	.459	.460	.462	.463	.465	.466	.468
28	0.469	.471	.473	.474	.476	.477	.479	.480	.482	.483
29	0.485	.486	.488	.489	.491	.492	.494	.495	.497	.498
30	0.500	.502	.503	.505	.506	.508	.509	.511	.512	.514
31	0.515	.517	.518	.520	.521	.522	.524	.525	.527	.528
32	0.530	.531	.533	.534	.536	.537	.539	.540	.542	.543
33	0.545	.546	.548	.549	.550	.552	.553	.555	.556	.558
34	0.559	.561	.562	.564	.565	.566	.568	.569	.571	.572
35	0.574	.575	.576	.578	.579	.581	.582	.584	.585	.586
36	0.588	.589	.591	.592	.593	.595	.596	.598	.599	.600
37	0.602	.603	.605	.606	.607	.609	.610	.612	.613	.614
38	0.616	.617	.618	.620	.621	.623	.624	.625	.627	.628
39	0.629	.631	.632	.633	.635	.636	.637	.639	.640	.641
40	0.643	.644	.645	.647	.648	.649	.651	.652	.653	.655
41	0.656	.657	.659	.660	.661	.663	.664	.665	.667	.668
42	0.669	.670	.672	.673	.674	.676	.677	.678	.679	.681
43	0.682	.683	.685	.686	.687	.688	.690	.691	.692	.693
44	0.695	.696	.697	.698	.700	.701	.702	.703	.705	.706
45	0.707	.708	.710	.711	.712	.713	.714	.716	.717	.718

TABLE OF SINES – *continued*

Angle in degrees	.0	.1	.2	.3	.4	.5	.6	.7	.8	.9
45	0.707	.708	.710	.711	.712	.713	.714	.716	.717	.718
46	0.719	.721	.722	.723	.724	.725	.727	.728	.729	.730
47	0.731	.733	.734	.735	.736	.737	.738	.740	.741	.742
48	0.743	.744	.745	.747	.748	.749	.750	.751	.752	.754
49	0.755	.756	.757	.758	.759	.760	.762	.763	.764	.765
50	0.766	.767	.768	.769	.771	.772	.773	.774	.775	.776
51	0.777	.778	.779	.780	.782	.783	.784	.785	.786	.787
52	0.788	.789	.790	.791	.792	.793	.794	.795	.797	.798
53	0.799	.800	.801	.802	.803	.804	.805	.806	.807	.808
54	0.809	.810	.811	.812	.813	.814	.815	.816	.817	.818
55	0.819	.820	.821	.822	.823	.824	.825	.826	.827	.828
56	0.829	.830	.831	.832	.833	.834	.835	.836	.837	.838
57	0.839	.840	.841	.842	.842	.843	.844	.845	.846	.847
58	0.848	.849	.850	.851	.852	.853	.854	.854	.855	.856
59	0.857	.858	.859	.860	.861	.862	.863	.863	.864	.865
60	0.866	.867	.868	.869	.869	.870	.871	.872	.873	.874
61	0.875	.875	.876	.877	.878	.879	.880	.880	.881	.882
62	0.883	.884	.885	.885	.886	.887	.888	.889	.889	.890
63	0.891	.892	.893	.893	.894	.895	.896	.896	.897	.898
64	0.899	.900	.900	.901	.902	.903	.903	.904	.905	.906
65	0.906	.907	.908	.909	.909	.910	.911	.911	.912	.913
66	0.914	.914	.915	.916	.916	.917	.918	.918	.919	.920
67	0.921	.921	.922	.923	.923	.924	.925	.925	.926	.927
68	0.927	.928	.928	.929	.930	.930	.931	.932	.932	.933
69	0.934	.934	.935	.935	.936	.937	.937	.938	.938	.939
70	0.940	.940	.941	.941	.942	.943	.943	.944	.944	.945
71	0.946	.946	.947	.947	.948	.948	.949	.949	.950	.951
72	0.951	.952	.952	.953	.953	.954	.954	.955	.955	.956
73	0.956	.957	.957	.958	.958	.959	.959	.960	.960	.961
74	0.961	.962	.962	.963	.963	.964	.964	.965	.965	.965
75	0.966	.966	.967	.967	.968	.968	.969	.969	.969	.970
76	0.970	.971	.971	.972	.972	.972	.973	.973	.974	.974
77	0.974	.975	.975	.976	.976	.976	.977	.977	.977	.978
78	0.978	.979	.979	.979	.980	.980	.980	.981	.981	.981
79	0.982	.982	.982	.983	.983	.983	.984	.984	.984	.985
80	0.985	.985	.985	.986	.986	.986	.987	.987	.987	.987
81	0.988	.988	.988	.988	.989	.989	.989	.990	.990	.990
82	0.990	.991	.991	.991	.991	.991	.992	.992	.992	.992
83	0.993	.993	.993	.993	.993	.994	.994	.994	.994	.994
84	0.995	.995	.995	.995	.995	.995	.996	.996	.996	.996
85	0.996	.996	.996	.997	.997	.997	.997	.997	.997	.997
86	0.998	.998	.998	.998	.998	.998	.998	.998	.998	.999
87	0.999	.999	.999	.999	.999	.999	.999	.999	.999	.999
88	0.999	.999	1.000	1.000	1.000	1.000	1.000	1.000	1.000	1.000
89	1.000	1.000	1.000	1.000	1.000	1.000	1.000	1.000	1.000	1.000
90	1.000									

TABLE OF COSINES

Angle in degrees	.0	.1	.2	.3	.4	.5	.6	.7	.8	.9
0	1.000	1.000	1.000	1.000	1.000	1.000	1.000	1.000	1.000	1.000
1	1.000	1.000	1.000	1.000	1.000	1.000	1.000	1.000	1.000	0.999
2	0.999	.999	.999	.999	.999	.999	.999	.999	.999	.999
3	0.999	.999	.998	.998	.998	.998	.998	.998	.998	.998
4	0.998	.997	.997	.997	.997	.997	.997	.997	.996	.996
5	0.996	.996	.996	.996	.996	.995	.995	.995	.995	.995
6	0.995	.994	.994	.994	.994	.994	.993	.993	.993	.993
7	0.993	.992	.992	.992	.992	.991	.991	.991	.991	.991
8	0.990	.990	.990	.990	.989	.989	.989	.988	.988	.988
9	0.988	.987	.987	.987	.987	.986	.986	.986	.985	.985
10	0.985	.985	.984	.984	.984	.983	.983	.983	.982	.982
11	0.982	.981	.981	.981	.980	.980	.980	.979	.979	.979
12	0.978	.978	.977	.977	.977	.976	.976	.976	.975	.975
13	0.974	.974	.974	.973	.973	.972	.972	.972	.971	.971
14	0.970	.970	.969	.969	.969	.968	.968	.967	.967	.966
15	0.966	.965	.965	.965	.964	.964	.963	.963	.962	.962
16	0.961	.961	.960	.960	.959	.959	.958	.958	.957	.957
17	0.956	.956	.955	.955	.954	.954	.953	.953	.952	.952
18	0.951	.951	.950	.949	.949	.948	.948	.947	.947	.946
19	0.946	.945	.944	.944	.943	.943	.942	.941	.941	.940
20	0.940	.939	.938	.938	.937	.937	.936	.935	.935	.934
21	0.934	.933	.932	.932	.931	.930	.930	.929	.928	.928
22	0.927	.927	.926	.925	.925	.924	.923	.923	.922	.921
23	0.921	.920	.919	.918	.918	.917	.916	.916	.915	.914
24	0.914	.913	.912	.911	.911	.910	.909	.909	.908	.907
25	0.906	.906	.905	.904	.903	.903	.902	.901	.900	.900
26	0.899	.898	.897	.896	.896	.895	.894	.893	.893	.892
27	0.891	.890	.889	.889	.888	.887	.886	.885	.885	.884
28	0.883	.882	.881	.880	.880	.879	.878	.877	.876	.875
29	0.875	.874	.873	.872	.871	.870	.869	.869	.868	.867
30	0.866	.865	.864	.863	.863	.862	.861	.860	.859	.858
31	0.857	.856	.855	.854	.854	.853	.852	.851	.850	.849
32	0.848	.847	.846	.845	.844	.843	.842	.842	.841	.840
33	0.839	.838	.837	.836	.835	.834	.833	.832	.831	.830
34	0.829	.828	.827	.826	.825	.824	.823	.822	.821	.820
35	0.819	.818	.817	.816	.815	.814	.813	.812	.811	.810
36	0.809	.808	.807	.806	.805	.804	.803	.802	.801	.800
37	0.799	.798	.797	.795	.794	.793	.792	.791	.790	.789
38	0.788	.787	.786	.785	.784	.783	.782	.780	.779	.778
39	0.777	.776	.775	.774	.773	.772	.771	.769	.768	.767
40	0.766	.765	.764	.763	.762	.760	.759	.758	.757	.756
41	0.755	.754	.752	.751	.750	.749	.748	.747	.745	.744
42	0.743	.742	.741	.740	.738	.737	.736	.735	.734	.733
43	0.731	.730	.729	.728	.727	.725	.724	.723	.722	.721
44	0.719	.718	.717	.716	.714	.713	.712	.711	.710	.708
45	0.707	.706	.705	.703	.702	.701	.700	.698	.697	.696

TABLE OF COSINES – *continued*

Angle in degrees	.0	.1	.2	.3	.4	.5	.6	.7	.8	.9
45	0.707	.706	.705	.703	.702	.701	.700	.698	.697	.696
46	0.695	.693	.692	.691	.690	.688	.687	.686	.685	.683
47	0.682	.681	.679	.678	.677	.676	.674	.673	.672	.670
48	0.669	.668	.667	.665	.664	.663	.661	.660	.659	.657
49	0.656	.655	.653	.652	.651	.649	.648	.647	.645	.644
50	0.643	.641	.640	.639	.637	.636	.635	.633	.632	.631
51	0.629	.628	.627	.625	.624	.623	.621	.620	.618	.617
52	0.616	.614	.613	.612	.610	.609	.607	.606	.605	.603
53	0.602	.600	.599	.598	.596	.595	.593	.592	.591	.589
54	0.588	.586	.585	.584	.582	.581	.579	.578	.576	.575
55	0.574	.572	.571	.569	.568	.566	.565	.564	.562	.561
56	0.559	.558	.556	.555	.553	.552	.550	.549	.548	.546
57	0.545	.543	.542	.540	.539	.537	.536	.534	.533	.531
58	0.530	.528	.527	.525	.524	.522	.521	.520	.518	.517
59	0.515	.514	.512	.511	.509	.508	.506	.505	.503	.502
60	0.500	.498	.497	.495	.494	.492	.491	.489	.488	.486
61	0.485	.483	.482	.480	.479	.477	.476	.474	.473	.471
62	0.469	.468	.466	.465	.463	.462	.460	.459	.457	.456
63	0.454	.452	.451	.449	.448	.446	.445	.443	.442	.440
64	0.438	.437	.435	.434	.432	.431	.429	.427	.426	.424
65	0.423	.421	.419	.418	.416	.415	.413	.412	.410	.408
66	0.407	.405	.404	.402	.400	.399	.397	.396	.394	.392
67	0.391	.389	.388	.386	.384	.383	.381	.379	.378	.376
68	0.375	.373	.371	.370	.368	.367	.365	.363	.362	.360
69	0.358	.357	.355	.353	.352	.350	.349	.347	.345	.344
70	0.342	.340	.339	.337	.335	.334	.332	.331	.329	.327
71	0.326	.324	.322	.321	.319	.317	.316	.314	.312	.311
72	0.309	.307	.306	.304	.302	.301	.299	.297	.296	.294
73	0.292	.291	.289	.287	.286	.284	.282	.281	.279	.277
74	0.276	.274	.272	.271	.269	.267	.266	.264	.262	.261
75	0.259	.257	.255	.254	.252	.250	.249	.247	.245	.244
76	0.242	.240	.239	.237	.235	.233	.232	.230	.228	.227
77	0.225	.223	.222	.220	.218	.216	.215	.213	.211	.210
78	0.208	.206	.204	.203	.201	.199	.198	.196	.194	.193
79	0.191	.189	.187	.186	.184	.182	.181	.179	.177	.175
80	0.174	.172	.170	.168	.167	.165	.163	.162	.160	.158
81	0.156	.155	.153	.151	.150	.148	.146	.144	.143	.141
82	0.139	.137	.136	.134	.132	.131	.129	.127	.125	.124
83	0.122	.120	.118	.117	.115	.113	.111	.110	.108	.106
84	0.105	.103	.101	.099	.098	.096	.094	.092	.091	.089
85	0.087	.085	.084	.082	.080	.078	.077	.075	.073	.071
86	0.070	.068	.066	.065	.063	.061	.059	.058	.056	.054
87	0.052	.051	.049	.047	.045	.044	.042	.040	.038	.037
88	0.035	.033	.031	.030	.028	.026	.024	.023	.021	.019
89	0.017	.016	.014	.012	.010	.009	.007	.005	.003	.002
90	0.000									

TABLE OF TANGENTS

Angle in degrees	.0	.1	.2	.3	.4	.5	.6	.7	.8	.9
0	0.000	.002	.003	.005	.007	.000	.010	.012	.014	.016
1	0.017	.019	.021	.023	.024	.026	.028	.030	.031	.033
2	0.035	.037	.038	.040	.042	.044	.045	.047	.049	.051
3	0.052	.054	.056	.058	.059	.061	.063	.065	.066	.068
4	0.070	.072	.073	.075	.077	.079	.080	.082	.084	.086
5	0.087	.089	.091	.093	.095	.096	.098	.100	.102	.103
6	0.105	.107	.109	.110	.112	.114	.116	.117	.119	.121
7	0.123	.125	.126	.128	.130	.132	.133	.135	.137	.139
8	0.141	.142	.144	.146	.148	.149	.151	.153	.155	.157
9	0.158	.160	.162	.164	.166	.167	.169	.171	.173	.175
10	0.176	.178	.180	.182	.184	.185	.187	.189	.191	.193
11	0.194	.196	.198	.200	.202	.203	.205	.207	.209	.211
12	0.213	.214	.216	.218	.220	.222	.224	.225	.227	.229
13	0.231	.233	.235	.236	.238	.240	.242	.244	.246	.247
14	0.249	.251	.253	.255	.257	.259	.260	.262	.264	.266
15	0.268	.270	.272	.274	.275	.277	.279	.281	.283	.285
16	0.287	.289	.291	.292	.294	.296	.298	.300	.302	.304
17	0.306	.308	.310	.311	.313	.315	.317	.319	.321	.323
18	0.325	.327	.329	.331	.333	.335	.337	.338	.340	.342
19	0.344	.346	.348	.350	.352	.354	.356	.358	.360	.362
20	0.364	.366	.368	.370	.372	.374	.376	.378	.380	.382
21	0.384	.386	.388	.390	.392	.394	.396	.398	.400	.402
22	0.404	.406	.408	.410	.412	.414	.416	.418	.420	.422
23	0.424	.427	.429	.431	.433	.435	.437	.439	.441	.443
24	0.445	.447	.449	.452	.454	.456	.458	.460	.462	.464
25	0.466	.468	.471	.473	.475	.477	.479	.481	.483	.486
26	0.488	.490	.492	.494	.496	.499	.501	.503	.505	.507
27	0.510	.512	.514	.516	.518	.521	.523	.525	.527	.529
28	0.532	.534	.536	.538	.541	.543	.545	.547	.550	.552
29	0.554	.557	.559	.561	.563	.566	.568	.570	.573	.575
30	0.577	.580	.582	.584	.587	.589	.591	.594	.596	.598
31	0.601	.603	.606	.608	.610	.613	.615	.618	.620	.622
32	0.625	.627	.630	.632	.635	.637	.640	.642	.644	.647
33	0.649	.652	.654	.657	.659	.662	.664	.667	.669	.672
34	0.675	.677	.680	.682	.685	.687	.690	.692	.695	.698
35	0.700	.703	.705	.708	.711	.713	.716	.719	.721	.724
36	0.727	.729	.732	.735	.737	.740	.743	.745	.748	.751
37	0.754	.756	.759	.762	.765	.767	.770	.773	.776	.778
38	0.781	.784	.787	.790	.793	.795	.798	.801	.804	.807
39	0.810	.813	.816	.818	.821	.824	.827	.830	.833	.836
40	0.839	.842	.845	.848	.851	.854	.857	.860	.863	.866
41	0.869	.872	.875	.879	.882	.885	.888	.891	.894	.897
42	0.900	.904	.907	.910	.913	.916	.920	.923	.926	.929
43	0.933	.936	.939	.942	.946	.949	.952	.956	.959	.962
44	0.966	.969	.972	.976	.979	.983	.986	.990	.993	.997
45	1.00	1.00	1.01	1.01	1.01	1.02	1.02	1.02	1.03	1.03

TABLE OF TANGENTS – *continued*

Angle in degrees	.0	.1	.2	.3	.4	.5	.6	.7	.8	.9
45	1.00	1.00	1.01	1.01	1.01	1.02	1.02	1.02	1.03	1.03
46	1.04	1.04	1.04	1.05	1.05	1.05	1.06	1.06	1.06	1.07
47	1.07	1.08	1.08	1.08	1.09	1.09	1.10	1.10	1.10	1.11
48	1.11	1.11	1.12	1.12	1.13	1.13	1.13	1.14	1.14	1.15
49	1.15	1.15	1.16	1.16	1.17	1.17	1.17	1.18	1.18	1.19
50	1.19	1.20	1.20	1.20	1.21	1.21	1.22	1.22	1.23	1.23
51	1.23	1.24	1.24	1.25	1.25	1.26	1.26	1.27	1.27	1.28
52	1.28	1.28	1.29	1.29	1.30	1.30	1.31	1.31	1.32	1.32
53	1.33	1.33	1.34	1.34	1.35	1.35	1.36	1.36	1.37	1.37
54	1.38	1.38	1.39	1.39	1.40	1.40	1.41	1.41	1.42	1.42
55	1.43	1.43	1.44	1.44	1.45	1.46	1.46	1.47	1.47	1.48
56	1.48	1.49	1.49	1.50	1.51	1.51	1.52	1.52	1.53	1.53
57	1.54	1.55	1.55	1.56	1.56	1.57	1.58	1.58	1.59	1.59
58	1.60	1.61	1.61	1.62	1.63	1.63	1.64	1.64	1.65	1.66
59	1.66	1.67	1.68	1.68	1.69	1.70	1.70	1.71	1.72	1.73
60	1.73	1.74	1.75	1.75	1.76	1.77	1.77	1.78	1.79	1.80
61	1.80	1.81	1.82	1.83	1.83	1.84	1.85	1.86	1.86	1.87
62	1.88	1.89	1.90	1.90	1.91	1.92	1.93	1.94	1.95	1.95
63	1.96	1.97	1.98	1.99	2.00	2.01	2.01	2.02	2.03	2.04
64	2.05	2.06	2.07	2.08	2.09	2.10	2.11	2.12	2.13	2.13
65	2.14	2.15	2.16	2.17	2.18	2.19	2.20	2.21	2.23	2.24
66	2.25	2.26	2.27	2.28	2.29	2.30	2.31	2.32	2.33	2.34
67	2.36	2.37	2.38	2.39	2.40	2.41	2.43	2.44	2.45	2.46
68	2.48	2.49	2.50	2.51	2.53	2.54	2.55	2.56	2.58	2.59
69	2.61	2.62	2.63	2.65	2.66	2.67	2.69	2.70	2.72	2.73
70	2.75	2.76	2.78	2.79	2.81	2.82	2.84	2.86	2.87	2.89
71	2.90	2.92	2.94	2.95	2.97	2.99	3.01	3.02	3.04	3.06
72	3.08	3.10	3.11	3.13	3.15	3.17	3.19	3.21	3.23	3.25
73	3.27	3.29	3.31	3.33	3.35	3.38	3.40	3.42	3.44	3.46
74	3.49	3.51	3.53	3.56	3.58	3.61	3.63	3.66	3.68	3.71
75	3.73	3.76	3.78	3.81	3.84	3.87	3.89	3.92	3.95	3.98
76	4.01	4.04	4.07	4.10	4.13	4.17	4.20	4.23	4.26	4.30
77	4.33	4.37	4.40	4.44	4.47	4.51	4.55	4.59	4.63	4.66
78	4.70	4.75	4.79	4.83	4.87	4.92	4.96	5.00	5.05	5.10
79	5.14	5.19	5.24	5.29	5.34	5.40	5.45	5.50	5.56	5.61
80	5.67	5.73	5.79	5.85	5.91	5.98	6.04	6.11	6.17	6.24
81	6.31	6.39	6.46	6.54	6.61	6.69	6.77	6.85	6.94	7.03
82	7.12	7.21	7.30	7.40	7.49	7.60	7.70	7.81	7.92	8.03
83	8.14	8.26	8.39	8.51	8.64	8.78	8.92	9.06	9.21	9.36
84	9.51	9.68	9.84	10.0	10.2	10.4	10.6	10.8	11.0	11.2
85	11.4	11.7	11.9	12.2	12.4	12.7	13.0	13.3	13.6	14.0
86	14.3	14.7	15.1	15.5	15.9	16.3	16.8	17.3	17.9	18.5
87	19.1	19.7	20.4	21.2	22.0	22.9	23.9	24.9	26.0	27.3
88	28.6	30.1	31.8	33.7	35.8	38.2	40.9	44.1	47.7	52.1
89	57.3	63.7	71.6	81.8	95.5	115	143	191	286	573